# UCLA FORUM IN MEDICAL SCIENCES

UNIVERSITY OF CALIFORNIA LOS ANGELES

# BRAIN FUNCTION

## VOLUME III

# SPEECH, LANGUAGE, AND COMMUNICATION

UCLA FORUM IN MEDICAL SCIENCES

NUMBER 4

# BRAIN FUNCTION

VOLUME III

Proceedings of the Third Conference, November 1963

## SPEECH, LANGUAGE, AND COMMUNICATION

Sponsored by the Brain Research Institute, University of California Los Angeles
with the support of the United States Air Force Office of Scientific Research

EDITOR

### EDWARD C. CARTERETTE

UNIVERSITY OF CALIFORNIA PRESS

BERKELEY AND LOS ANGELES

1966

## EDITORIAL NOTE

The present volume contains the proceedings of the third in a series of conferences on Brain Function, supported by grants made to Dr. H. W. Magoun of the Brain Research Institute of the University of California Los Angeles. The first and second conferences of the series, on *Cortical Excitability and Steady Potentials* and on *RNA and Brain Function*, respectively, appeared as Numbers 1 and 2 of the UCLA Forum in Medical Sciences; both were edited by Dr. M. A. B. Brazier. The fourth conference, on Brain Function and Learning (November 1964) will appear as UCLA Forum in Medical Sciences No. 6. The fifth conference, dealing with Brain Mechanisms of Aggression and Defense, was held November 1965.

CITATION FORM

Carterette, E. C. (Ed.), *Brain Function, Vol. III: Speech, Language, and Communication.* UCLA Forum Med. Sci. No. 4, Univ. of California Press, Los Angeles, 1966.

University of California Press
Berkeley and Los Angeles, California

Cambridge University Press
London, England

# PARTICIPANTS IN THE CONFERENCE

H. W. Magoun, *Chairman*
Brain Research Institute, University of California Los Angeles
Los Angeles, California

Edward C. Carterette, *Editor*
Department of Psychology, University of California Los Angeles
Los Angeles, California


Julián de Ajuriaguerra
Clinique Psychiatrique de L'Université de Genève
Bel-Air près Genève, Switzerland

Joseph Applegate
Department of Near Eastern and African Languages
University of California Los Angeles
Los Angeles, California

Mary A. B. Brazier
Brain Research Institute, University of California Los Angeles
Los Angeles, California

William O. Bright
Department of Anthropology
University of California Los Angeles
Los Angeles, California

Katrina de Hirsch
Pediatric Language Disorder Clinic
Columbia Presbyterian Medical Center
New York, New York

Peter B. Denes
Bell Telephone Laboratories, Inc.
Murray. Hill, New Jersey

Susan M. Ervin-Tripp
Department of Speech, University of California
Berkeley, California

CHARLES A. FERGUSON
Center for Applied Linguistics
Washington, D. C.

HAROLD GARFINKEL
Department of Sociology
University of California Los Angeles
Los Angeles, California

PAUL L. GARVIN
Language Analysis and Translation, The Bunker-Ramo Corporation
Canoga Park, California

NORMAN GESCHWIND
Aphasia Research Section, Veterans Administration Hospital
Boston, Massachusetts

VICTOR GOODHILL
Department of Surgery, University of California Los Angeles
Los Angeles, California

WILLIAM G. HARDY
The Hearing and Speech Center
The Johns Hopkins Medical Institutions
Baltimore, Maryland

IRA J. HIRSH
Central Institute for the Deaf
St. Louis, Missouri

HARRY HOIJER
Department of Anthropology
University of California Los Angeles
Los Angeles, California

ROMAN JAKOBSON
Harvard University and Massachusetts Institute of Technology
Cambridge, Massachusetts

PETER LADEFOGED
Department of Linguistics, University of California Los Angeles
Los Angeles, California

SYDNEY M. LAMB
Department of Linguistics, University of California
Berkeley, California

Eric H. Lenneberg
Speech Research Laboratory, The Children's Hospital Medical Center
Boston, Massachusetts

Donald B. Lindsley
Department of Psychology, University of California Los Angeles
Los Angeles, California

Floyd G. Lounsbury
Department of Anthropology, Yale University
New Haven, Connecticut

Jacob Marschak
Western Management Science Institute
University of California Los Angeles
Los Angeles, California

Richard L. Masland
National Institute of Neurological Diseases and Blindness
National Institutes of Health
Bethesda, Maryland

Michel A. Melkanoff
Department of Engineering, University of California Los Angeles
Los Angeles, California

Charles E. Osgood
Institute of Communications Research, The University of Illinois
Urbana, Illinois

Jaan Puhvel
Center for Research in Languages and Linguistics
University of California Los Angeles
Los Angeles, California

Lamar Roberts
Division of Neurosurgery
Teaching Hospital and Clinics, University of Florida
Gainesville, Florida

A. Kimball Romney
Department of Anthropology, Stanford University
Stanford, California

Harvey E. Savely
Life Sciences Division, Air Force Office of Scientific Research
United States Air Force
Washington, D. C.

Joseph G. Sheehan
Department of Psychology, University of California Los Angeles
Los Angeles, California

Robert P. Stockwell
Department of English, University of California Los Angeles
Los Angeles, California

Marcel Verzeano*
Department of Biophysics and Nuclear Medicine
University of California Los Angeles
Los Angeles, California

Hans von Leden
Department of Surgery, University of California Los Angeles
Los Angeles, California

Joseph M. Wepman
Departments of Psychology and Surgery
The University of Chicago
Chicago, Illinois

---

* Not present

**CARL WERNICKE**

1848–1905

The publication of Wernicke's epochal *Der aphasische Symptomen-complex. Eine psychologische Studie auf anatomischer Basis* in 1874 marks the start of the development of a scientific approach to aphasia.

# CONTENTS

# CARL WERNICKE, THE BRESLAU SCHOOL, AND THE HISTORY OF APHASIA*

NORMAN GESCHWIND

Veterans Administration Hospital

Boston

The political difficulties of Germany at the close of the eighteenth century were reflected in the fortunes of the German universities, a large number of which either disappeared or merged with other institutions. The list of the universities affected included some of the most distinguished of the medieval foundations. Wittenberg, so closely associated with Luther and the origins of the Reformation, dissolved to be united with Halle in 1815. It was not alone. The two decades from 1798 to 1818 also witnessed the total or partial dissolution of the universities of Mainz, Cologne, Bamberg, Dillingen, Duisburg, Rinteln, Helmstedt, Salzburg, Erfurt, Altdorf, Frankfurt-an-der-Oder, Ingolstadt, and Münster.

It might have been expected that this massive disappearance of ancient seats of learning would have weakened seriously the position of German scholarship. The political conditions of the time might appear at first view to have been equally unfavorable to the flowering of learning. After the Congress of Vienna, Germany consisted of thirty-five princely states and four free cities, each in total control of its own internal affairs.

As is so often the case, however, the obvious rational expectation turns out to be incorrect, and the 19th century was in fact a period of great success for German scholarship. There were several factors which played a role in this upsurge of learning. For one, periods of confusion are sometimes more conducive to that passion and freedom which is so essential to great scholarship than are periods of undisturbed tranquillity. The professor who lives under the threats of major disturbances consequent on political upheaval may well feel it worth his while to be daring in the precious periods available to him for research and may not see the use of those cautious attempts to climb the academic ladder that are more likely to take precedence in periods of relative quiet. The many German scholars who made their positions even more untenable by their participation in forbidden po-

* Some of the work discussed was done under a grant (MH 08472) from the National Institute of Mental Health to the Department of Neurology, Boston University Medical School.

1

litical activities must also frequently have paid little attention to the long-range effects of their scholarly works on their formal academic careers.

But there were perhaps deeper reasons for the growth of the German universities despite the buffetings of the time. Reforms are often easier in periods of upheaval, when ancient practices lose their emotional force. Many of the universities which disappeared in the early 1800's were in fact, despite their illustrious histories, only medieval relics which deserved to vanish. Their dissolution in some cases strengthened other institutions which absorbed their faculties. The place of these extinct institutions was taken by newer and more vigorous centers more suited to the new times. Two of the greatest universities, Berlin and Bonn, were founded in the second decade of the 19th century, while Munich, another great seat of learning, was reorganized.

The crazy-quilt pattern of independent principalities probably was favorable rather than detrimental to the growth of learning. In such countries as France and England, where the medieval fractionation of power among independent duchies and baronies had long since been abolished, there had been a powerful trend toward centralization of cultural life in or near the capital, to the detriment of provincial cities and universities. In Germany, by contrast, almost any professor could feel satisfied that he was in or near a capital. Julius Caesar is said to have asserted that it was better to be first in some remote village than second in Rome. How much better, however, to be first in some remote village if it is also the seat of a king. Another benefit of the decentralization of power was that many states took pride in their universities and supported them more handsomely than would a central government anxious to concentrate its efforts on the aggrandizement of the capital. Many of the German princes prided themselves on their roles as patrons of learning.

There was still one further element in German university life which was beneficial to the widespread development of scholarship. One of the most useful features of medieval German university life had been carried over into the 19th century despite the decline of so many of the outworn traditions. The German student (often the able and ambitious one, although all too frequently the one whose main qualification was wealth) was likely to spend time at several universities, wandering like his medieval forbear to sit at the feet of great masters of learning. The professor who could build a metaphorical better mousetrap did indeed find the wandering scholars beating a path to his door. The great scholar or scientist could thus build his own prestige and not have to depend on that of his institution. This system also favored an interchange of ideas that kept intellectual life in ferment. Even if the German professor was perhaps too often the supremely remote *Geheimrat* who brooked no disagreement, the tendency for the student to go elsewhere insured the infusion of new ideas into the system. Moreover, there was a strong tradition of appointment of professors from the outside, which tended to prevent departments from freezing into a uniform pattern. This tendency to appoint outsiders extended even beyond national boundaries to include all of the German-speaking world and even some non-German speaking countries where German scholarship was dominant. The orbit thus included not only the German states but also much of the Austrian empire and Switzerland, and even Holland.

German neurology and psychiatry, like the rest of German medicine, shared in the benefits of this system. It received tremendous impetus from the growth of nationalism, yet enjoyed the psychological and material advantages of decentralization, and so participated in the cross-fertilization resulting from the free movement of scholars. While in France and England the growth of neurology and psychiatry was very closely tied to London and Paris, these fields of knowledge flowered widely throughout the German-speaking world. The independence of the many great centers was so well established that it survived even the unification of Germany and the increased emphasis on Berlin as the capital of the amalgamated empire. This impetus carried well into the 20th century. Permanent major contributions came from such widely dispersed centers as Berlin, Breslau, Frankfurt-am-Main, Graz, Halle, Heidelberg, Jena, Königsberg, Leipzig, Munich, Prague, Vienna, and Zürich, and from such workers as Westphal, Jolly, Bonhoeffer, Wernicke, Alzheimer, Liepmann, Oppenheim, Edinger, Goldstein, Kleist, Krafft-Ebing, Wagner von Jauregg, Anton, Freud, Hitzig, Kraepelin, Nissl, Berger, Flechsig, Meynert, von Gudden, Grashey, Pick, Forel, Bleuler, Foerster, von Monakow, Vogt, Brodmann and Spielmeyer, to name only the most distinguished of those working at the turn of the century or immediately afterwards.

Aphasia was one of the most vigorously pursued areas of neurological study in the forty years from 1874 to 1914, and its fountainhead was Carl Wernicke, working in one of the most peripheral of the German universities, Breslau. This, the eighth largest of the German cities and a major industrial center, was the capital of the Prussian province of lower Silesia. It must have been very different from the great universities of the German heartland because of its nearness to and long historical associations with Slavic Europe. It bordered on the Polish province of Galicia, which itself had a very heavy admixture of Jews on a background of Poles and other Slavs.

Carl Wernicke was born in Silesia, in Tarnowitz (now Tarnowskie Gory), not far from the Galician border and now also part of Poland. He grew up in a family of very reduced circumstances, worsened by his father's death when Wernicke was 17. His mother was nevertheless able to provide for his further education in the hope of his becoming a minister. Just before his final examinations, she too died. In 1870, at the age of 22, Wernicke was graduated in medicine. After a brief period in the university's eye clinic and as assistant to a surgeon in the Franco-Prussian war, he joined the psychiatric service at Breslau.

In 1874, when only 26, he published his epoch-making work on aphasia, *Der aphasische Symptomencomplex,* subtitled *Eine psychologische Studie auf anatomischer Basis* (34). This 72-page monograph was to set the tone for research in aphasia over the next forty years. Aphasic disorders had been recognized sporadically over several centuries and there had even been some impressive clinical studies; Professor Arthur Benton (2) has reviewed these early developments. The modern history of aphasia clearly begins with Paul Broca, whose achievements have recently been reviewed by Macdonald Critchley (4) and Robert Joynt (17). There has been considerable argument between the supporters of Broca and those of Dax over the difficult question of priority. However, it appears that the work of Dax, like that of the other forerunners, was at best an isolated flash of insight which set no new activities in motion.

Why was Wernicke's work so important? He was certainly not the first to study aphasia after Broca. Hughlings Jackson indeed had already entered this field actively by the mid-1860's. Credit is often given to Wernicke for the discovery of those forms of aphasia in which comprehension is impaired. Yet Bastian (1) had described such disturbances in 1869, as had Schmidt (29) in 1871. Nevertheless, it was Wernicke's paper, not the observations of Bastian and Schmidt, which brought home to the neurological world the existence of the sensory varieties of aphasia. Furthermore, Wernicke's publication also succeeded in showing with postmortem material that this type of aphasia had a different localization from that described by Broca. Thus he resolved the confusion that had followed on the finding of aphasic patients without lesions in Broca's area. Yet the most important contribution in this paper lay at a still deeper level: it is reflected in Wernicke's subtitle, "A Psychological Study on an Anatomical Basis." It is worthwhile to consider the previous history of aphasia in order to understand this point fully.

Broca's discovery resulted from an attempt to test a prediction made by workers in the phrenological tradition. It might have been anticipated that his success would have strengthened the cause of phrenology; actually, it hastened the downfall of that system since it increased the demand of neurologists for a theory which could link the new knowledge meaningfully with other knowledge—something phrenology, even in its most sophisticated form, could not supply. It was precisely this demand that Wernicke satisfied. Not only did he provide new evidence for the localization of aphasia but also set forth a theory which tied these phenomena to existing neurological knowledge. He thus made possible the development of a scientific approach to aphasia. On the basis of this theory it was possible to predict the existence of syndromes not previously seen and to devise experimental means of testing hypotheses. No one had previously supplied this. Little wonder that the appearance of this paper by an unknown 26-year-old physician, with less than four years of clinical experience and only six months study of anatomy under Meynert in Vienna, was considered so astonishing.

It was the theoretical aspect of Wernicke's approach that made it so fruitful over the next forty years and gave it such viability. However brilliant the clinical insights of a Jackson or a Head may have been, they suffered from not being readily derivable from anatomical facts nor being fruitful in devising new experiments. The Wernicke approach has been forced to adapt itself repeatedly to criticism, but in the end the core of Wernicke's method has remained consistently useful over the years.

Wernicke's reasoning was simple. He applied Meynert's teaching on the fiber tracts of the brain to the problem of aphasia. The phrenologists, he argued, had been wrong in their attempt to localize such complex mental attributes as magnanimity or filial love; what was actually localizable were much simpler perceptual and motor functions. All the complex array of human intellectual attributes must somehow be woven from these few threads of different texture. The cortex could at its simplest provide two means of achieving this higher integration: it could store sensory traces in cells for long periods of time and, by means of association fiber tracts, it could link together different parts of the system. Meynert had already pointed out that what lay anterior to the fissure of Rolando was motor in function, what lay behind it was sensory. It seemed most reasonable to assume that traces of sensory impressions or of motor patterns should somehow be stored in regions adjacent to the appropriate elementary zones in the cortex.

The application to speech was immediate. Hitzig had already shown that at the lower end of the Rolandic cortex was a zone which, when stimulated on one side, led to bilateral movements of the mouth and the tongue. It was reasonable to assume that immediately in front of this zone lay a region where patterns of articulatory movements might be stored. This was exactly where Broca had placed the lesions in his cases, a localization repeatedly to be confirmed.

Meynert had asserted that the central end of the acoustic pathways lay in the vicinity of the Sylvian fissure. Thus it was reasonable to assume that traces of words should be stored near this zone. If this were the case, then an aphasia with loss of comprehension should result from lesions in this neighborhood. Necropsy of the patients recorded in Wernicke's paper amply confirmed these hypotheses.

Wernicke went further. The fact that these patients also showed an inability to comprehend written language was attributed to the circumstance that script is taught as an association to sounds and should therefore suffer with impairment in understanding sounds. Writing is lost for the same reason. The ability to repeat would obviously be lost. The speech of the patient would be fluent, even rapid and paraphasic* because of the loss of the internal correction of the activities of the motor speech zone by the receptive speech zone.

He argued further that a different lesion, sparing the receptive and motor speech zones but destroying the pathway connecting them, should lead to a characteristic syndrome, that of paraphasic speech (again, because of loss of the internal correction of the motor speech area by the receptive speech zone), and yet normal comprehension. He thought the lesions would lie in the insula.

This he called *Leitungsaphasie* or conduction aphasia. A severe critic of his own work, Wernicke was haunted by the problem of conduction aphasia over the next thirty years, since it seemed to him that the clinical pictures and anatomical findings he had expected did not seem to concord. Although he saw many patients with paraphasic speech and good comprehension, he did not always find the expected lesions. Further, he had seen lesions of the insula unaccompanied by this clinical picture. This confusing situation became clarified in two ways. Wernicke had first placed the pathway between the posterior and anterior speech regions in the insula, but he was later to be convinced by von Monakow's researches that the major pathway between the two speech areas lay in the arcuate (or superior longitudinal) fasciculus in the lower parietal region. Most later students of the problem have agreed with this localization.

There was, however, an even more important source of error which resulted from Wernicke having failed to analyze his own diagram correctly: he had omitted the deduction that there should be a disturbance of repetition in conduction aphasia. Lichtheim (21) in 1885 correctly added the deduction and cited a patient showing this condition. Freud (7) returned to this problem in 1891 and, although he cited Lichtheim extensively, he seemed to have missed in part some of Lichtheim's extension of Wernicke's theory. Freud argued, as Lichtheim had, that the lesion disconnecting the motor from the sensory speech area should produce a loss of repetition in the face of intact comprehension, and went on to remark that this situation is highly unlikely. Yet within the next twenty years the triad of paraphasia, intact comprehension and impaired repetition was to become well known. In 1904 Karl Kleist, then an assistant of Wernicke's at Halle, demonstrated a case which finally convinced Wernicke of the existence of this entity. Kleist was to describe several such cases. In addition, the syndrome was described by others, such as Liepmann, Pappenheim, Pötzl, and Stengel. Kurt Goldstein (10) (who had also been a student under Wernicke) called the complex of paraphasia with intact comprehension and poor repetition "central

---

* The term "paraphasic" is used to characterize particular incorrect word usages in the speech of aphasics. Paraphasias may consist in omission of parts of the word, substitution of incorrect sounds in the word, correct words incorrectly used, or complete neologisms.

aphasia".* In recent years interest has again revived in this entity and its existence has been reconfirmed.

Wernicke's mode of analysis was quickly taken up. Lichtheim (21) was able to predict the lesion necessary to produce pure word-deafness. It remained for Liepmann (23, 27) to confirm this hypothesis by a necropsy on a superbly studied patient.† Dejerine's brilliant analysis of isolated acquired reading defects (5) was developed on a further extension of Wernicke's original analysis.

The final reason for Wernicke's importance extends beyond his work on aphasia. He had the ability, not common to all distinguished figures, of developing great students. The roster of those who came under his influence at Breslau is impressive: it was not merely that his students were distinguished; they learned to develop to full advantage that combination of talents which had served Wernicke so well, a profound respect for careful observation and a feeling for the elucidation of mechanisms.

His own activities extended into many fields and most of his contributions are now part of the foundations of neurology. He elucidated (with Mann, cf. 18) the pattern of weakness in spastic hemiplegias, described what is now known as Wernicke's disease and its pathology, proved the origin of cortical deafness in bilateral temporal lesions, traced the pyramidal tract to the spinal cord, and established much of the picture of cortical sensory loss. He contributed greatly to developing the symptom picture of organic psychoses. He brought to recognition the important distinction between remote memory and the ability to learn new material.

This great productivity had a profound effect on his pupils. Karl Bonhoeffer was the first of Wernicke's assistants to be offered the "Habilitation" (the first step in being formally permitted to teach publicly at a university). This followed Bonhoeffer's demonstration that a patient with unilateral chorea (until then always regarded as a functional psychiatric disorder) had a lesion in the midbrain. Bonhoeffer became professor in Breslau after Wernicke's departure for Halle, and subsequently was to hold the chair of psychiatry and neurology in Berlin. He devoted himself to many problems, including aphasia and cerebellar speech disturbances; he wrote the classical descriptions of alcoholic delirium and other alcoholic psychoses and of the memory disturbances in Korsakoff's syndrome; he delineated the generally accepted clinical manifestations of the toxic psychoses.

If the leading academic psychiatrist of Germany after World War I was a pupil of Wernicke's, so was the leading German neurosurgeon, Otfrid Foerster, who eventually became chief of the neurological clinic in Breslau.

---

* Some authors have recently used Goldstein's term "central aphasia" in a much broader sense than Goldstein. He specifically equated his "central aphasia" to conduction aphasia.
† Some authors mistakenly assume that Wernicke described pure word-deafness in his 1874 monograph. He did not and, as already noted, the aphasia he described involved all aspects of speech. Lichtheim predicted and Liepmann demonstrated that pure word-deafness was the result of disconnection of auditory stimulation from an intact Wernicke's area.

In a series of papers (cf. 33, 36) published over a period of nearly forty years he recorded an impressive list of contributions. He pioneered in the field of rehabilitation, made extensive studies of disturbances of movement and coordination and of the surgical treatment of these disorders. His work on sensation is classical and includes studies on the anatomy of the sensory pathways and on the neurosurgical treatment of pain. Some of his greatest contributions came from his studies of stimulation of the human brain and of epilepsy and its surgical treatment. He wrote little on aphasia but even this little reflected the influence of Wernicke's teaching. For example, the first description of the speech disturbances resulting from frontal parasagittal excisions was presented by Schwab and Foerster in 1927 (30).

While Bonhoeffer and Foerster were the most prominent of his pupils, other students of Wernicke also made great advances, especially in the study of the aphasias and related disorders. His assistant Lissauer was to apply the same principles to an analysis of the study of the agnosias. Hugo Liepmann, another assistant, produced almost singlehandedly in a few years the classical clinical pictures and methods of analyses of the apraxias. Of all his students Liepmann brought Wernicke's method of analysis of the higher functions to its most brilliant and most significant development; his name in this field deserves a place with those of Broca and Wernicke.

Liepmann's early background contrasted sharply with that of Wernicke. While the master had grown up in difficult circumstances, Liepmann was born in 1863 to wealth, and remained a man of independent means throughout his life. He had begun his career in philosophy with a Ph.D. thesis on the atomistic ideas of Leucippus and Democritus, and later on he published a work on Schopenhauer. Liepmann received his second degree, in medicine, in 1894 at the age of 31. Already five years older than Wernicke when the latter produced his early masterwork, Liepmann was not long in making up for lost time. In 1895 he published his first neurological work (22), a pioneer study on the experimental production of hallucinations —a neglected pathfinding work in a field in which interest has revived only since the last war. That same year he went to Breslau to spend his four most important formative years. In this period he made his study of pure word-deafness and confirmed at postmortem examination Lichtheim's anatomical predictions. In 1900 he returned to Berlin and during the next decade wrote his series of papers on apraxia; he was the first to use this term in its modern sense. Liepmann's first important paper in this area, the study of the *Regierungsrat* (24), was published in 1900. His accomplishment was twofold: he began by demonstrating that a patient who at first appeared to be globally demented had in fact an unprecedented combination of remarkable disturbances; he then proceeded to predict, on the basis of the known anatomy of the cortex and its fiber pathways, the localization of the lesions. Two years after the publication of this paper and its predictions as to the underlying pathology, the patient died and the necropsy confirmed Liepmann's expectations. Wernicke was especially delighted with this work, as well he might be: it remains to this day the most brilliant example of the "psychological analysis on an anatomical basis" which the master had first developed a quarter of a century earlier.

Liepmann continued this work in the following years. In 1907 he and Otto Maas (26) described the clinical picture resulting from disconnection of the hemispheres by a lesion in the corpus callosum which was demonstrated at necropsy. Goldstein, also a former student of Wernicke's, was to confirm this a year later with another proven case (9). Other case reports followed, including one published by Bonhoeffer (3). This work was generally neglected in the English-speaking world and only today are we rediscovering the callosal syndromes which were common knowledge to Liepmann's contemporaries.

It may seem to some that this account of the Breslau school and its approach to aphasia neglects the existence of other streams in the history of the study of the higher functions of the nervous system. It might appear that there were really two separate streams, that initiated by Wernicke, which emphasized localization, and that including Marie, Head, von Monakow, Goldstein, and Pick, which was anti-localizationist. It would take us too far afield from our discussion of the history of the Breslau school to treat this problem thoroughly. None of their critics brought evidence to discredit the major conclusions of Wernicke and his followers. Head's clinical description and localization of syntactic aphasia, for example, were the same that half a century earlier Wernicke had given to that form of aphasia which now bears his name. Head's verbal aphasia obviously corresponds to the classical Broca's aphasia and indeed was given the same localization. Similarly, Pierre Marie's localizations of aphasia were highly classical despite his criticism of earlier approaches. As Liepmann was to point out, the list of the localizations of apraxic lesions advanced by the great Russian-Swiss neurologist von Monakow was identical with Liepmann's much older list. Finally, Goldstein, in his writings over forty years (including his 1948 book on language, 11), supported the main conclusions of the Wernicke approach and has always praised Liepmann's epoch-making work.

Why this apparent discrepancy with the common view of two opposed streams? I believe that the answer will be found in a closer examination of the European literature on aphasia prior to World War I, on reading which one soon realizes that there was no wholesale rejection of the Wernicke approach by any of the major figures. But if the Wernicke approach remained, as it were, the central theme of nearly all the later efforts, it was to be elaborated in different ways. Wernicke had placed the pivot in his subtitle, "A Psychological Study on an Anatomical Basis." In one direction the theory could lead to an excessive multiplication of specific centers, a neophrenological approach, so to speak. Such proliferation of *ad hoc* centers had been as far from Wernicke's mind in 1874 as it was from Liepmann's a generation later. The extreme mosaicist view suffers from the same shortcomings as the phrenological view: mechanisms become unimportant and the whole point of linking psychology and anatomy vanishes. This pole of extreme mosaicism was supported not by Wernicke or his great student Liepmann, but by others such as Jendrassik, Henschen and Kleist.

If the theory ran into danger from a tendency of some toward excessive parcellation, it also ran into difficulties from the tendency of others to overemphasize the psychological study of aphasia, an approach which in its extreme form denied the importance of anatomy, or argued that aphasia must be considered completely separately on the psychological and anatomical levels. Even this view, however, was generally built on the core of the Wernicke approach. Thus Goldstein, who is often regarded as the spearhead of the psychological orientation, actually supported the main anatomical tenets of the Wernicke school; indeed some of Goldstein's writings, for example on callosal syndromes (8, 10), explicitly supported Liepmann's analysis, which was obviously in the classical Wernicke tradition. It is striking that advocates of precise localization were often criticized for speaking of the concept of "center", yet this notion reappeared extensively in Goldstein's writings as the "concept field" (Begriffsfeld). Goldstein hastened to add that by this he meant no localized region but an extensive area of the brain outside the speech region (which he divided classically into sensory and motor zones). Yet Wernicke himself had disavowed a concept center as a localized entity and used this term in essentially the same sense as Goldstein's later use of Begriffsfeld.

It is perhaps not surprising that the differences between views lessen when they are considered from our current vantage point. In the heat of scientific dispute it may be easily overlooked that investigators, in fact, agree far more than they disagree. The central theme of Wernicke's approach survived the extremist pressures, and actually the study of aphasia gained from the criticisms. The attacks by the holistically oriented forced a constant reappraisal of clinical criteria so that nonfocal phenomena could be distinguished from focal disturbances; although such advocates of localization as Charcot had stressed the effects of early experience, the holists had also asserted the importance of this factor; it was the localizer Bastian who was praised by Freud (7) and Goldstein for emphasizing that differences in the clinical picture might reflect not the site but the intensity of damage—the holists, however, advanced this point more persistently. Writers like Goldstein, agreeing with such highly anatomically oriented workers as Niessl von Mayendorf, stressed the equipotentiality not of the whole brain, which was clearly untenable in any strict sense, but of the individual more or less localizable "center"; it was the holist Goldstein with his emphasis on the flexibility of the brain who made the strongest attack on the problem of re-education in aphasia, yet it was the localizer Foerster, one of Wernicke's leading pupils, who had been the first to establish rehabilitation as a major neurological activity. The holists were more active in linking linguistics to aphasia, yet Pick, one of the pioneers in this approach, had been of the first to support Wernicke's views on the localization of sensory aphasias. If the holists were excessively outspoken, they were certainly not unimportant and they left their permanent seal on our thinking about aphasia; they studied new areas, fostered therapy, and forced refinement of clinical observation and anatomy. They had a profound effect on the course of the stream but they did not establish a new channel.

The mosaicists were also useful. If their anatomy had no link to psychology, their researches could be used by others who were more oriented in that direction. They made fundamental advances in our knowledge of the gross and fine anatomy of the cortex. If the holists had an aversion to discovering new syndromes, the mosaicists performed a valuable service in discovering remarkably isolated disturbances which cried out for explanation. It is perhaps comforting to consider that the activities of highly skilled and intelligent men are rarely totally wasted, even when wrong. The history of discovery in aphasia would have been poorer if the field had been diverted into either channel; its future history will be the richer if the many channels explored by those on either bank of the main stream are investigated further.

The Breslau school, so richly rewarded in its scientific activities, was not to find the outside world quite so satisfying. Inadequate formal recognition, indeed even active administrative persecution, and violent events harassed the careers of the major figures of this school. Wernicke was involved in difficulties from the start. Following the publication of his early masterwork in 1874 he left Breslau to Work in Berlin at the Charité Hospital under Westphal. But within two years he was dismissed because, as Liepmann (25) put it, "he came into conflict with the direction of the Charité in a non-scientific and nonofficial situation, which was intensified by Wernicke's obstinacy. . ." What the situation was I have not found recorded, but one rumor at least is that it concerned a woman. Wernicke went into private practice with no academic connection. A possible appointment at Heidelberg was lost when he fell ill for six months. He applied for an appointment at Dalldorf, the Berlin municipal mental hospital, but was turned down, it is said at the instigation of the great pathologist Virchow, who was a powerful force in medicine in Berlin and who would not forgive the battle at the Charité. Wernicke was never allowed to forget the Charité incident. Not only was Virchow angered, but also Althoff, the Ministerial Director who harassed Wernicke for the rest of his life.

Finally, in 1885 an appointment at Breslau was realized. Wernicke's old friend, Förster, head of the ophthalmic clinic, succeeded in obtaining a post for his brilliant former pupil despite the opposition of Althoff, who had succeeded in blocking all other routes of advance. The years at Breslau were to have a bitter end, however. Wernicke had used the municipal psychiatric hospital as the source of most of his clinical material. He had tried fruitlessly for some years to have a university clinic built but had repeatedly been refused on economic grounds. Liepmann (25) records his repeated complaint, only too familiar to those in academic life, that "twelve million [marks] are granted without any further question for a warship, but the paltry million for a clinic is not to be had." The city fathers of Breslau, who had disliked the arrangement from the start, finally terminated the hospital connection; the psychiatric clinic now existed only on paper. For the next two years Wernicke was permitted to use patients for demonstrations in clinical lectures to students, but even this privilege was later withdrawn. Wernicke still had access to a neurological clinic and a private clinic. At least the marked decline in the work load of the department had the advantage of giving him considerably more free time to finish his *Foundations of Psychiatry* (35). It seems clear, however, that he lacked the ability to convince himself of the benefits of adversity.

Wernicke had more to suffer in these years. Three major professorships fell vacant. According to some he refused the chair vacated by Krafft-Ebing in Vienna in 1902. Niessl von Mayendorf claims that Wernicke would have been delighted to take over the chair once held by Meynert but that before he was approached several Viennese newspapers carried the statement that Wernicke would refuse if offered the position; according to von Mayendorf the rumor became generally accepted and therefore Wernicke never actually received the offer. A vacancy was created at Munich by the retirement of Bumm but was filled by Kraepelin, Wernicke's great opponent in purely psychiatric matters. Finally, the death of Jolly made available the directorship of the University Nerve Clinic at the Charité in Berlin, which Wernicke had left so unceremoniously twenty-eight years before. The medical faculty of the university nominated Wernicke as their first choice for the chair. But the Ministry of Education, under the direction of Wernicke's lifelong antagonist Althoff, turned him down and Ziehen, the professor at Halle, was chosen instead.

In 1903 the direction of the Breslau psychiatric hospital was returned to Wernicke. Five years of frustration could not but leave their mark, however, and in 1904 Wernicke accepted an offer from Halle for the position being vacated by Ziehen in his move to Berlin. He thus took over the chair founded by Hitzig, the originator of the experimental study of localization in the human brain. A brief period of slightly more than a year was then to be perhaps the happiest in Wernicke's life; at last he had achieved his desire for a university clinic.

He also developed other interests: he had never participated in sports because of his slight build but now took enthusiastically to mountain climbing, skating and cycling. On June 13, 1905 Wernicke and his assistant, Berthold Pfeifer, went cycling in the Thuringian forest. They met a wagon loaded with logs and as they cycled past it, Wernicke fell. A rear wheel of the wagon ran over his breastbone. He apparently surmised that his injury was fatal and told Pfeifer that he probably had a hemorrhage into the pericardium. He was taken to a nearby country inn. Concerned that the wagon driver should not be held responsible, he insisted that the blame was only his; it is recorded that in a quiet moment during this period he said, in the terminology of his own psychiatric textbook, "I am dying as the result of autopsychic disorientation." Kleist interprets this as meaning incorrect assessment of his own ability (to ride a bicycle). He died of his injuries on June 17, 1905, at the age of 57. The advances in thoracic surgery to be made a few years later might have saved him.

Of Wernicke's important pupils, Bonhoeffer was perhaps the most different personally. He appears from the descriptions of his biographers and the accounts of those who worked with him to have had the classical Greek quality of measure in all things. His own career had none of the upsetting character of Wernicke's. He left Breslau in 1903 for Königsberg and within a year took over the chair at Heidelberg which Kraepelin had vacated to move to Munich. Althoff, Wernicke's old nemesis, was angered by this change and threatened that Bonhoeffer would never again receive an appointment at a Prussian university. But with Wernicke's departure from Breslau, Bonhoeffer was called to take over his chair in that city. Althoff could not interfere since he was no longer in office. In 1912 Bonhoeffer went to Berlin, where he stayed for the remainder of his life.

This early history of uninterrupted success did not test Bonhoeffer's mettle and it was not until the tragic rise of Nazism in Germany that his tremendous personal strength was demonstrated. The rise of Hitler disturbed the usually well-ordered life of a professorial neuropsychiatric unit. Bonhoeffer handled these problems, as he had all others, with Apollonian equanimity. Quadfasel, one of his assistants, had shown his dislike of the new regime and was imprisoned despite his East Prussian Protestant ancestry; Bonhoeffer with the help of others was able to obtain for Quadfasel the immunity of a diplomatic railroad car to leave the country. Bonhoeffer's difficulties as the leading psychiatrist of the capital city of the Reich must have been prodigious but, as recorded by Stertz (32), he dealt with these problems with sovereign calm. He never had a picture of Hitler in his office, and after the passage of the sterilization laws by the Nazis he never reported a patient as hereditarily defective. Yet to a remark by an assistant that he hated the Nazis he replied, "A psychiatrist does not hate, he understands." His moral fiber seems to have been conveyed to others of his family circle. Of these the most distinguished was his son, Pastor Dietrich Bonhoeffer, who was despite his youth one of the leading figures in German protestant theology. He was one of the leading conspirators, along with his brother-in-law Dohnyani, in a plot to overthrow Hitler; arrested and imprisoned, he refused under torture to give the names of his co-conspirators. He and his brother Klaus were killed within a month of the end of the war.

Somehow the elder Bonhoeffer survived it all. A son who had also come through this period became one of Germany's leading physical chemists. Karl Bonhoeffer lived to enjoy an eightieth birthday. The *Monatsschrift für Psychiatrie und Neurologie*, founded by Wernicke and Ziehen and edited by Bonhoeffer for many years, honored him with a special Jubilee issue.*

---

* *Mschr. Psychiat. Neurol.*, 1949, *117*, No. 4/5/6.

The American Psychiatric Association elected him an honorary member. Bonhoeffer regarded this, as Jossmann (16) pointed out, as a token of the revived internationality of science rather than as a personal honor. He had himself noticed the warning signs of the stroke of which he was to die on December 4, 1948. In the announcement of his death was the phrase, "Despite severe suffering, a happy life."

Of all of Wernicke's pupils, Otfrid Foerster was to have the most brilliant worldly success. He refused to leave Breslau but the world came to his door. The list of those who studied with him is a roll call of the modern leaders of neurosurgery. Sherrington even expressed the view that he was worthy of a Nobel prize. Personal tragedies, however, clouded his life. The coming of the Nazis added further burdens. His wife was of Jewish extraction and some of his outstanding assistants had been Jewish. In addition he was himself probably suspect for having spent two years in Russia as the physician of the hemiplegic and aphasic Lenin. Foerster lacked Bonhoeffer's Olympian detachment in the face of the Nazis and personally suffered more from the political changes. He died June 15, 1941 of tuberculosis.

Of all of Wernicke's assistants at Breslau, Liepmann is recorder by Kleist as being closest to him, and it was certainly he who was to repeat most exactly the first brilliant achievement of the master. His career was much like Wernicke's. After leaving Breslau, he returned to Berlin to work at Dalldorf, where Wernicke had been refused a post many years earlier. For nearly all the remainder of his career he stayed there, never to be offered a professorial chair despite the wide recognition of his work and his acceptance in Berlin as one of the outstanding lights of German neuropsychiatry. He was Jewish and, as Max Weber pointed out, Jews could not expect to advance in German academic life. Goldstein (13) mentions that Liepmann was told he would be offered an academic position if he changed his name and adopted Protestantism; although not religious, he refused on principle. His later years were darkened by the onset of Parkinson's disease. On his sixtieth birthday the *Zeitschrift für die gesamte Neurologie und Psychiatrie* honored him (15). Two years later, faced with the relentless progression of his disease, he committed suicide. So died Wernicke's most direct heir, "a worthy representative," as Goldstein put it, "of a great creative epoch in neurology."

## REFERENCES

In writing this paper the author has drawn heavily on many personal conversations with Drs. Fred A. Quadfasel and Paul Jossmann, both former assistants of Bonhoeffer in Berlin, and Professor Ernst Jokl, a former assistant of Foerster's, all widely cognizant of the history of German neurology and psychiatry. He has also consulted extensively the original scientific writings of the members of the Breslau school and their contemporaries. Other information sources are included in the following list.

1. BASTIAN, H. C., On the various forms of loss of speech in cerebral disease. *Brit. For. Med.-Chir. Rev.*, 1869, **43**: 209-236; 470-492.

2. BENTON, A. L., Contributions to aphasia before Broca. *Cortex*, 1964, **1**: 314-327.

3. BONHOEFFER, K., Klinischer und anatomischer Befund zur Lehre von der Apraxie und der "motorischen Sprachbahn". *Mschr. Psychiat. Neurol.*, 1914, **35**: 113-128.

4. CRITCHLEY, M., Broca's contribution to aphasia reviewed a century later. In: *Scientific Aspects of Neurology* (H. Garland, Ed.). Williams & Wilkins, Baltimore, 1961: 131-141.

5. DEJERINE, J., Contribution à l'étude anatomo-pathologique et clinique des différentes variétés de cécité verbale. *C. R. Soc. Biol.* (Paris), 1892, **44**: 61-90.

6. *Encyclopaedia Britannica*, 1960.

7. FREUD, S., *On Aphasia; a Critical Study.* International Universities Press, New York, 1953.

8. GESCHWIND, N., The paradoxical position of Kurt Goldstein in the history of aphasia. *Cortex*, 1964, **1**: 214-224.

9. GOLDSTEIN, K., Zur Lehre von der motorischen Apraxie. *J. Psychol. u. Neurol.*, 1908, **11**: 169-187; 270-283.

10. ———, Die Lokalisation in der Grosshirnrinde; nach den Erfahrungen am kranken Menschen. In: *Handbuch der Normalen und Pathologischen Physiologie*, Vol X (A. Bethe et al., Eds.). Springer, Berlin, 1927: 600-842.

11. ———, *Language and Language Disturbances; Aphasic Symptom Complexes and Their Significance for Medicine and Theory of Language.* Grune & Stratton, New York, 1948.

12. ———, Carl Wernicke (1848-1904). In: *The Founders of Neurology* (W. Haymaker, Ed.). Thomas, Springfield, 1953: 406-409.

13. ———, Hugo Karl Liepmann (1863-1925). In: *The Founders of Neurology* (W. Haymaker, Ed.). Thomas, Springfield, 1953: 326-329.

14. HAYMAKER, W. (Ed.), *The Founders of Neurology.* Thomas, Springfield, 1953.

15. ISSERLIN, M., Hugo Liepmann zum Gedächtnis. *Zschr. Neurol. Psychiat.*, 1925, **99**: 635-650.

16. JOSSMANN, P. B., Professor Karl Bonhoeffer, 1868-1948. *Am. J. Psychiat.*, 1949, **106**: 159-160.

17. JOYNT, R., Paul Pierre Broca: his contribution to the knowledge of aphasia. *Cortex*, 1964, **1**: 206-213.

18. KIRCHHOFF, T. (Ed.), *Deutsche Irrenärzte* (2 vols.). Springer, Berlin, 1921, 1922.

19. KLEIST, K., Carl Wernicke (1848-1905). In: *Grosse Nervenärzte*, Vol. II (K. Kolle, Ed.). Thieme, Stuttgart, 1959: 106-128.

20. KOLLE, K. (Ed.), *Grosse Nervenärzte* (3 vols.). Thieme, Stuttgart, 1956, 1959, 1963.

21. LICHTHEIM, L., On aphasia. *Brain*, 1885, **7**: 433-484.

22. LIEPMANN, H., Ueber die Delirien der Alkoholisten und über künstlich bei ihnen hervorgerufene Visionen. *Arch. Psychiat. Nervenkr.*, 1895, **27**: 172-232.

23. ———, *Ein Fall von reiner Sprachtaubheit.* Psychiatrische Abhandlungen, Breslau, 1898.

24. Liepmann, H., Das Krankheitsbild der Apraxie ("motorischen Asymbolie") auf Grund eines Falles von einseitiger Apraxie. *Mschr. Psychiat. Neurol.*, 1900, **8**: 15-44; 102-132; 182-197.

25. ———, Wernicke, Carl. In: *Deutsche Irrenärzte*, Vol. II (T. Kirchhoff, Ed.). Springer, Berlin, 1922: 238-250.

26. Liepmann, H., and Maas, O., Fall von linksseitiger Agraphie und Apraxie bei rechtsseitiger Lähmung. *J. Psychol. u. Neurol.*, 1907, **10**: 214-227.

27. Liepmann, H., and Storch, E., Der mikroskopische Gehirnbefund bei dem Fall Gorstelle. *Mschr. Psychiat. Neurol.*, 1902, **11**: 115-120.

28. Niessl von Mayendorff, E., Hugo Liepmann (1863-1925). *Psychol. Med.*, 1925-1926, **1**: 257-277.

29. Schmidt, J. B., Casuistik. Gehörs- und Sprachstörung in Folge von Apoplexie. *Allg. Zschr. Psychiat.*, 1871, **27**: 304-306.

30. Schwab, O., Über vorübergehende aphasische Störungen nach Rindenexzision aus dem linken Stirnhirn bei Epileptikern. *Dtsche. Zschr. Nervenhlk.*, 1926, **94**: 177-184.

31. Shirer, W. L., *The Rise and Fall of the Third Reich.* Simon & Schuster, New York, 1960.

32. Stertz, G., Karl Bonhoeffer (1868-1948). In: *Grosse Nervenärzte*, Vol. I (K. Kolle, Ed.). Thieme, Stuttgart, 1956: 17-26.

33. Wartenberg, R., Otfrid Foerster (1873-1941). In: *The Founders of Neurology* (W. Haymaker, Ed.). Thomas, Springfield, 1953: 422-425.

34. Wernicke, C., *Der aphasische Symptomencomplex. Eine psychologische Studie auf anatomischer Basis.* Cohn & Weigert, Breslau, 1874.

35. ———, *Grundriss der Psychiatrie in klinischen Vorlesungen* (2nd rev. ed.). Thieme, Liepzig, 1906.

36. Zülch, K. J., Otfrid Foerster (1873-1941). In: *Grosse Nervenärzte*, Vol. 1 (K. Kolle, Ed.). Thieme, Stuttgart, 1956: 81-98.

# CENTRAL BRAIN MECHANISMS IN SPEECH

**LAMAR ROBERTS**
University of Florida
Gainesville

One of the oldest and most classic approaches to speech was through cerebral dominance and, accordingly, I turn to this area first. Mark Dax in 1836 supposedly read, but probably did not, a paper to the Medical Society of Montpellier, France, stating that loss of speech was associated with right hemiplegia and, therefore, with a lesion of the left hemisphere. This manuscript (6) was published by his son in 1865, four years after Paul Broca's excellent first publication in this field (3).

At first, handedness as an index of cerebral dominance or its relationship to speech was not considered. Later it was theorized that, a person being right-handed, speech therefore must be localized in the left cerebral hemisphere. Furthermore, it was assumed that speech would be localized in the right cerebral hemisphere of the left-handed.

Handedness was mentioned in practically all the reported cases of aphasia. These confirmed the fact that speech disturbances occurred in the right-handed who had left cerebral damage. A case was then reported of a left-handed man who suffered very extensive destruction of the left cerebral hemisphere and had no speech difficulty the remainder of his life. The theory was therefore confirmed! It should be noted, however, that this man had a right hemiplegia in infancy, so that the destruction of the left cerebral hemisphere occurred before, during, or shortly after birth. As time went on the majority of the cases reported were of the preceding two types, that is, aphasia or no aphasia, with left cerebral damage in the right- or left-handed respectively. Then left-handed cases appeared in which there was no previous history of brain damage, but in which aphasia was associated either with a right or a left cerebral injury. Later, ambidexterity came under consideration, and finally occurred the rare case of a right-handed man with right cerebral damage who had aphasia. Such theories as Foster Kennedy's (13) "stock brainedness" subsequently followed.

What do we know about handedness? Many animals prefer one paw or hand, but man is the only predominantly right-handed species. As far as I can ascertain, the time when man became right-handed is unknown, but approximately five per cent of the armies of Biblical Israel were left-handed.

What determines handedness? All of the studies of homozygous and heterozygous twins could be interpreted to make it appear as being due either to hereditary or environmental factors. By "environmental" is meant direct or indirect attempts by the parents and culture to induce conformity to right-handedness. The best evidence I can find in the literature to sustain a genetic position concerns the percentage of whorls and loops in the first interdigital fold in the right- and left-handed. The difference between ten per cent of the presence of whorls and loops for the right-handed and fourteen per cent for the left-handed is highly significant statistically (20, 23). However, this is not very impressive to me.

Blau (2), in a very interesting monograph, came to the conclusion that left-handedness was due to negativism. Subirana et al. (23) showed that abnormal electroencephalograms were more common in otherwise normal left-handed school children than in right-handed ones. Some people are ambidextrous but practically all of them prefer one hand, and I have preferred to classify them as predominantly left-handed or predominantly right-handed. Many of the so-called ambidextrous are actually ambilevous; that is, they are clumsy with both hands.

Handedness is a form of behavior in a particular individual. It may be influenced by psychological abnormalities, heredity, environment, brain damage, and perhaps other factors.

### Handedness and Speech Dominance

With the exception of individuals who incurred left cerebral damage early in life, the left cerebral hemisphere is usually dominant for speech, regardless of handedness. Therefore it would seem to me that the most important thing man inherits is a left cerebral hemisphere dominant for speech. Thus, it seems quite possible that right-handedness may have developed secondarily to speech dominance. It seems quite clear though, that if the right hemisphere is dominant for speech, the individual is more likely to be left-handed.

It has been suggested for a number of years that speech may be represented bilaterally, particularly in the left-handed. I do not believe that this has been proven in the literature as regards lesions in various areas. The Wada sodium amytal intracarotid arterial test (29) has added much information: in this test, following injection of sodium amytal into one carotid artery, there is contralateral hemiplegia, with or without aphasia, for a period of about five to ten minutes; the appearance of dysphasia following the injection indicates that the hemisphere tested is dominant for speech. It has been reported (I have not personally seen this demonstration) that aphasia has occurred with injection on each side, although to a greater degree on one side than on the other. Such cases are extremely rare and have been seen only in individuals with one or more previous cerebral injuries. The argument set forth here, nonetheless, is that the left cerebral hemisphere is usually dominant for speech, regardless of the handedness of the individual.

### The Development of Language

THE ORIGIN OF LANGUAGE. Of the numerous theories concerning the origin of language, the most reasonable in my opinion (although there is no real proof for it) is the action theory, i.e., to tell what is to be done in a given situation. As a beginning, this probably consisted of the second person singular of a verb of action; for example, "do that". It was used in the hunt for food, in attack, and in defense against animal and man.

THE MAKE-UP OF LANGUAGE. Each language has its own code but there are no fundamental differences in the codes. The basic unit in each code is the phoneme. In English there are 33 segmental phonemes, comprising nine vowels, twenty-one consonants, and three semi-vowels (h, w, y) (32). The number of segmental phonemes in other languages varies from as few as 13 to possibly as many as 45. In the normal enunciation of English speech there are 12 supra-segmental phonemes: four levels of pitch, four degrees of accent or stress or loudness, and four lengths of pause between phonemes, morphemes, work linkages, and utterances or sentences. A morpheme is the smallest meaningful linguistic unit.

In a very interesting monograph, Warfel (32) defines language as follows: "Language is a structural system of overt, learned and therefore noninstinctive, sequentially produced, voluntary, human, symbol-carrying vocal sounds by which communication is carried on between two or more persons." Thus, all that can be said in English results from a combination of the 33 segmental and 12 supra-segmental phonemes, just as all that can be written can be transliterated into 26 alphabetical letters, a unit of space, and 12 marks of punctuation, for a total of 39 symbols.

I mention this simply because I am convinced of the value of linguistic science in the study of aphasia and the cerebral localization of speech. It points to the complexity and yet analyzability of this response with which we are concerned.

THE LEARNING OF LANGUAGE. It is necessary for the auditory, kinesthetic, and visual systems to be intact to learn to speak normally. Can the child with loss of one or more of these systems learn to speak? Yes, but not as well as the normal child; there is something lacking in the deaf or blind child. The infant hears sounds in the environment, and he learns to babble. When he babbles, three things happen almost simultaneously: he hears the sound of his own voice, he receives kinesthetic sensations of the movements made in producing the sounds, and he sees the reactions to his sounds on the face of his mother or other persons. All three of these perceptions are necessary to learn to speak normally.

As the child is learning to speak, he is continually watching the face of his parents or siblings; at least, all six of my children did. Of course, at the same time there is reinforcement of the auditory and kinesthetic sensations.

Language must be, and is, simple. Despite the fact that our voices are all different and, therefore, our phonemes are different too, the child is able to understand his mother, father and siblings. The child learns to generalize, to abstract and, at the same time, to be specific or to be concrete.

The child has much more difficulty with some phonemes than with others. In recent years, with the coming of the electronics age, there have been many experiments in speech concerned with variation of the frequency, intensity, and time relationships. One might interpret a sound as a $p$ or $k$ depending upon its frequency and the vowel which follows it. Also, there is considerable variation among individuals as to the exact end point in the interpretation of the sounds heard. Cineradiograms have been made of the vocal apparatus—lips, mouth, pharynx, larynx, diaphragm, and so forth—of individuals while they were speaking. These films have been converted into sound signals and played back. Considerable alterations can be made in these films, and yet, when they are converted into sound signals and played back, they can still be understood.

Spoken language is simple, and every normal person can learn to speak. The same is true of reading and writing. Most children are able to learn to read and write, regardless of the methods employed to teach them. Some seem to have difficulty with the newer and faster scanning methods and do better with a system based on phonetics. A combination of the scanning and phonetic methods is perhaps the best.

EFFECTS OF LESIONS. It has been shown that peripheral lesions may produce defects which may be called partial auditory agnosia. These defects have occurred with eighth nerve tumors. The alterations seen in the speech audiograms of these patients are comparable to some of the defects classically described in auditory agnosia. My point here is that peripheral mechanisms appear to play a substantially greater role in complex auditory and speech discrimination than was formerly assumed.

Bilateral lesions in the region of the posterior part of the Sylvian fissure will produce cortical deafness. The exact extent of the auditory cortex in man is unknown; in lower primates it seems to go up into the inferior parietal lobule. Bilateral lesions in the region of the calcarine area will produce cortical blindness. The relationship between the primary occipital visual cortex and the inferior temporal cortex is unclear. In infrahuman primates, bilateral inferior temporal lesions are required to bring about visual disturbances. In man it seems that lesions of the nondominant, usually right, inferior temporal cortex produce difficulties in visual-motor tasks. Bilateral lesions in the region of the inferior Rolandic fissure will produce pseudobulbar palsy and inability to make the movements necessary for speech.

Lesions of the frontal lobes produce alterations in behavior which seem to be related to initiatives, rewards and punishments, fighting, fleeing, eating, and mating. Lesions in the inferior mesial temporal regions, particularly the hippocampi, induce disturbances in immediate memory. These patients have intact remote memories but are completely unable to recall what they had for breakfast five minutes before.

Now let us consider those lesions which have specific effects upon speech. I agree that a lesion anywhere in the cerebrum may be associated with the inability to recall a specific word at a specific time. This is the same type of effect that occurs with fatigue or drugs. I also agree with Hughlings Jackson's statement (12) that any acute lesion of the left cerebral hemisphere will result in some defect in speech. This defect, however, will very quickly disappear unless it involves specific speech areas.

Lesions in the supplementary motor area of Penfield will produce dysphasia. Disturbances in the execution of rapidly alternating movements, particularly of the opposite foot, occur with these lesions; the speech disturbances may be similar, namely a difficulty in rapid, coordinated responses. The entire supplementary motor area may be excised without permanent dysphasia. Lesions in the region of the posterior part of the second frontal convolution produce dysphasia associated with difficulty in writing, which certainly has comparable characteristics to speech; this is not simply a motor defect, as illustrated by our own and other cases in the literature—at any rate, it is transient. Lesions in the region of the posterior part of the third frontal convolution (Broca's area) produce a dysphasia; this defect is similar to the writing disturbances seen with the preceding lesion; it, too, will clear.

The most pronounced and prolonged disturbances in speech occur with lesions of the posterior speech area—the posterior temporal, inferior parietal, and anterior occipital region. The more anterior the lesion, the more the auditory aspects of speech are involved, and the more posterior the lesion the more the visual aspects are effected. The longest lasting dysphasias have occurred with lesions in this posterior temporoparietal area.

EFFECTS OF STIMULATION. With the patient under local anesthesia, electric current can be applied to various parts of the cortex to see what effects might be produced. Both positive and negative ones have occurred. The positive effect is vocalization—an either continuous or intermittent vowel cry, sometimes with consonant components; the patient continues to cry until the electrode is withdrawn or until he has to take a breath. This vocalization results from stimulation of the motor areas (primary and supplementary) of both hemispheres; similar vocalization occurs in lower primates.

Negative aspects such as complete arrest of speech, hesitation, slurring and repetition of words or syllables have occurred from stimulation in the motor areas of both hemispheres and in the dominant Broca's and temporoparietal regions. These effects are considered to be due to interference with either motor or speech systems. Other negative effects include confusion of numbers while counting, inability to name with retained ability to speak, and misnaming with or without perseveration. These dysphasic aspects have been evoked from the dominant Broca's, supplementary motor, and temporoparietal regions. In such cases, the dominant hemisphere has usually been the left one; and there is no difference in the effects produced by electrical interference in any of these speech areas.

### ANATOMICAL, PHYSIOLOGICAL AND PSYCHOLOGICAL CONSIDERATIONS

Auditory impulses are transmitted to the auditory cortex of both hemispheres; from there they are transmitted to interact with activity in the speech system. Comprehension of speech occurs during these transactions. The speech system consists of the three cortical areas (Broca's, supplementary motor and temporoparietal regions) and interrelated subcortical structures which probably include the pulvinar of the thalamus and other areas; the most important cortical area is the temporoparietal region. A further vital aspect is the participation of the ascending reticular activating system in focusing attention upon auditory stimuli.

Visual impulses are received in the visual cortex of both hemispheres and are then transmitted to interact with the speech system; probably there is also interaction with the auditory system. Comprehension of written material occurs during these transactions.

The mechanism of the energy source which initiates the original process of the production of speech and writing remains unknown. I prefer a holistic to a dualistic theory of behavior, but I do not know how to prove either, and so I would view speech and writing simply as different forms of verbal behavior. At any rate, following whatever does occur, impulses from the speech center system interact with those of the motor system, and the production of speech or writing occurs during these transactions.

In summary:

*a)* Handedness is determined by multiple factors: hereditary, environmental, psychological (normal and abnormal), brain damage, and perhaps others.

*b)* The left cerebral hemisphere is usually dominant for speech, regardless of the handedness of the individual.

*c)* Language must be, and is, simple.

*d)* Lesions in various locations produce specific defects.

*e)* Electrical interference in the dominant Broca's, supplementary motor, and temporoparietal regions produces dysphasic responses.

*f)* My preference for a holistic over a dualistic theory of behavior leads me to view speech and writing as simply different forms of verbal behavior.

### Discussion

*Masland:* I am greatly indebted to Dr. Roberts for this very succinct review of a tremendous amount of information now available regarding the localization of function in the central nervous system. Much of this information he himself contributed in the course of surgical explorations.

I recognize that in this review it has been necessary to pass over one or two of the fascinating enigmas of language development and structure. Dr. Roberts has documented the fact that in the large majority of adults the left hemisphere contains those structures whose integrity is essential for the normal processes of language. He mentioned in passing that this is not the case in those individuals whose left hemisphere had been injured in infancy. In fact, there is now substantial evidence to indicate that when the left hemisphere is severely damaged in infancy or childhood (up to, say, eight years of age) the language function may be handled excellently by the remaining portions of the nervous system.

In my personal experience and, certainly, in that of many others, it is possible to remove surgically the entire left hemisphere from such individuals without even a transitory disturbance of speech. This means, then, that in the infant the occurrence of lesions which are capable of producing severe and, in fact, permanent loss of language function in the adult, is without permanent effect. This being the case, how do we account for the language disabilities of infancy and childhood? Obviously, they must depend upon a different anatomical substrate from that which is characteristic of the adult.

There are several possible explanations, of which Dr. Roberts has mentioned one. Perhaps we should direct a more thorough investigation toward the role of the major afferent pathways for language, hearing, and perception; these are structures which are essential in the child or adult for the development of normal language function.

Only recently has it become evident that asphyxia of infancy and neonatal jaundice are important etiological factors in many of the language disabilities of childhood. Pathological investigations of such conditions, conducted by a number of people, more recently by Windle (33) in asphyxiated monkeys, have demonstrated that important lesions produced by these insults reside in the central structures of the brain and brain stem. Thus, one possible explanation for the language disabilities of the child is that they are in the central structures.

A second possibility is that we are dealing with bilateral lesions of the brain, and that the language disabilities of the child occur when both hemispheres have been injured. There would certainly be language disability if there is a bilateral disturbance or injury of the major afferent pathways to the hemispheres.

A third possibility concerns minor injury. Whereas a complete injury of the left hemisphere permits the language function to be transferred to the right hemisphere, partial or incomplete lesions of the left hemisphere in infancy may possibly lead to distortions of function worse than would occur with a complete lesion. We know that in many adults the existence of distorted brain tissue may be more disruptive of intellectual function than the complete absence of that portion of the brain.

There is a fourth possibility which relates to the fact that there appears to be a strong genetic factor in many instances of language disabilities in children. Possibly there are genetically based deviations of anatomical and physiological function which are associated with an intrinsic or constitutional inability to carry on some essential component function of language.

As our studies of these disabilities proceed, possibly we will be able to classify language-disabled children according to such basic characteristics. It is certain that the anatomical substrate of the adult aphasic must be different from the anatomical substrate underlying the developmental language disabilities of the child.

*Roberts:* I would just like to add one word of caution to what Dr. Masland said about hemispherectomies in childhood. In some of these patients, even though there is extensive destruction within the temporal and occipital region, there may be transient or persistent postoperative dysphasia following temporal or occipital lobectomies. There are cases reported of children with persistent difficulty in speech following hemispherectomy.

I agree completely that the speech cortex is involved in a developmental process, but I would not agree with Dr. Masland's statement that an entirely different anatomical substrate is involved in children. I think it is the same anatomical substrate we see in adults. I believe the most important factor is the fact that the plasticity of the brain of the child is so much greater than that of the adult that it allows him to function with his remaining brain to a much better extent than would be possible for the adult.

*Ajuriaguerra:* Organization of language centers in the child is fundamentally different from that in the adult. Up to a point I agree that there are no preformed language centers in the brain. In children, basic structures exist which are probably crucial, but they are less fixed and less organized. Only in rare cases do we find unilateral centers which are critical for language disorders in a child of three.

I feel that there are three underlying principles: (*a*) in the child, any interference with sensory motor processes may result in language disorganization; (*b*) there are no preformed centers of language in the young organism, but these centers spring into life easily in the very process of organization, becoming functional in the course of the process itself; (*c*) hemispheric dominance is much more labile in the child than in the adult.

In the last instance, although language is based on certain structural units in the central nervous system, it is not functional without participation in the process of communication. As Pierre Janet says, for every function there are organizations laid down in the central nervous system, but they will not be functional without the process itself, which works back on these structures. Language function is realized in the process of communication on the basis of certain possibilities; I do not mean to deny the fact that there are crucial structures in the nervous system. Apart from certain specific structural units, language comes into life in the making; it becomes functional in the process of use and in the framework of a certain code which is imposed on this activity.

In the adult, something happens similar to what Dr. Masland mentioned. In the dysphasic adult the results are better, the reading is better, if the occipital region is excised than if ablations are performed. On the other hand, if the larger insult is made in the other hemisphere, greater difficulty will be found. It is often preferable to have no structures than structures which lead to disorganization. I think the same is true for the temporal hemisphere as for the occipital. It is important to note that the process of language is a process in time, and this temporal process is different, not always coinciding with the structural type.

*Lindsley:* Going back to the differentiation between dominant and nondominant hemispheres, particularly the Wada test (29), which has been followed up by various investigators (17, 21, 25, 30, 31), I would like to mention the interesting use of the test by Rossi and his group (17, 21). They have found that intracarotid injections of sodium amytal or amobarbital on the side ipsilateral to the dominant hemisphere produced speech disturbances and emotionally depressive effects, whereas injections in the opposite internal or common carotid corresponding to the nondominant hemisphere caused no speech defects but did induce euphoric symptoms. Along with this, the injection on the dominant side accentuates contralateral peripheral reflexes and induces the Babinski response, suggesting that there is a peripheral release effect. At the same time, though, there is the interesting depressive effect when the dominant hemisphere is involved, and the euphoric effect in the contralateral or nondominant hemisphere. Rossi and his collaborators (21) find too that the electroencephalogram also distinguishes the dominant hemisphere after unilateral injections. Incidentally, they find that if sodium amytal is injected intravenously into the general circulation, about 400 mg are required to produce an effect, whereas 100 mg or less will suffice if injected in the carotid artery.

I wonder if Dr. Roberts, who no doubt has had experience with this test since Wada first described it (29), would care to comment further about that. One wonders how these barbiturates produce such selective and differential effects. We know that there are very well defined effects in the EEG after peripheral infusion, as Dr. Brazier and others have shown.

*Roberts:* I agree with Dr. Lindsley that there is a difference in the emotional response after injection of amobarbital into the cerebral circulation of the nondominant hemisphere as compared with the dominant hemisphere.

The euphoric effect seen with nondominant hemispheral injections is usually associated with denial of the contralateral hemiplegia; it is also true that
anosognosia is seen usually with nondominant hemispheral lesions. The de-
pressant effect which occurs with dominant hemispheral injections is associated with and may be related to the marked dysphasia.

*Magoun:* I was interested to note that Dr. Roberts differentiated origins
of language under the two headings, the phylogenetic and the development
in individual ontogeny. The phylogenetic aspects of language development
have, of course, long been of interest to the anthropologist but, because
speech has preceded writing, records of initial stages are inevitably missing.

The related ontogenetic development of speech and cerebral dominance
in contemporary man makes it of interest to note instances of the appearance of handedness in hominid prehistory. In Davidson Black's account (1)
of Sinanthropus, or Peking Man, artifacts of a rough stone nature were proposed as fitting themselves better toward use in the right hand than in the
left (14). At this intermediate stage of hominid evolution in the Middle
Pleistocene, approximately 350,000 years ago, one anthropologist has thus
proposed an indication of handedness in the use of tools.

There is a more precise indication of handedness in some of the cave
paintings of the Cro-Magnon period 25,000 to 50,000 years ago in Europe.
It was not uncommon for the human hand to be depicted in silhouette on
the cave wall. One hand was placed on the wall and pigment was blown or
paint was daubed around it, leaving the silhouette of the hand on the wall.
In one of the caves in which 35 hands were depicted, 28 of them represented the left hand and seven the right. When the left hand was represented, it can be assumed that it was placed on the wall and the right hand
used to make a silhouette of it. If this is so, in 80 per cent of the instances,
the right hand was employed for this procedure, implying a left cerebral
dominance.

*Roberts:* I certainly agree with Dr. Magoun's statements. I am not sure,
though, exactly how we ought to interpret them from the standpoint of
when these primitive individuals developed speech before the drawings of
the hands were made. And the exact relationship between the origin of
speech and handedness as interpreted from the cave drawings is unknown.

*Geschwind:* For anyone interested in language, the opportunity to deal
directly with the human brain of a live, conscious patient is a unique one.
The first to do this were Fritsch and Hitzig who, on the battlefield of Sé-
dan, made stimulation studies on exposed brains of wounded soldiers. Fortunately, their method is no longer used. The study of language changes
through brain stimulation was probably pioneered by Otfrid Foerster, the
great German neurosurgeon; Penfield & Roberts (16) have since conducted
the most extensive program of its kind. Despite the presence of a large
number of neurosurgical centers, this type of study has been attempted in

only a few places. We owe a debt to those carrying on this work because brain stimulation is one of the major areas of potential advancement.

I would like to comment first on the question of anatomical differences in the two hemispheres. Recently Bonin (26) discussed the data which purport to show that there are differences in the right and left hemispheres; while he was certainly correct in being cautious, I think in his conservatism he failed to show that at least some of the studies he cited deserve to be followed up.

The most important investigation of this type was done by Pfeifer (18), who studied the superior surface of the temporal lobes in both hemispheres. Economo & Horn (28) essentially confirmed his results. Pfeifer pointed out that in monkey there are usually two transverse gyri of Heschl (these are the cortical structures involved in hearing; they lie on the superior surface of the temporal lobe), which run more or less at right angles to the Sylvian fissure. This "simian pattern" is the same on the right and left sides and turns out to be the one which Pfeifer says is usually seen on the right side in humans. In the left hemisphere of man, another pattern is now seen more often, according to Pfeifer; instead of two clearly separate Heschl's gyri, there may be any of the following: one large gyrus, one large and one small gyrus, or two gyri which are incompletely separated. Another common feature on the left side is that the Heschl's gyri are angled forward more sharply. The intersection of the Heschl's gyri with the superior temporal gyrus is therefore seen further forward on the lateral surface of the left temporal lobe. The angling forward of the Heschl's gyri results in the presence of a small flat area behind them, the so-called planum temporale.

The difficulty with both Pfeifer's (18) and Economo & Horn's (28) papers is that neither provided statistics as to the relative prevalence of each type of pattern on the right and left sides. My colleague, Dr. Walter Levitsky, and I have therefore embarked on a large-scale survey of upper surfaces of temporal lobes to see if we can definitively confirm or reject Pfeifer's conclusions.

Assuming for the moment that Pfeifer's conclusions are correct, what significance can we attach to them? I think the probable reason that the Heschl's gyri are angled forward is that Wernicke's area, which is part of the auditory association cortex, has grown so extensively that it can be pictured as pushing the primary auditory cortex forward. It is particularly the expansion of Wernicke's area into the planum temporale which has this effect.

In order to deal with the problem of the phylogeny of language,* let us first consider how the human brain differs from that of lower animals. I may add parenthetically that occasionally the statement is made that there is no

---

* *Dr. Geschwind's note, after the Conference:* A more extensive discussion of the phylogeny of language was presented by the author at the 15th Annual Round Table Meeting on Linguistics and Language Studies (10).

obvious difference between the human brain and that of, say, a chimpanzee. This is of course not true, and the brain of man is significantly advanced
over that of even the highest of the anthropoid apes.

Where does the human brain differ? Its most striking development lies in
two regions: the frontal pole and the posterior inferior parietal region. Some
authors (e.g., Goldstein, 11) assert that these regions are not even present
below man. Others (e.g., Bonin & Bailey, 27) believe that the posterior inferior parietal region is in fact present below man, but even these authors
point out that relatively speaking the greatest increase in size in the human
brain as compared with the anthropoid brain is in the parietal region. If we
look further, we find other evidences for the advanced character of this region. Thus, as Flechsig (9) pointed out many years ago (Figure 1*), the posterior inferior parietal region is one of the last four regions of the human
brain to myelinate. Similarly, Yakovlev (35) has indicated that this region
matures very late in respect to its cellular architecture.

Let us consider the possible significance of the fact that this posterior inferior parietal region is relatively much more developed in man than in any
other animal. First I want to make a digression to consider some aspects of
the anatomical background of learning in the monkey, specifically concerning visual learning.

The visual cortex of a monkey sends connections mainly to adjacent regions of cortex, which form the visual association cortex. The largest long
connection of the visual association cortex is to the lateral and basal temporal lobe. The major connections of the lateral and basal temporal region are
to the limbic structures lying on the medial surface of the temporal lobe.
This section of the temporal lobe contains structures which make up part of
the so-called limbic system, that portion of the brain which connects with
the regions in which are represented both the subjective and objective manifestations of behavior related to the survival of the individual or the species
—the motor aspects of rage, flight and sexual behavior, the feelings of hun-
ger or thirst with the corresponding feelings of satiation, and other similar
behaviors and emotions. The main connections of the visual system in the
monkey thus run eventually to the limbic system. What is the reason for
this arrangement?

Consider the task of teaching a monkey to choose a visually presented
circle rather than a cross. In the usual experiments the monkey receives a
peanut if it chooses the circle, nothing if it chooses the cross. It has thus
formed an association between a visual stimulus and a food stimulus; in
more general terms, for the monkey to learn, it must form a visual-limbic

---

* Figure 1 is based on Flechsig's later modifications of his early maps (9), which show 36
  myelinogenetic regions. The changes are not major: thus in the earlier map the angular
  gyrus region is No. 34 and so was regarded as one of the last three zones to myelinate,
  while in the later figure the angular gyrus is denoted by No. 42, i.e., as one of the last four
  zones to myelinate.

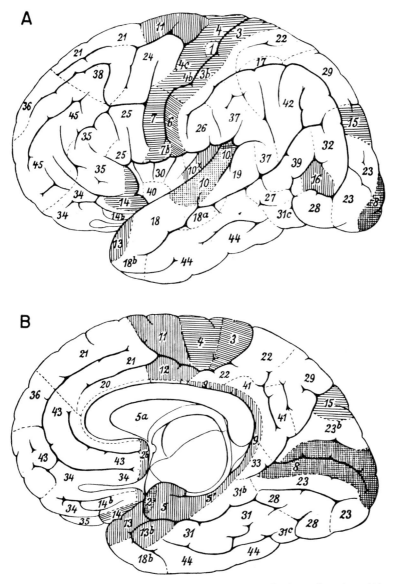

**Figure 1.** Flechsig's maps of myelinogenesis on the lateral surface (A) and the medial surface (B) of the human brain. The myelinogenetic areas are numbered in the order in which they myelinate, No. 1 being the earliest and No. 45 the last. In the view shown in A, the Sylvian fissure is opened so as to expose the insula. (Modified from Flechsig, 9.)

association. A monkey finds this sort of task easy, and it appears clear that it is designed anatomically to form such associations readily, since the largest connections of the visual system are with the limbic system. Thus the monkey can form visual-limbic associations, tactile-limbic associations, and auditory-limbic associations. One might say that the sign-systems of a monkey are concerned with forming associations between a non-limbic and a limbic modality.

It is sometimes stated that inter-modal or cross-modal associations, that is, associations between stimuli in two different sensory modalities, cannot be formed in the monkey. It is obvious, however, that the monkey can form such a connection as long as the association is between a non-limbic and a limbic stimulus. What is difficult for the monkey is to form a connection between two non-limbic stimuli.

This difficulty is demonstrated by several types of experiments using conditioning techniques. Another type of experiment is one performed by Ettlinger (7), who taught monkeys to choose one of two patterns visually; when the monkeys had learned this task, they were tested with the same patterns presented tactilely: the monkeys showed no evidence of any carryover and had to learn the tactile task completely anew.[*]

Such a task is, of course, extremely easy for man in contrast to its difficulty for the monkey. The usual answer is that man does the task by "verbal mediation", that is, he learns in the visual experiment to choose the object named "circle"; when the tactile experiment is done he again chooses the object named "circle". But a little reflection shows that by a simple inversion of this point of view we can arrive at a more important conclusion. What is important is not that we need language in order to have cross-modal associations: it is rather that in order to develop language we must be able to form non-limbic cross-modal associations. Thus, we learn to name objects by forming an association between the sight or feel of an object and a particular auditory stimulus, the "name" of the object. It is precisely this type of non-limbic cross-modal association which is difficult in the monkey.

This entire problem of intermodal associations represents a vast area for study. In studying their presence in children it is most important, however, that studies be conducted before the development of language, so that one can tell the age at which the child can begin to form non-limbic cross-modal associations. Presumably they will not be readily formed at first; as the child starts to acquire this type of association, he will be able to acquire language which is just a special case of this kind of non-limbic cross-modal connection.

*Osgood:* Are you familiar with the perceptual transposition studies of preverbal *versus* verbal children? Different effects are seen.

*Geschwind:* After language has developed, the cross-modal association to an auditory stimulus (the name) should dominate in transposition experiments. In younger children, particularly before cross-modal associations are readily made, one would expect a different pattern.

Animals below man also possess symbolic systems. What they lack, how-

---

[*] Ettlinger's result, strictly speaking, shows a failure of cross-modal transfer rather than cross-modal association. This does not, however, appreciably alter the conclusion. As already noted, experiments on cross-modal association in the strict sense show the great difficulty that subhuman forms have in carrying out this type of task.

ever, is non-limbic cross-modal symbolic systems. It is interesting that there is some suggestive evidence that the purest associations of this type are difficult to form. Thus children acquire object-naming early: seen objects usually have rich tactile associations. Color-naming tends to occur later, and the naming of a color is, of course, the formation of a rather pure visual-auditory association.

What is the basis for the fact that man can form these non-limbic cross-modal associations? It is, in my view, related to the development of that region of the brain which is most highly developed in a human compared to that of a subhuman primate, i.e., the angular gyrus region. This region myelinates, as I have noted, quite late.

*Lenneberg:* Flechsig's original myelogenetic map (9) seems to show that the entire area is late.

*Geschwind:* I do not think that the entire posterior parietal region develops equally late. Thus, if one consults Flechsig's diagram (Figure 1A) of the order of myelination, one finds the angular gyrus to be area 42. (This is not the Brodmann numbering of cortical areas but simply indicates that this is the forty-second region to myelinate.) Since there are 45 regions in Flechsig's diagram, the angular gyrus is one of the last four regions to myelinate. Immediately above and behind the angular gyrus are areas numbered 17, 29, 15, and 32. Immediately in front and below are the relatively late regions 39 and 37.

Yakovlev (35) has pointed out that the angular gyrus probably matures late in cellular structure and, in addition, he thinks it has a more complicated fissural pattern than is generally seen elsewhere on the surface of the brain.

As I noted, the visual system in the monkey eventually feeds into the limbic system. The same appears to be true for the somesthetic and auditory systems. Associations between these non-limbic modalities are formed only with difficulty. This in turn corresponds to the anatomical fact that anatomical connections between non-limbic association cortexes are sparse. Thus Sugar, French & Chusid (24), in their strychnine neuronographic experiments, did show some fibers between the auditory and visual association cortex, but in far smaller number than the large band of fibers running from the visual association cortex to the lateral and basal temporal lobe and eventually feeding into the limbic system.

The angular gyrus region in man probably makes up for this deficiency. Notice that it lies at the junction of the classical visual, auditory, and somesthetic association regions and is therefore admirably suited to act as an association area of association areas. It is, in my opinion, the anatomical substrate for the ready ability of man to make non-limbic cross-modal transfers. Yakovlev* has also suggested—very tentatively—that on the basis of some preliminary evidence it appears possible that the angular gyrus re-

---

* Personal communication.

ceives fewer thalamic afferents than the surrounding regions. If this is true, then it would truly be an association area of association areas since it would depend for its connections almost entirely on adjacent cortical regions.

While non-limbic cross-modal associations are easier for a human than for a monkey, they are not especially easy. It does take several years to learn speech.

Let us now further consider Flechsig's map (Figure 1) indicating the times of myelination of different brain regions mentioned by Dr. Lenneberg. All primary motor and sensory regions myelinate early (Figure 1A): the classical motor cortex includes the regions No. 1, 4 and 7; the classic sensory cortex Nos. 3 and 6; the visual cortex No. 8; and the auditory cortex No. 10. The brain of a rabbit might be considered to consist almost entirely of the low-numbered regions bunched together; the higher numbers are absent or the areas represented by them are very small. In the brain of the monkey the regions numbered 42 to 45 are very small or absent. The area numbered 37 in man probably is present in the monkey, although probably not as well developed as in man. Number 42 is the area which is the most markedly developed in man relative to its development in any lower form.

The same pattern is found in Flechsig's diagram of the medial surface of the hemisphere (Figure 1B); the association areas have the later numbers, the limbic and projectional regions have earlier numbers.

*Lenneberg:* I have some objections to your statement regarding Flechsig's myelogenetic area No. 42 and its absence in the monkey, in view of the fact that the homology of gyri in primates is very difficult to establish.

*Geschwind:* I agree with Dr. Lenneberg on this point. One would be in trouble if one were to make judgments only on the basis of homology of gyri. It is indeed often said that a certain part of the monkey's parietal lobe is the "angular gyrus". We must therefore find independent criteria: (a) the parietal lobe has grown more in man than any other lobe in comparison to the lower forms; (b) the monkey has no large area of cellular architecture similar to the human angular gyrus in its posterior parietal region; (c) along the interparietal fissure in man lies a band of cortex and white matter, the so-called visuo-sensory band of Elliot Smith (22), while below the angular gyrus region lies a similar band, and these bands, which have a distinctive cytoarchitecture and myelinate early, are said not to exist in apes; Smith suggested that these bands are residues of earlier connections which were left behind as the inferior parietal region grew so extensively in man.

*Lenneberg:* Myelogenesis has not been worked out for primates lower than man. How can you know what corresponds to what? I have not seen any theory of myelogenesis in anything but man.

*Geschwind:* I agree that myelinogenesis has not been studied in subhuman primates. I would, however, point out that every criterion for phylogenetic advancement is met by the angular gyrus region in man.

*Osgood:* I would like to ask a question before we leave this. Dr. Geschwind, you said that area 45 is also athalamic? I thought the frontal areas were quite richly connected. And let me ask a second question about areas 42 and 45: is it true that the systems from which these do receive thalamic afferents are not as richly supplied with thalamic afferents as the primary projection areas?

*Geschwind:* Yes, the region in Flechsig's diagram numbered 45 and lying in the frontal lobe receives very few thalamic afferents. Yakovlev (34) has studied the problem and has found from lobotomy material that this part of the frontal pole receives very few thalamic afferents. A monkey does not have a similar region or, if it does, it is very small. This means that human and monkey lobotomies are probably not quite the same procedure anatomically.

*Lindsley:* In speaking about the visual cortex of the monkey, Dr. Geschwind, you seemed to portray its organization in a fashion similar to that in the human. In my understanding, area 17 extends over the convexity of the occipital lobe almost to the lunate sulcus, which is bordered by area 18; area 19 is a small strip still more anterior. Marshall & Talbot (15) indicate that the center of the macular projection is far lateral and forward toward the sulcus lunatus. Poliak (19) also locates the cortical projection of the fovea very far forward and laterally. Areas 18 and 19, I believe, are regions where Le Gros Clark & Northfield (5) have found a richness of projections of the pulvinar, as in the superior temporal gyrus, despite the fact that the pulvinar does not receive auditory or optic tract afferent fibers directly.

*Geschwind:* These visual regions are really not reversed in monkey and man and are organized similarly in both species. Brodmann's area 17, which is the visual cortex, does extend more onto the convexity in a monkey than in a man, but it also extends onto the medial surface. Brodmann's area 18 is visual association cortex, and is probably the region that receives connections from the pulvinar. It lies anterior to the visual cortex on the convexity in both man and monkey.

*Roberts:* I should like to differ considerably with Dr. Geschwind's view that non-limbic cross-modal associations are easy for the child to learn but difficult for the monkey. I think it is difficult for the child as well as for the monkey. It is not an easy task for a child to convert from the visual to the tactile or to the auditory, and I think it takes a considerable period of time. I believe that this period of time is comparable to that seen in the monkey for learning cross-modal association between a visual and tactile task or other non-limbic association.

Against the view that areas 42 and 45 are completely without connections to the thalamus, we have several cases now which have been studied at postmortem showing definite pulvinar connections with this posterior inferior parietal and junction of temporal region. I am afraid I would have to see Yakovlev's data in order to compare the interpretation of our data with his.

*Lenneberg:* I should add that I do not essentially disagree with Dr. Geschwind, but I think one can become very puzzled by the lack of congruence between cytoarchitectural, myelogenetic, dendrogenetic, and other maps. As an illustration, I would mention a map showing the cortical projection areas of thalamic nuclei in man, the work of Feremutsch (8), a German anatomist who has made comparative studies of chimpanzee and man. His problem was to work out homologies between the two forms, since projection area borderlines have never been defined exactly. Another example is Bonin's cytoarchitectural map, familiar to many of you, I am sure. Since cytoarchitecture is very far from being coterminous with behavioral maps such as cortical maps for language function, one wonders whether there is any connection between speech function and architecture.

*Lindsley:* In that connection, I wonder if the work of Buser, Borenstein & Bruner (4) on electrophysiological responses of this general area, which seems to be considerably broader than had been conceived before in terms of cytoarchitecture, may not contribute something further along this line. It seems to me that neurophysiological studies, together with behavioral studies of perceptual discrimination, may give us considerably more information than we obtain from architectonic studies based solely on histology.

## REFERENCES

1. BLACK, D., YOUNG, C. C., PEI, W. C., and DE CHARDIN, T., Fossil man in China. *Mem. Geol. Surv. China*, Ser. A., 1933, No. 11.
2. BLAU, A., *The Master Hand. A Study of the Origin and Meaning of Right and Left Sidedness and Its Relation to Personality and Language.* Res. Monog. No. 5, Am. Orthopsychiat. Ass., New York, 1946.
3. BROCA, P., Remarques sur le siège de la faculté du langage articulé, suivi d'une observation d'aphémie. *Bull. Soc. Anatomie*, S2, 1861, **6**: 330-357.
4. BUSER, P., BORENSTEIN, P., and BRUNER, J., Étude des systèmes "associatifs" visuels et auditifs chez le chat anesthésié au chloralose. *EEG Clin. Neurophysiol.*, 1959, **11**: 305-324.
5. CLARK, W. E. L., and NORTHFIELD, D. W. C., The cortical projection of the pulvinar in the macaque monkey. *Brain*, 1937, **60**: 126-142.
6. DAX, M., Lesions de la moitie gauche de l'encèphale coincident avec l'oubli des signes de la pensée. *Gaz. Hebdom.*, 1865, S2, **11**: 259-260.
7. ETTLINGER, G., Cross-modal transfer of training in monkeys. *Behavior*, 1960, **16**: 56-65.
8. FEREMUTSCH, K., Thalamus. In: *Primatologia; Handbook of Primatology*, Vol. II/2, No. 6 (H. Hofer, A. H. Schultz, and D. Starck, Eds.). Karger, Basel, 1963.
9. FLECHSIG, P., Developmental (myelogenetic) localisation of the cerebral cortex in the human subject. *Lancet*, 1901, **2**: 1027-1029.

10. GESCHWIND, N., The development of the brain and the evolution of language. In: *Report of the 15th Annual Round Table Meeting on Linguistic and Language Studies,* Monog. Ser. Languages and Linguistics No. 17 (C. I. J. M. Stuart, Ed.). Georgetown Univ. Press, Washington, D. C., 1964.

11. GOLDSTEIN, K., Die Lokalisation in der Grosshirnrinde; nach den Erfahrungen am kranken Menschen. In: *Handbuch der Normalen und Pathologischen Physiologie,* Vol. X (A. Bethe et al., Eds.). Springer, Berlin, 1927: 600-842.

12. JACKSON, J. H., Hughlings Jackson on aphasia and kindred affections of speech; together with a complete bibliography of Dr. Jackson's publications on speech, and a reprint of some of the more important papers. *Brain,* 1915, **38**: 1-190.

13. KENNEDY, F., Stock-brainedness, the causative factor in the so-called "crossed aphasias". *Am. J. Med. Sci.,* 1916, **152**: 849-859.

14. MAGOUN, H. W., DARLING, L., and PROST, J., The evolution of man's brain. In: *The Central Nervous System and Behavior,* Trans. 3rd Conf. (M. A. B. Brazier, Ed.). Josiah Macy, Jr. Found., New York, 1960: 33-126.

15. MARSHALL, W. H., and TALBOT, S. A., Recent evidence for neural mechanisms in vision leading to a general theory of sensory acuity. *Biol. Symp.,* 1942, **7**: 117-164.

16. PENFIELD, W., and ROBERTS, L., *Speech and Brain-Mechanisms.* Princeton Univ. Press, Princeton, 1959.

17. PERRIA, L., ROSADINI, G., and ROSSI, G. F., Determination of side of cerebral dominance with amobarbital. *Arch. Neurol.,* 1961, **4**: 173-181.

18. PFEIFER, R. A., Pathologie der Hörstrahlung und der corticalen Hörsphäre. In: *Handbuch der Neurologie,* Vol. VI (O. Bumke and O. Foerster, Eds.). Springer, Berlin, 1936: 533-626.

19. POLIAK, S. L., The main afferent fiber systems of the cerebral cortex in primates. *Univ. Calif. Publ. Anat.,* 1932, **2**: 1-370.

20. RIFE, D. C., Heredity and handedness. *Sci. Mon.,* 1951, **73**: 188-191.

21. ROSADINI, G., and ROSSI, G. F., Ricerche sugli effetti elettroencefalografici, neurologici e psichici della somministrazione intracarotidea di amytal sodico nell 'uomo. *Acta Neurochir.,* 1961, **9**: 234-250.

22. SMITH, G. E., A new topographical survey of the human cerebral cortex; being an account of the distribution of the anatomically distinct cortical areas and their relationship to the cerebral sulci. *J. Anat. Physiol.,* 1907, **41**: 237-254.

23. SUBIRANA, A., COROMINAS, J., PUNCERNAU, R., OLLER-DAURELLA, L., and MONTEYS, J., Nueva contribución al estudio de la dominancia cerebral. *Medicamenta,* 1952, **10**: 255-258.

24. SUGAR, O., FRENCH, J. D., and CHUSID, J. G., Corticocortical connections of the superior surface of the temporal operculum in the monkey (*Macaca mulatta*). *J. Neurophysiol.,* 1948, **11**: 175-184.

25. TERZIAN, H., and CECOTTO, C., Su un nuovo metodo per la determinazione e lo studio della dominanza emisferica. *Giorn. Psichiat. Neuropat.,* 1959, **87**: 889-923.

26. von Bonin, G., Anatomical asymmetries of the cerebral hemispheres. In: *Interhemispheric Relations and Cerebral Dominance* (V. B. Mountcastle, Ed.). Johns Hopkins Press, Baltimore, 1962: 1-6.

27. von Bonin, G., and Bailey, P. Pattern of the cerebral isocortex. In: *Primatologia; Handbook of Primatology*, Vol II/2, No. 10 (H. Hofer, A. H. Schultz, and D. Starck, Eds.). Karger, Basel, 1961.

28. von Economo, C., and Horn, L., Über Windungsrelief, Masse und Rindenarchitektonik der Supratemporalfläche, ihre individuellen und ihre Seitenunterschiede. *Z. Neurol. Psychiat.*, 1930, **130**: 678-757.

29. Wada, J., A new method for the determination of the side of cerebral speech dominance: a preliminary report on the intracarotid injection of sodium amytal in man. *Med. Biol.*, 1949, **14**: 221-222.

30. Wada, J., and Kirikae, T., Neurological contribution to the induced unilateral paralysis of human cerebral hemisphere: special emphasis on the experimentally induced aphasia. *Acta Med. Hokkaido*, 1949, **24**: 1-10.

31. Wada, J., and Rasmussen, T., Intracarotid injection of sodium amytal for the lateralization of cerebral speech dominance. Experimental and clinical observations. *J. Neurosurg.*, 1960, **17**: 266-282.

32. Warfel, H. R., *Language; a Science of Human Behavior.* Allen, Cleveland, 1962.

33. Windle, W. F., Neuropathology of certain forms of mental retardation; experiments on monkeys illustrate probable mechanisms of brain damage in human infants. *Science*, 1963, **140**: 1186-1189.

34. Yakovlev, P. I., Anatomical studies in frontal leucotomies: II. Cortical origin of the fronto-pontine tract and organization of the thalamo-frontal projections. *Trans. Am. Neurol. Ass.*, 1954, **79**: 53-56.

35. ———, Morphological criteria of growth and maturation of the nervous system in man. *Res. Publ. Ass. Res. Nerv. Ment. Dis.*, 1962, **39**: 3-46.

# SPEECH DEVELOPMENT: ITS ANATOMICAL AND PHYSIOLOGICAL CONCOMITANTS

ERIC H. LENNEBERG
The Children's Hospital Medical Center
Boston

This presentation roughly falls into three divisions. First, I shall describe some developmental milestones in the acquisition of speech, and I should also like to adduce evidence that the facility for acquisition of speech sharply declines around puberty; for brevity's sake I shall refer to this first point simply as the onset and decline of language acquisition, and I shall think of it as a special type of "critical period". Second, I should like to show that the critical period for language acquisition is accompanied by certain milestones in the physical maturation of the brain; thus, I shall compare a certain aspect of man's maturational history with his behavioral, i.e., language, history. Third, I shall demonstrate that the maturational history of the human brain is different from that of the chimpanzee and, in fact, is very likely to be unique to our species.

### ONSET AND DECLINE OF SPEECH ACQUISITION SKILLS

The first of my points is so obvious that we need not waste many words over it. I have done considerable research on vocalization of infants before they begin language (22, 24). There is a very orderly progression from pure crying to additional cooing sounds, then babbling and the introduction of intonation patterns. Figure 2 shows three independent statistics on some arbitrary, gross milestones in the development of speech. The first ogive shows the suddenness with which children come out with one, two, or three single words; this material was gathered by trained observers (8, 27) who may be trusted to have been relatively uniform in their identification of this particular phenomenon. By nine months of age only 20 per cent of children in the two groups (Austrian and British) were said to have one or more words, but by the completion of the first year about 75 per cent of the children had acquired at least one word, illustrating the very steep increase in percentages.

The second ogive is more gradual. Morley (27) defined phrases as any two-word composition including such stereotypes as "all gone" or "come

37

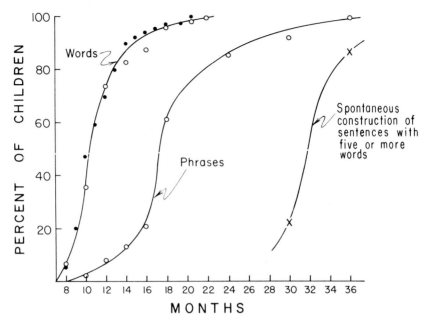

**Figure 2.** Emergence of various developmental milestones in the acquisition of language. Black circles indicate results obtained by Bühler (8) in 49 Austrian children; white circles show results of tests conducted by Morley (27) in 114 British children; the third curve (X) compiles the results of the author's observations in 500 American children (Boston).

here". Once more we see a very sharp rise in the percentage of children who have such phrases. At this age, incidentally, children are not yet able to join spontaneously two independent items of their word repertoire; they may be able to say "all gone" and also something that corresponds to "milk"; ordinarily, however, they are not heard to make up such primitive sentences as "milk all gone". Spontaneous joining of independent words does not occur before 18 months, and an ogive drawn for this milestone would have its most rapid rise between the 20th and 24th months.

The third ogive is based on my own observations: a language test was devised consisting of extent of vocabulary, degree of intelligibility, ability to repeat syntactically and correctly certain complex sentences as well as certain tests of verbal comprehension. About 90 per cent of these lower middle class children passed the test at age three years.

*Hirsh:* These data have to do with production only, that is, verbalizations produced by the child, not comprehended by it?

*Lenneberg:* Yes; similar charts can also be made for comprehension. The times are not the same; comprehension regularly precedes production.

*Wepman:* Would this indicate, for the total sample, that 100 per cent of the children had developed words by the 22nd month? Is this the upper level of the normal development of language?

*Lenneberg:* In the samples studied by Bühler (8) and Morley (27), all of the children were reported to have had one or more words by age 22 months. This is just one milestone in language development; there are other milestones. The onset of language is not a single event: the most primitive step is the development of one or more words.

*Wepman:* I understand; the lower level of language in your estimation is 22 months. What if a child does not say his first word until 24 months? Would you consider that child delayed?

*Lenneberg:* Yes, if a child has not been able to say a single word before the 24th month, I would consider him to be outside the normal range. Actually, this is somewhat beside the point right now. Here I wish to stress that the vast majority of children do have words by 12 months of age. It goes without saying that there are abnormalities in this as in any other aspect of development. I believe one may characterize health and normalcy without at the same time giving a complete repertoire of abnormal conditions.

*Osgood:* What impresses me most about these curves is their extreme sharpness, which means that a considerable portion of the children are shifting at the same time.

*Roberts:* Has this been broken down into boys and girls?

*Lenneberg:* No.

*Hoijer:* What about the child between siblings?

*Lenneberg:* The appearance of milestones is statistically the same in second children as in first. However, second children have a statistically higher incidence of unintelligibility. All of these statistics have been published in several sources and are easily available. The only point of interest here is that there is evidence that language begins at a characteristic time in the human developmental history.

In Figure 3 we have another type of statistic, showing how the estimated size of vocabulary very suddenly increases after 36 months of age. We must assume that there are days during which a child acquires as many as ten or twelve new words.

I would like now to propose that the regularity of the appearance of speech acquisition milestones is not due to a cultural factor but is directly related to factors of maturation. Let us think of the appearance of motor milestones such as the age at which a baby develops a grasp with thumb and finger opposition, or the age at which he is able to sit without support, or to stand without holding on, or to take his first three steps, and so on. Most students of development would agree that these milestones are dependent on growth and maturation of skeletal and neurological structures. We do not believe that a child learns to stand and walk because he sees other people stand and walk or because he is reinforced to do it (blind children stand and walk at the usual time). When we now compare the developmental history of speech with the developmental history of motor milestones, we find that the two histories intercalate in a normal and regular way. It is very rare indeed that a child can join words into primitive sentences before he

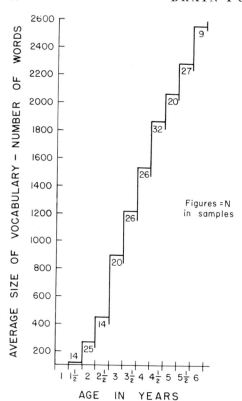

Figures = N
in samples

**Figure 3.** Average vocabulary size of ten samples of children at various ages. (Based on data by M. E. Smith, 33.)

has learned to walk. When one studies general retardation of development, such as in the mongoloid (25), one finds that the entire developmental history is stretched out, that motor milestones emerge at a much slower rate, that the speech developmental milestones are still slower, and that the intercalation of these two developmental histories tends to be undisturbed. Not all retarded children develop good speech but many show an arrest of speech development at primitive stages. This is due to the fact that the history of speech development extends much beyond the history of the most elementary motor development.

We are presently conducting cross-cultural comparisons in which motor development and speech development are studied simultaneously in children among the natives of New Guinea and Central Brazil. So far, the data seem to show quite clearly that the developmental relationships between speech and motor development are the same in those cultures as in Boston. Generally speaking, then, the onset of language occurs at a specific period during the development of the child.

Let us now review the evidence for a decline in language acquisition skills around the age of puberty. I have elsewhere (23) discussed different types of evidence, so that I can confine myself here to essentially one class, namely the effect of acquired lesions.

TABLE 1

CLINICAL COURSE OF LEFT-SIDED TRAUMA IN 88 WAR VETERANS*

|  | Number | Percentage |
|---|---|---|
| Aphasia cleared within 3 months or less | 29 | 32 |
| Permanent aphasic residues | 26 | 30 |
| Slow and protracted improvement, final status not reported | 5 | 6 |
| Initial aphasia cleared but permanent associated symptoms | 7 | 8 |
| Clinical course not reported | 7 | 8 |
| No aphasia | 14 | 16 |

* Based on Russell & Espir (30).

It is well known that left-sided cortical lesions in the vicinity of the Rolandic and Sylvian junctures produce aphasic states. It is not so generally
known that the chances for recovery from acquired aphasia are very
different during childhood than during adult life. Let me start with statistics from Russell & Espir (30) on the clinical course of left-sided traumas in
young war veterans (Table 1). Unfortunately, the follow-up of these cases is
not very complete; the monograph may serve as a baseline, however, and
the figures reported conform roughly to the practical experience of neurology. Notice that those patients who did have aphasia fall into two distinct
groups. The first group recovers quickly from the behavioral disturbance,
whereas the second group shows aphasic symptoms that do not improve
after the first three months and remain quite stable, usually for the rest of
the subject's life. Gradual and protracted improvement over periods longer
than three months is very rare in the traumatic aphasias. The six per cent in
Table 1 who show slow and protracted improvement includes patients
whose follow-up story is not reproduced exactly, so I gave them the benefit
of the doubt. It is more likely that less than six per cent will have an aphasia
that keeps improving slowly over many months, perhaps even years, clearing
up after a prolonged recovery of, say, two years or more. This group certainly
is an exception.

Compare now this picture with acquired aphasia in childhood. The most
clearly described cases in the literature are summarized in Table 2, with the
addition of some cases of children seen at the Children's Hospital in Boston.
Table 2, in contrast to Table 1, shows that these patients only experienced
transient aphasia subsequent to acquired lesions. This, then, corresponds to
the first two lines of Table 1. In Table 1 half the patients with aphasia have
permanent language deficits. Table 2, on the other hand, shows that lesions
which caused acquired aphasia have a totally different prognosis during
childhood, that is, before age nine or ten. I must stress that the patients
shown in Table 2 only include children with a definitely one-sided and acquired lesion. The youngest child, twenty months old, had just begun to develop words and phrases. During this age and up to about three years children tend to recover from aphasia very rapidly, usually by repeating once

TABLE 2

RECOVERY FROM APHASIA

| Patient's age at insult (years) | Residual deficit remained after: | | | Etiology or Pathology | Comments | Source | Case |
|---|---|---|---|---|---|---|---|
| | 3 mos. | 1 yr. | 2 or more yrs. | | | | |
| 1.7 | + | + | 0 | Trauma, L hemisphere worse than R | Complete speech loss; new onset 16 mos. later. L hemispherectomy at 12 followed by aphasia clearing within 9 mos. postoperative | Basser (4) | 28 |
| 2 | + | + | 0 | Diphtheria with convulsions | | Basser (4) | I |
| 2.3 | + | 0 | – | Measles followed by right-sided spasm and hemiplegia | | Bateman (5) | |
| 3 | + | + | 0 | Trauma followed by CVA, left | | CHMC* | 63 |
| 4 | + | 0 | 0 | Trauma, L forehead | | Guttmann (17) | TP |
| 4 | ?+ | ?0 | – | Abscess, L temporal lobe with operative evacuation to internal capsule | Last follow-up 8 wks. postop. Child steadily improving, but speech not yet normal | Brunner & Stengel (7) | |
| 5 | + | + | 0 | Sudden hemiplegia of unknown origin | | Basser (4) | XII |
| 6 | + | 0 | 0 | Ruptured aneurysm, left | | CHMC* | 34 |
| 6 | 0 | 0 | 0 | Sudden hemiplegia of unknown origin | | Basser (4) | I |
| 6 | 0 | 0 | 0 | Trauma, left side | | Guttmann (17) | AC |
| 6 | 0 | 0 | 0 | Trauma, left side | | Guttmann (17) | JK |

| | | | | | | | |
|---|---|---|---|---|---|---|---|
| 6 | + | − | − | Meningo-encephalopathy | Satisfactory improvement reported, but follow-up not clear | LeFèvre (20) | MR |
| 6 | + | 0 | 0 | Trauma, left temporo-parietal | | André-Thomas (3) | |
| 7 | + | 0 | 0 | CVA, R hemisphere (confirmed by arteriogram) | | CHMC* | 39 |
| 7 | + | 0 | 0 | Unknown | Comprehension and expression deteriorating over 3 mos. period, followed by slow improvement over 9 mos. | Pötzl (28) | |
| 8 | + | 0 | 0 | Trauma, left temporal | | CHMC* | 00 |
| 8 | + | + | 0 | CVA, left | | CHMC* | 51 |
| 9 | + | + | + | ? Convulsions with hemiplegia | Permanent residue | Basser (4) | III |
| 10 | + | 0 | 0 | Trauma, left | | Guttmann (17) | JJ |
| 11 | + | 0 | 0 | Trauma, left, probably followed by CVA | | CHMC* | 63 |
| 11 | + | + | + | Left otogenic abscess | Mild permanent residue: hesitation & grammatical mistakes | Guttmann (17) | JW |
| 12 | + | − | + | Trauma, left | No follow-up but substantial though slow improvement reported | LeFèvre (20) | AJ |
| 14 | + | + | + | Trauma, left | Slight aphasic symptoms, permanent; marked agraphia and alexia, permanent | LeFèvre (20) | MCS |
| 15 | + | + | + | Tumor, left parietal | Receptive aphasia preop.: jargon aphasia postop., clearing within 9 mos.: other aphasic symptoms unchanged 2 yrs. postop. | CHMC* | 14 |
| 18 | + | + | + | Trauma, left temporo-parietal | Marked aphasia, permanent | CHMC* | 70 |

CVA = cerebrovascular accident

*CHMC: The Children's Hospital Medical Center, Boston.

more the early stages of language development. Given this pathology, there is virtually not a single case known to me in which a child who suffered insult at or before age eight years failed to recover from his aphasia. Yet, in contrast to the adult population, the recovery period from aphasia may take much longer in childhood; it is not at all uncommon for a child to recover some of his earlier speech three months after the trauma and then continue to improve for another year or so. By the end of the second year after the disease the children have all recovered their full command of language provided the underlying disease process had been arrested at the time of the first insult. Between age 11 and 14, aphasic symptoms do not disappear with the same ease as in the younger children. Permanent residues only make their appearance at about the time of puberty or thereafter.

So far I have said nothing about the phenomenon of lateralization of function in the human brain. At what age does the left hemisphere become specialized for speech? Up to what age is it possible to make the right hemisphere transact neurophysiology of speech? An important article by Basser (4) throws light on this problem; Table 3, based on it, shows children who acquired lesions before they began to speak, that is, infants of less than 14 months of age. In slightly more than half of these children, unilateral lesions did not delay onset of speech. In somewhat less than half of them the onset of speech was delayed, but once it began it developed normally. Notice that the speech delay may be caused by insult to either the right or the left hemisphere; this seems to indicate that both hemispheres are involved in speech at the very onset of development. In this age group there is no evidence yet of cerebral lateralization of function. I am somewhat puzzled about the third column, listing children who never develop speech. According to our experience with traumatic aphasia in older children, we should have expected the total in this third column to be even less than shown. Even so, the incidence reported here is only 7.5 per cent. Perhaps it is due to the fact that it is not always easy to ascertain exclusive laterality of lesion during infancy.

Turning now to Table 4, based also on Basser's article (4), there is a comparable tabulation of children whose lesions occurred after they had acquired at least primitive stages of language, but who were no older than ten at the time of the insult. Notice that in this age group lateralization of func-

TABLE 3

LESIONS BEFORE ONSET OF SPEECH*

| | Onset of Speech | | |
|---|---|---|---|
| | Normal | Delayed | Never |
| L hemisphere | 18 | 15 | 1 |
| R hemisphere | 19 | 15 | 4 |

* Based on Basser (4).

TABLE 4

LESIONS AFTER ONSET OF SPEECH AND BEFORE AGE 10*

| | Speech After Catastrophe | |
| --- | --- | --- |
| | Normal | Disturbed |
| L hemisphere | 2 | 13 |
| R hemisphere | 8 | 7 |

* Based on Basser (4).

tion is becoming apparent, although it is not yet perfect. Left hemisphere lesions are more likely to cause speech disturbances than right hemisphere lesions but, as Dr. Ajuriaguerra has pointed out, children have a much higher incidence of speech disturbances following right hemisphere lesions than do adult patients. After the age of 18 years aphasia is only very rarely produced by right hemisphere lesions. Thus we see that the lateralization of speech function appears during the very first few years of childhood but does not become established until the early teens.

Further and more dramatic evidence for that observation may be adduced from the operation known as hemispherectomy, the removal of one of the cerebral hemispheres. It is undertaken primarily for the correction of certain uncontrollable seizures; it may also be undertaken for large infiltrating tumors, but in the present paper only a single such case will be discussed. Seizures are a common consequence of localized lesions; it does not matter here whether the pathology is congenital or acquired. A lesion may constitute an epileptogenic focus from which waves of physiological disturbances emanate. The function of an entire hemisphere may be profoundly disturbed or even suspended due to the large amount of destroyed tissue or because of the constant waves of physiological disturbances. It is very common that the structurally healthy hemisphere is also disturbed by the contralateral abnormality; the physiological disturbances that radiate out from the epileptogenic focus are very likely to cross over to the other hemisphere through the fiber tracts that connect the two, particularly the corpus callosum. One might say that the disease leading to hemispherectomy may be described on three distinct levels: on a structural level there is a distinct unilateral lesion; on a physiological level there are disturbances that begin in the vicinity of the lesion but then sweep over into the other hemisphere; on a behavioral level there may be disturbances that can be directly related to the structural abnormality and therefore are strictly lateralized, such as a paralysis on one side. There may also be behavioral disturbances that have nothing to do with lateralization, such as personality peculiarities, unmanageable behavior, or loss of intelligence.

In addition to these two types of behavioral disturbances it is possible that language is affected "phenotypically". That is, the patient actually may have learned to speak and to understand but, because of the constant and

severe epileptic discharges, may be so crippled in the execution of this behavior that he gives the impression of having a severe language deficit. One
might say that the diseased hemisphere troubles the healthy hemisphere to
such an extent that even potentially available behavior cannot be executed
properly. Once the "misbehaving" hemisphere is surgically removed, the
other may function in peace, and one can now see which behavior has actually been acquired and can be performed by the remaining side.

The left column in Table 5 indicates the age at which the patient suffered
the original lesion. The hemispherectomy itself was performed in most
cases, but not in all, after the patient had reached his early teens or even
adulthood. In no case did the hemispherectomy immediately follow the acquisition of the lesion. The entries in the third column from the left show
the number of patients who had no aphasia after the hemispherectomy.
This group includes all of those patients who had no speech disturbance before the hemispherectomy but only suffered from motor disturbances or inability to learn new material, as well as those patients who had in some way
abnormal speech before the operation and whose speech improved as a consequence of the operation. The last column lists the number of cases having
permanent aphasia after hemispherectomy and includes patients both with
and without aphasia before the operation had been performed.

From Table 5 it becomes quite clear that the lesion incurred in the left
hemisphere during childhood prevents the lateralization of the speech function to that hemisphere and forces the right hemisphere to continue in its
speech participation much the way it had done in normal children around
the time of the onset of speech. Note that if the lesion is on the left and hemispherectomy is performed later on in life—it does not matter at what age

TABLE 5

HEMISPHERECTOMY

| Lesions acquired | Hemisphere involved | Speech not affected or improved postop. | Permanent aphasia |
|---|---|---|---|
| Before teens* | oper. on L | 49 | 3 (had aphasia before oper.) |
| | oper. on R | 38 | 5 (ditto) |
| During puberty† (single case) | oper. on L | slow improvement | some residue to end of life (27 mos. postop.) |
| Adult* | oper. on L | none | 6 (one had aphasia before oper.) |
| | oper. on R | 25 | none |

* Based on Basser (4).
† Hillier (18, and personal communication).

—aphasia does not ordinarily occur. This seems to contrast with those patients who incur their lesions at an adult age, a developmental time when the right hemisphere can no longer be forced to perform speech activities (unless it had always done so throughout life). Thus, the six cases in which left hemispherectomy had to be performed were all aphasic after the operation. On the other hand, among those who incurred lesions on the right side as adults, not one had aphasia as a consequence of the hemispherectomy.

These data clearly show that cerebral lateralization of the speech function is to a certain extent a plastic phenomenon. No lateralization seems to be present before age two or three; then there is a period that lasts to about age ten or twelve during which cerebral lateralization for speech is gradually established but may still be pushed back into the right hemisphere if the left hemisphere is disturbed. After puberty, lateralization is normally firmly established to the left, and the right hemisphere is no further involved in speech functions; lesions to the left interfere with speech, but lesions to the right do not. There is no good evidence that this asymmetry may be altered after puberty through intensive conditioning procedures.

In summary, then, primary language acquisition before puberty may be accomplished by either the right or left hemisphere. Severe disruption of the language function during or after the early teens is difficult or impossible to correct.

### Cerebral Maturation in Man

Maturation of the brain will be considered here in three aspects: anatomical changes, biochemical changes, and physiological changes. The maturational history of the brain is relevant at this point to determine whether the two critical stages in speech developmental history are accompanied by any maturational changes in the brain. Are the second and twelfth years of life turning points as regards physical maturation? This section is essentially descriptive, for we shall map language history onto growth history. This procedure by itself cannot be called theoretical; however, if we should find landmarks that coincide in both histories, this would allow us to theorize or, if you will, to speculate that the two are related. I shall, in fact, take this theoretical step towards the end of my presentation, but I wish to stress right now that the changes which I am about to show in the physical substrate must not be considered to be specifically or exclusively related to language alone. They are general aspects of development, and the demonstration is merely to the effect that language acquisition is highly dependent upon these general physical correlates.

The next figures show different growth parameters for the human brain, correlated with chronological age expressed on a logarithmic scale. Language history is indicated by a stippled area, and it should be understood that onset and cessation are not quite as abrupt as would appear from these representations.

Figure 4 demonstrates that the most rapid rate of growth occurs during the first two years of life, when the brain more than triples its weight. It then continues to grow, but at a much slower pace, the weight increase from age two to age twelve being no more than less than one-third of the weight at age two. At age twelve or, a little more accurately, around puberty, an asymptote is reached: the brain has arrived at its mature size with no further changes taking place until old age and death. (Changes in head circumference are due entirely to bony growth and extracranial soft tissues.)

*Osgood:* I notice that the baseline has a very strange kind of unit. In fact, if I read it correctly, you are graphically underestimating the rapid rate of change in the first two years. Why did you do it this way? It is not logarithmic.

*Lenneberg:* It actually is logarithmic. My original drawing was plotted on log paper, but I chose a part of the grid that would give the best stretch for the childhood years. The transformation is log of $(N + 1)$. Of course, you are correct in that it under-represents the very rapid rate of change during the first couple of years. I will have more to say about this in the last part of my paper.

The gross changes of weight are also accompanied by changes in microscopic anatomy. Conel (13) has published voluminous atlases showing the change in the growth of the dendritic plexus in the various layers of the human cortex throughout infancy and childhood. A glance at Conel's pictures shows an ever increasing density of neuropil and an arborization and interconnection of dendrites beginning just about the time of birth which appears to have reached a certain level of maturity by age two years.

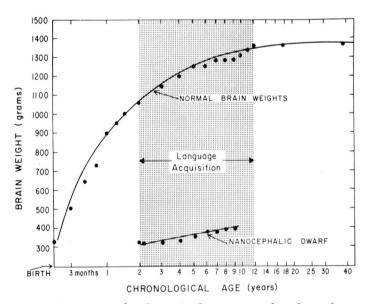

**Figure 4.** Brain weights determined at autopsy plotted as a function of patients' chronological age.

*Osgood:* Is this purely maturational, or are there usage effects?

*Lenneberg:* The progressive arborization described by Conel is thought to be purely maturational. I know of no empirical evidence that could support the notion that dendritic arborization in the cerebral cortex is the function of sensory input.

*Osgood:* Suppose one took the visual association areas and examined them in individuals who were functionally blind from birth. Do you think one would see exactly the same degree of development?

*Lenneberg:* I know of no histological study that would give me the basis for answering your question; Chow (11) found no such changes in monkeys. I believe, however, that we can make certain inferences. The German neurologist, Max De Crinis (13a), has tried to work out what he called the dendrogenetic map of the human cortex, attempting to plot those areas of the infantile cortex in which dendrites grow most rapidly at birth, and comparing these areas with other areas in which dendrites arise either more slowly or at a later stage of development. The work of De Crinis has not been universally accepted, although it is very clear today that dendrites have different growth and arborization rates in different areas of the cortex. The sensory and motor areas, including the striate area, are the first to show dendrogenesis. The areas of latest dendritic growth are in the frontal and middle part of the parietal lobe. In these late areas arborization is said to be completed at about forty months of age. Inasmuch as the same sequence of events has been observed in different brains by more than one worker, I find it hard to believe that the time table for dendrogenesis follows those for the behavioral patterns or for sensory experience, which ought to be much more random from child to child.

*Geschwind:* Dr. Osgood asked how one might study the effect of function on the development of the visual association areas; it would probably be necessary to remove the visual cortex proper in a young animal and then study the development of the visual association cortex. There have been experiments by Riesen (29) showing poor development of the retina in young animals deprived of light.

*de Hirsch:* Is there no relationship between function and maturation?

*Lenneberg:* There might be; we do not know at this time. There is a lot of evidence against it (9, 12, 16) and only the most indirect evidence for it, such as shown in the recent experiments by Wiesel and Hubel (34). In this latter work, however, there is no evidence that cortical histology may be influenced by use; the authors did find that light deprivation from birth on prevented cells in the geniculate body from growing. Interestingly enough, this observation was confined to light deprivation during the developmental months of kittens, whereas light deprivation in mature cats could not retroactively change the microscopic structure of nervous tissue studied.

Figure 5 presents data by Schadé & van Groeningen (31), who have done statistical research on the growth of neurons. Once more we see rapid rate

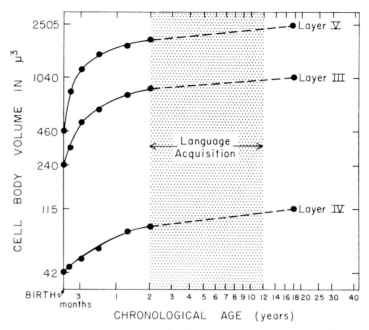

**Figure 5.** Neurons in the cerebral cortex grow in volume with age. The broken lines between ages 2 and 18 indicate that no measurements were made because brains of children dead between those ages were not available for histological study. (Redrawn from Schadé & van Groeningen, 31.)

of growth to age two, and from then on a slow approximation towards asymptote. The same authors studied other parameters of cortical development, shown in Figure 6. Again, the curves of neurodensity show that age two marks the slowing down of maturational change, and puberty appears to be the time at which full maturation is reached. Both Figures 5 and 6 are based on counts made on blocks of cortical tissue taken from a region a few millimeters above Broca's area.

Let us now take a brief look at biochemical maturation. Figure 7 shows the gradual change in percentage of certain components of the human cortex. Figure 8 shows comparable data for white matter. The tissues were obtained from blocks of brain taken at autopsy. The subjects were children, and the work was done by Brante (6) in Sweden. You may observe that in these two figures the general trend of rapid developmental change before age two, flattening out between two and puberty, and practical stabilization after this time, is again demonstrated.

Lastly, we come to physiological development. Here I am touching on material about which both Dr. Lindsley and Dr. Brazier know ever so much more than I do. The data in Figures 9 and 10 come from relatively old sources (15, 32). In fact, they are among the first studies in electroencephalography and may well be somewhat out of date now in terms of accuracy. What interests us in these two figures is that we once more see great

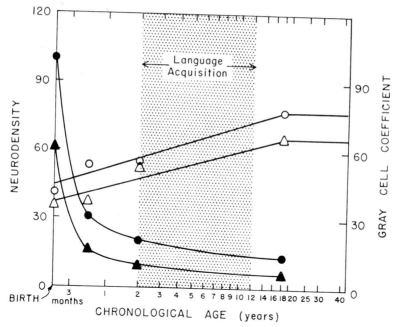

**Figure 6.** As the cerebrum expands with age the nerve cells in the cortex become less crowded and the neurodensity decreases. The rising curves indicate that the distances between the cells increasing with age are progressively filled with dendrites and neuropil, resulting in dense arborization. Neurodensity (number of cells $\times$ $10^3$ per mm³) in Layer III is indicated by black circles; that in Layer V by black triangles. The gray cell coefficient, computed by dividing the volume of gray matter by the volume of nerve cells contained in it, is indicated by white circles for Layer III and white triangles for Layer V. (Based on data by Schadé & van Groeningen, 31.)

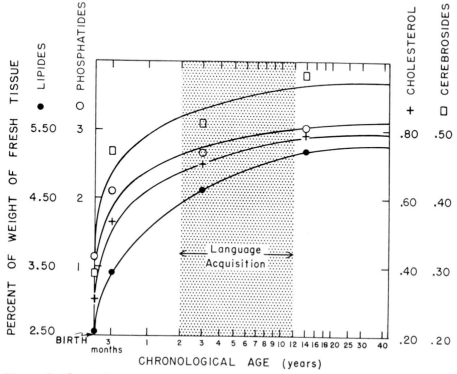

**Figure 7.** Chemical composition of human cerebral cortex plotted as a function of chronological age. (Based on data by Brante, 6, and Folch-Pi, 14.)

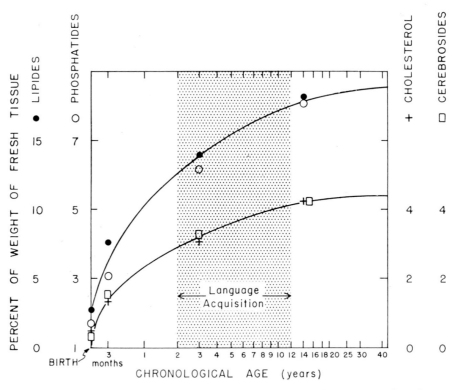

**Figure 8.** Chemical composition of human cerebral white matter plotted as a function of chronological age. (Based on data by Brante, 6, and Folch-Pi, 14.)

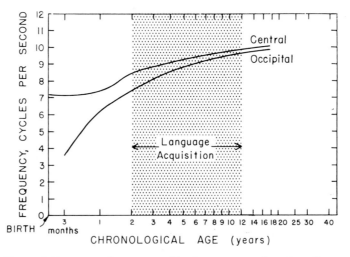

**Figure 9.** Dominant frequency of brain waves as a function of age. (Redrawn from Smith, 32.)

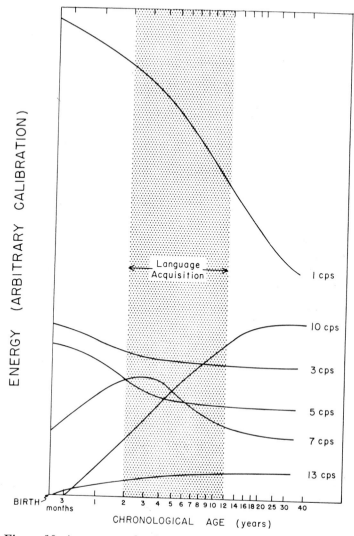

**Figure 10.** Average amplitude of various brain waves as a function of age. (Based on data by Gibbs & Knott, 15.)

variations before age two, then a period during which the mature state of affairs is being approached more gradually, reaching maturity just about puberty. I would like to ask Dr. Brazier whether these data are still acceptable, or is there now evidence that dominant frequencies keep changing after age twelve, that is, would the curve shown in Figure 9 continue to rise?

*Brazier:* The curve flattens out at about 15 years of age.

*Lenneberg:* To summarize: what I have done is merely to show what is meant by cerebral maturation. There are measurable anatomical, biochemical and physiological changes, and it is possible to plot the rate of change. In doing so we may see that on all fronts certain turning points are reached at about age two and at about age twelve. Please remember that I am not asserting that these changes have a specific relationship to language but merely that language skills may be heavily dependent on reaching a certain level of maturity as well as being dependent on a brain not fully matured and stable as yet.

### MATURATIONAL HISTORIES OF MAN AND CHIMPANZEE

If language should indeed be related to man's maturational history, as I have suggested, then we might do well to ask in what respect man's maturational history differs from that of our closest phylogenetic relative, the chimpanzee.

Attempts have been made to show similarities between the courses of pri-

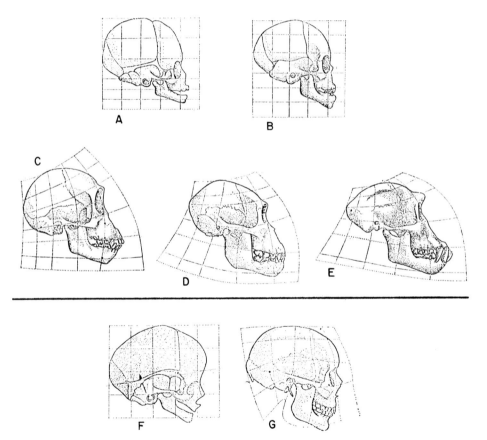

**Figure 11.** *Above line:* ontogenesis of chimpanzee skull. A: Female fetus, 214 mm sitting height; B: 74-day-old female; C: infantile specimen of unknown age and sex; D: juvenile specimen of unknown age, probably female; E: adult male. *Below line:* geometrical transformation of human skull. F: Human fetus during ninth month of gestation; G: adult skull. Comparison of chimpanzee development with human development shows the two to be entirely different from one another. Thus, the human growth patterns do not resemble any fetal stage of the other primate form. (From Kummer, 19.)

mate development. On some level of generality there must naturally be similarities for the entire order. At the same time, comparative zoology would
make it plausible for every species to have peculiarities. There have been
some who thought that man represents merely a fetal stage of monkey and
ape development. If this were so, then perhaps one would only have to
slow down the ape's development and perhaps arrest it at some primitive
stage in order to make a man out of an ape. But it turns out that this is considerably more difficult than to make an ape out of a man! Figure 11 repro-
duces some anatomical studies conducted by Kummer (19), which illustrate
the growth pattern of the chimpanzee's skull from late fetal stage to maturity. Comparison of these growth patterns with man's, as demonstrated by
the two lower skulls in Figure 11, makes it obvious that quite different developmental events take place in these two species. Man's developmental
history is not a part of the ape's history, nor is the reverse the case. Each
follows its own characteristic patterns as far as their skeletons are concerned.

Unfortunately there are no studies available that compare the biochemical or physiological maturation of the chimpanzee with man's. We must

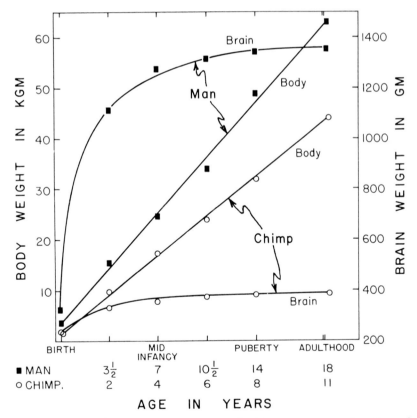

**Figure 12.** Weight increases in man and chimpanzee as a function of
maturational stage.

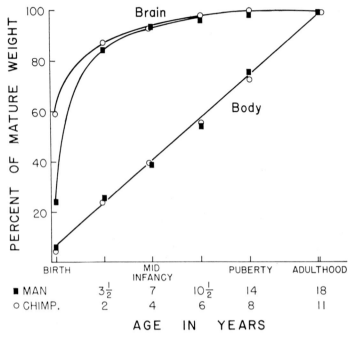

**Figure 13.** The same data as in Figure 12, with weights expressed in terms of percentages of mature weight. The parameter is now *rate* of growth. Note that the rate of body weight increase is practically identical in man and chimpanzee, whereas the rate of brain weight increase is quite different during the first quarter of their maturational histories.

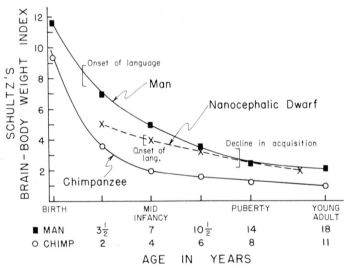

**Figure 14.** Brain-body weight ratio as a function of maturational stage. The adult proportions are attained in man much more gradually than in chimpanzee. Note that the developmental curve of nanocephalic dwarf resembles that of normally growing humans. (Based on tables published by Altman & Dittmer, 2.)

confine ourselves, therefore, to the simple index of the rate of growth of brain and body in the two forms. Such comparisons are made in Figures 12 and 13. Notice that in terms of percentages the increases in body weights are practically identical for the two species, while the brains follow very different developmental curves. Chimpanzee is born with a much more mature brain than man.

I have shown elsewhere (21) that the ability or inability for the acquisition of language cannot be explained simply by referring to the peculiar brain-body weight ratio of man. There is a certain form of dwarfism which reduces man to miniature proportions, and it is possible to show that some of the individuals afflicted by it have absolute brain weights and body weights identical with those of an infant chimpanzee. While the absolute brain weights do not give us a clue to the ability for speech, a comparison of developmental histories does give us such a clue. Figure 14 plots the brain-body weight ratio as a function of age. The index figures *per se* are not unique to the human species, but what is unique is the age at which that brain-body weight index is reached. For instance, the index number characteristic for adult man corresponds to the index number of chimpanzee at mid-infancy. Man's index number at mid-infancy corresponds to a chimpanzee index number after one-fifth of the latter's infancy. Generally speaking, we have indications that the maturational history and sequence of events observed in man are unique for his species. We do not know the significance of these specific developmental phenomena. All we can say at this point is that the phenomena of development and emergent behavior for each species must be studied separately.

### Summary and Conclusion

In the first part of this paper I tried to show that speech and language have a regular time of onset and that there is evidence that primary language acquisition may take place between two years of age and puberty. The most powerful evidence for this comes from cases of acquired aphasia. Structural lesions may interfere with the production and understanding of speech; during childhood individuals tend to overcome the interference; after puberty there is a rapid rise in the incidence of permanent speech deficits. Apparently this time table is related to the phenomenon of cerebral lateralization of function. Such asymmetry is not present at birth; it first appears at the time of onset of speech, and it does not become firmly established until puberty. There is also evidence that the acquisition of language after acquired aphasia is related to the brain's ability to subserve speech function by parts which had not carried out that activity before the occurrence of structural lesions. There is no good evidence that such transferral of function, for instance to the right hemisphere, may regularly take place in the adult brain-injured patient.

The maturational history of the brain gives credence to the theory that language acquisition requires a minimum level of maturation but is greatly limited if the brain has come to full maturation and "settled down", so to speak. This latter point seems to be contradicted by the ability to learn second languages after puberty. However, even this skill seems to suffer once the teens are reached and, furthermore, by definition it occurs only in individuals who already have neurophysiological organization for language itself.

In the third part of this presentation I stressed the differences in maturational history between chimpanzee and man. I would now like to propose, by way of conclusion, that man's two species-specific characteristics of neurophysiology, the regular asymmetry in brain function and the peculiar developmental history, are both related to man's most outstanding species-specific behavior, namely speech and language. This proposal is still very vague, neither is it new. However, I hope to have added some substance to earlier less specific claims.

## Discussion

*Ervin:* Dr. Lenneberg's paper was extremely informative about the probable neurological bases for the marked behavioral changes with age. Not being qualified to remark upon the neurological evidence he has presented, I shall shift emphasis to these behavioral implications. Some of my observations are based upon a longer first-draft version of Dr. Lenneberg's presentation, in which he expanded his own views of some of the behavioral correlates of the organic data he has been discussing.

I think Dr. Lenneberg is being very careful not to extrapolate in talking about the cause-and-effect relationship of structure and function. In looking at the lateral dominance he found in relation to age changes, I find it very tempting to infer that the acquisition of language does have some effect in stimulating changes in the brain. It is hard to resist the inference, and perhaps more attention will now be given this question.

One of the points he made is the intriguing observation that during relearning of language by children who suffered aphasias there seems to be a recapitulation of the learning process that occurred prior to injury. This recapitulation apparently is the more complete the earlier the injury occurs. Every time someone uses a recapitulation explanation I think it is very important to look with great detail at the process that actually takes place. I do not know whether there are enough such cases for us to find out more about this in the near future. An obvious thing to do is to use detailed observational and testing techniques on such children during reacquisition of language, to see if the same processes are found to go on as in normal acquisition before injury. Apparently, babbling has been observed to occur just as it does in both normal and deaf children at a regular, and probably organically-based, maturational stage. It would be quite important to find out whether there is the same kind of successive differentiation in the phonemic system and whether there are the same successive stages in the development of grammar as we observe in detailed studies of normal children.

Particularly important in such studies would be comparison between this kind of relearning in young and older children. Such a comparison might give more insight regarding the effects of organic changes at different ages on specific features of the learning sequence. In addition, if there are specific language functions of different parts of the brain, such behavioral studies based on damage and relearning may at some time be tied to studies of maturational rates in different parts of the brain.

A significant behavioral implication of neurological changes with age was suggested by Dr. Lenneberg in the earlier draft of his paper: the possibility that cortical maturation may affect the ease of second-language learning at various ages. In normal children this would be the performance in which neurological changes at puberty would have the most important behavioral impact. It is common belief that a very sudden change in facility in second-language learning, especially phonetic, occurs around puberty, but anybody who studies these cases is puzzled by the exceptions; for example, children of immigrants often have an American accent in their parents' language, even when their parents do not have an American accent. Phonetic interference is characteristic of adult learning of a second language, yet it also may appear in children who have learned two languages from childhood and are normally called bilingual.

We find at the other extreme great ranges of skill in second-language learning in adults. Without exception in the cases that I have studied, there are always effects of the second language on the first language, even in adults who learned a second language quite late. Thus children may fail to learn, while adults may learn a second language perfectly and lose the first. For these reasons, it appears that an organic explanation for the difficulties of second-language learning by adolescents and adults may not be as adequate as it first appears. There are very marked social, emotional and neurological changes at puberty which confound studies based on age change.

In general, I think the problem of age changes related to facility in second-language learning is simply that we do not have appropriate data. Obviously, what is needed is intensive second-language teaching to children of various ages, preferably with the social circumstances of learning kept constant if at all possible. It is obvious that adult second-language students learn under different circumstances than do children.

Finally, one of the things which interests me about Dr. Lenneberg's point of view is that it seems to fit in with a developing trend in the study of first-language learning. There is increasing criticism of the traditional emphasis of learning theorists on mimicry, overt practice and external social reward as highly important factors in natural language learning. We are beginning to believe that these factors are not of great importance in the early stages of the production of language and that, in fact, it is possible for language to be learned quite well with a minimum of overt practice, reward, and so on.

For instance, in the acquisition of grammatical patterns in two-year-olds, I have evidence that spontaneous mimicry is grammatically more primitive than the sentences the children make up by themselves. Grammatical development cannot be accounted for by the assumption that children simply imitate. There seems to be something more complicated going on that makes the reception system probably of far greater importance than we have hitherto believed.

Perhaps the critical events necessary for children to learn a language are a combination of the maturational factors mentioned by Dr. Lenneberg and something we might call exposure to language. Just what this entails I do not know. I do not know whether a child could learn to speak from listening to the radio, whether he needs to see referents for the terms he hears, or whether he has to make a response to what he hears. I hope this is something we are going to learn a great deal more about in the future. The point of view of workers in the field of first language is changing a great deal regarding the relative importance of overt practice in speaking as opposed to maturation and listening to language.

*Magoun:* Since language learning in the elementary and secondary schools now forms a part of our national defense effort, does anyone want to offer testimony from his own teaching, or from observations of his children's experience? I can say a word for the graduate level of education. Unquestionably, the worst time of one's life to try to learn a new language is as a graduate student.

*Brazier:* I should like to ask a question. Are there no data from the countries where a second language is compulsory from childhood? Have the Russians studied this, or the Hungarians, or the Dutch, or the Scandinavians? Is there something in their literature?

*de Hirsch:* There are a number of studies dealing with bilingualism. Children in Belgium and Holland do learn two or three languages very early. It seems that children of comparable intelligence differ in ability to cope with two or three languages at the same time.

Bilingual children must shift between different receptive and expressive frameworks. Speaking two languages involves constant choosing between different patterns. There is a good deal of research to the effect that bilingualism is detrimental to oral and printed language development (10, 26). However, since in this country bilingualism is found most frequently in lower socioeconomic groups, one cannot be sure to what degree language retardation in these children is related to specific linguistic or sociological factors.

Actually, we do not really know what a second language means in psychological terms. The "mother language" is the mother's own language and must be of enormous importance in terms of the basic communicative attitudes of mother and child.

*Ladefoged:* There is an unpublished study by Mrs. E. Ingram of the University of Edinburgh, Scotland, who took children at a variety of ages (starting at five, I think, and going only up to twelve) and tried to correlate age with language learning ability. It was a nicely controlled experiment with a language none of the children would have otherwise learned; unfortunately, it did not go far enough. The criteria used were related only to how well the children managed to acquire the pronunciation of this language; they were not concerned with how well the children managed to use the language. There was no significant correlation with age: up to age twelve, all the children seemed to acquire an equally good pronunciation.

*Lenneberg:* As Dr. Ervin pointed out, this part of the discussion centered around the weakest type of behavioral observations we can make. Second-language learning is a very confusing phenomenon. There are about a hundred different variables: Who taught the child? Where did the child learn? Possibly the child's intelligence. What two languages were involved? At what ages? What was the social value system that surrounded the learner? It is very difficult to evaluate second-language learning. I think very few people can take issue with the fact that foreign accents are much more difficult to overcome in adulthood than in childhood.

*Geschwind:* Dr. Ervin also said that the adult learner of a second language usually does not learn in the same situation as a child. I believe that this is true in a quite literal sense. The adult rarely learns a language in the sort of situation that is provided by children playing together. In *The Education of Henry Adams* (1) there is a charming account of how Adams learned German. Having gone to Germany to study law, he had simply not managed to pick up the language. A German friend arranged for him to spend his days in the lowest grade of a German primary school, where he was rapidly accepted by the children. Adams commented, as I recall, that by this method one could teach German to a puppy in three months. In this case the childhood situation of first-language learning was much more closely reproduced than is usual in adult life.

There is another sense in which second-language learning usually takes place in circumstances different from first-language learning: we probably learn a second language in an anatomically different way than that in which we learned our first language. In first-language learning, associations are made between actual objects in the environment and their names, the largest number being visual-auditory and tactile-auditory associations. By contrast, when a second language is learned by an adult, it is primarily done by translating from the first language, i.e., by auditory-auditory associations, not by dealing directly with the environment. Different anatomical regions are used in the two cases. There are attempts to avoid this, such as the Berlitz method, but I suspect that most of us really translate from our first language even when learning by another technique.

I suspect that the parts of the brain most relevant to language learning are those which mature slowly rather than those which mature rapidly, since the phylogenetically most advanced areas mature last.

*Lenneberg:* I think there is evidence in favor of the notion that some parts of the brain mature at different periods. The brain and the cortex do not mature uniformly. Unfortunately, our information on this topic is very sketchy. I believe what is important is that by age two maturation is not yet complete, as determined by most of the measurements taken so far, yet it is well advanced according to all those criteria. On the other hand, by age twelve to fourteen maturation seems to be complete on all counts, at least insofar as I know. I would like to hear whether there are any exceptions to these statements. Do you have any evidence?

*Geschwind:* There are some indicators of maturation of the brain which show that development is not complete by age three or four. You have pointed out that myelination may continue beyond this age.

*Lenneberg:* Yes, this is the one exception. Myelination does continue, but at a very much slower rate.

*Geschwind:* Yakovlev (35) has evidence that in some individuals certain areas do not mature in their cellular architecture until the age of ten or twelve, although the age of three or four is more typical. The areas most delayed in some are the most phylogenetically advanced.

*Wepman:* I should like to make one more comment about the age of 22 months being the accepted upper limit for the development of normal language or the acquisition of words.

*Lenneberg:* For the single first word.

*Wepman:* Such as "mama"? We would have to define what the word is. This, in itself, is difficult. What does being impaired mean? Using your yardstick for that would mean, to me, that a child who did not say his first word until he was three years of age should be considered impaired by about eight months. Would this be a fair estimate? This uncertainty plagues us when we talk of language impairment as though we knew what we meant by it. Those of us trying to do research do not think we are able to define it that nicely. It seems to me that we have seen many patients who developed their first words after 22 months of age and went on to quite normal development.

*Hardy:* Is it not possible there is innate confusion between words and language, that is, speech? What is at stake is that the appearance of the first word may not at all be indicative of the state of development of language comprehension.

*Wepman:* Yes, but even using verbal expressive language, not just language comprehension, the curve for phrases goes along too closely with the development of words themselves to say that we are just talking of the first word. We are talking of the acquisition of phrases, etc., and we have a very difficult time determining whether, let us say, a four-year-old child who has six words is delayed, or aphasic, or at what stage of language impairment. At what stage should he be? One of the most acute problems that we have in deciding this arises from the terrific burden of the notion of average development rate.

I have never yet known a parent who believed that his child should ever fall below the average. Consequently, our reports of the development of language are invariably related to an implicit average: "My child began to speak a few words at six months (or 'nine months', or 'ten months'), but then he did not develop any more words." One gets quite a different picture from the parents of aphasic patients than one does from studying a group of 100 or 150 so-called normal children. Those parents relate the extreme delay in onset of language rather than the "early" acquisition of words. I wonder if a clinic population might not be a good one to add to this type of study.

*Lenneberg:* I think the last two criticisms are very well taken, inasmuch as they are criticisms of what I did not say. On the first point, I did not use the word "impairment" at all. When we talk about emergence of behavior, we talk about modal events. If we say a normal child begins to take his first step by age 12 months, we do not imply that a child who begins to walk at 18 months has an impairment of ambulation. This is no different from saying that normally children are born after nine months of gestation. A baby that is born after seven or eight months of gestation is born prematurely and thus outside the norm. A child who cannot take a single step after 18 months of life is retarded with respect to gait. A child who cannot yet say "mama" or "daddy" at age two has delayed onset of speech and is brought to Dr. Wepman's clinic because the mother, the pediatrician, and probably Dr. Wepman himself, recognize that there is some aspect of the development which is not within normal limits. This assertion does not imply that such a child is mentally retarded or will not eventually have good speech development. In my presentation I was merely concerned with the statistical distribution of the appearance of one or more words. I also agree with Dr. Wepman and Dr. Hardy that the notion of first word is vague and one may not rely on mothers' reports of when this event occurred. In the material (8) that I reviewed in my talk, the occurrence of the first word was a milestone observed by trained child psychologists, and the observers for all of these children were always the same, so that we may assume that the distributions demonstrated do not suffer from lack of reliability of observation. If one were to describe speech development to a class of students in speech therapy, one would most certainly have to point out that there is a certain percentage of children who do not reach milestones at the exact modal time but who are, nevertheless, not mentally retarded and need not necessarily give cause for alarm.

In conclusion, I would like to make a final summary: the overall view is that there is a minimum level of maturation that the brain has to attain; then there is a state of flux that Dr. Roberts would call the state of plasticity. I think Dr. Ajuriaguerra referred to it as a state at which organization takes place. All these are types of theoretical conceptualization of the maturation process. Something that stops in adult life seems to be going on in the brain during childhood. That is about all we can say at this point.

*Hirsh:* May I add one comment. I think it is not irrelevant for me to report on some of the observations of my colleagues in the education of the deaf. I am as interested in the top part of Dr. Lenneberg's curves as in the bottom. If you had asked me independently at what age does it become extremely difficult to teach speech to a deaf child, I would have said about ten. If the child has not been recognized as deaf, or has been in an institution where he has learned only a sign language, or if he comes to us after the age of ten, it is a very difficult task. Below the age of ten, it simply becomes easier the earlier it is attempted. I do not know whether there is a lower limit on this since society does not take responsibility for education until age five.

## REFERENCES

1. ADAMS, H., *The Education of Henry Adams*. Modern Library, New York, 1931.
2. ALTMAN, P. L., and DITTMER, D. S. (Eds.), *Growth, Including Reproduction and Morphological Development*. Fed. Am. Soc. Exp. Biol., Washington, D. C., 1962.
3. ANDRÉ-THOMAS, SORREL, E., and SORREL-DEJERINE, MME., Un cas d'aphasie motrice par traumatisme cranio-cérébral chez l'enfant. *Revue Neurol.*, 1935, **63**: 893-896.
4. BASSER, L. S., Hemiplegia of early onset and the faculty of speech with special reference to the effects of hemispherectomy. *Brain*, 1962, **85**: 427-460.
5. BATEMAN, F., *On Aphasia or Loss of Speech and the Localization of the Faculty of Articulate Language*. Churchill, London, 1870.
6. BRANTE, G., Studies on lipids in the nervous system; with special reference to quantitative chemical determination and topical distribution. *Acta Physiol. Scand.*, 1949, **18**: Supp. 63.
7. BRUNNER, H., and STENGEL, E., Zur Lehre von den Aphasien im Kindesalter. *Zschr. Neurol. Psychiat.*, 1932, **142**: 430-450.
8. BÜHLER, C., *Kindheit und Jugend*, 3rd ed. Hirzel, Leipzig, 1930.
9. CARMICHAEL, L., The onset and early development of behavior. In: *Manual of Child Psychology* (L. Carmichael, Ed.). Wiley, New York, 1954: 60-185.
10. CARROLL, J. B., Language development. In: *Encyclopedia of Educational Research* (C. W. Harris, Ed.). Macmillan, New York, 1960: 744-752.
11. CHOW, K. L., Failure to demonstrate changes in the visual system of monkeys kept in darkness or in colored lights. *J. Comp. Neurol.*, 1955, **102**: 597-606.

12. Coghill, G. E., *Anatomy and the Problem of Behavior*. Macmillan, New York, 1929.

13. Conel, J. L., *The Postnatal Development of the Human Cerebral Cortex*, Vols. I-VII. Harvard Univ. Press, Cambridge, 1939-1963.

13a. De Crinis, M., *Aufbau und Abbau der Grosshirnleistungen und ihre anatomischen Gründe*. Karger, Berlin, 1934.

14. Folch-Pi, J., Composition of the brain in relation to maturation. In: *Biochemistry of the Developing Nervous System* (H. Waelsch, Ed.). Academic Press, New York, 1955: 121-136.

15. Gibbs, F. A., and Knott, J. R., Growth of the electrical activity of the cortex. *EEG Clin. Neurophysiol.*, 1949, **1**:223-229.

16. Grohmann, J., Modifikation oder Funktionsreifung. Ein Beitrag zur Klärung der wechselseitigen Bezeihungen zwischen Instinkthandlung und Erfahrung. *Zschr. Tierpsychol.*, 1938, **2**: 132-144.

17. Guttmann, E., Aphasia in children. *Brain*, 1942, **65**: 205-219.

18. Hillier, W. F., Jr., Total left cerebral hemispherectomy for malignant glioma. *Neurology*, 1954, **4**: 718-721.

19. Kummer, B., Untersuchungen über die Entwicklung der Schädelform des Menschen und einiger Anthropoiden. *Abhandl. Exakt. Biol.*, 1953, **3**: 1-44.

20. Lefèvre, A. B., Contribuição para o estudo da psicopatologia da afasia em crianças. *Arq. Neuro-Psiquiat.*, 1950, **8**: 345-393.

21. Lenneberg, E. H., Biological perspectives of language. In: *New Directions in the Study of Language* (E. H. Lenneberg, Ed.). M.I.T. Press, Cambridge, 1964: 65-88.

22. ———, Speech as a motor skill with special reference to nonaphasic disorders. *Monogr. Soc. Res. Child Dev.*, 1964, **29**/1: 115-127.

23. ———, *Biological Foundations of Language* (in preparation).

24. Lenneberg, E. H., Rebelsky, F. G., and Nichols, I. A., The vocalization of infants born to deaf and hearing parents. *Hum. Developm.*, 1965, **8**: 23-27.

25. Lenneberg, E. H., Nichols, I. A., and Rosenberger, E. F., Primitive stages of language development in mongolism. *Res. Publ. Ass. Res. Nerv. Ment. Dis.*, 1964, **42**: 119-137.

26. McCarthy, D., Language development in children. In: *Manual of Child Psychology* (L. Carmichael, Ed.). Wiley, New York, 1954: 492-630.

27. Morley, M., *The Development and Disorders of Speech in Childhood*. Livingstone, Edinburgh, 1957.

28. Pötzl, O., Ueber sensorische Aphasie im Kindesalter. *Zschr. Hals- N.-Ohrenhlk.*, 1926, **14**: 190-216.

29. Riesen, A. H., Effects of stimulus deprivation on the development and atrophy of the visual sensory system. *Am. J. Orthopsychiat.*, 1960, **30**: 23-36.

30. Russell, W. R., and Espir, M. L. E., *Traumatic Aphasia. A Study of Aphasia in War Wounds of the Brain*. Oxford Univ. Press, London, 1961.

31. Schadé, J. P., and van Groeningen, W. B., Structural organization of the human cerebral cortex; maturation of the middle frontal gyrus. *Acta Anat.*, 1961, **47**: 74-111.

32. SMITH, J. R., The frequency growth of the human alpha rhythms during normal infancy and childhood. *J. Psychol.*, 1941, **11**: 177-198.

33. SMITH, M. E., An investigation of the development of the sentence and the extent of vocabulary in young children. *Univ. Iowa Stud. Child. Welfare*, 1926, **3**: No. 5.

34. WIESEL, T. N., and HUBEL, D. H., Effects of visual deprivation on morphology and physiology of cells in the cat's lateral geniculate body. *J. Neurophysiol.*, 1963, **26**: 978-993.

35. YAKOVLEV, P. I., Morphological criteria of growth and maturation of the nervous system in man. *Res. Publ. Ass. Res. Nerv. Ment. Dis.*, 1962, **39**: 3-46.

# LINGUISTIC TYPES OF APHASIA

ROMAN JAKOBSON
Harvard University
and Massachusetts Institute of Technology
Cambridge

While anthropologists consider the monologue a more sophisticated super-structure upon the dialogue and find communities which use only dialogues, monologues in scientific life are less subtle and less productive than dialogues. Therefore, I will be most grateful if you transform my paper in an exchange of opinions; interruptions manifest a genuine cooperation between speaker and listeners.

It seems to me that there are very few workers remaining in the field of language disorders who still believe that the role of linguistics in the study of aphasia is unimportant. At present, in various parts of America and Europe, there are groups of diverse specialists attempting joint inquiry into various questions of aphasia and other disturbances of language. There are several centers where neurologists, psychologists, linguists, and other specialists work together to describe, to examine, to analyze aphasia, and to obtain the most exact diagnoses and prognoses.

In a recent interdisciplinary Ciba symposium (5) devoted to the disorders of language, it was expressly stated that for a very long time linguistics had been unable to participate efficiently in the investigation of aphasia because the development of structural analysis in linguistics is a relatively recent phenomenon. But now, with the intensive development of such scrutiny, linguists must also have their say on the disruptions of language. The participation of linguists in such research proves to be important for the study of aphasia, on the one hand, and for linguistics on the other, because there obviously exists a very intimate interrelation between problems of normal language in operation, language in build-up, i.e., the acquisition of language by children, and the disintegration of language, exemplified by the various types of aphasic impairments. It becomes more and more clear that such impairments have their own order, so to say an orderly hierarchy of disorders; this order actually exists and must be analyzed. Lord Brain, the initiator of the Ciba Symposium, went even farther: he said that the same analytic methods may be applied to psychotic, especially schizophrenic, speech

(3). The linguistic work in this wider field has scarcely begun but one can already see that schizophrenia gives clues that enable a linguist to catch certain phases and facets in the process of the illness which could otherwise easily remain unnoticed.

During the earlier period, when linguistics played only a minor role in the study of language disorders, there arose among nonlinguists certain conceptions of aphasia which show, to put it bluntly, a complete disregard for the linguistic aspect of speech pathology. Such intentional neglect is intolerable for, if aphasia affects uniquely or primarily our language, it is the science of language which has to offer the first tentative answer as to the kind of aphasia encountered in any given case. Unfortunately many psychologists came to believe that aphasia presents a single unitary type only, and that no qualitative, but merely quantitative, differences may be found among the diverse varieties of verbal disturbances. This theory is in glaring contradiction with all the extant empiric data about aphasic impairments. It is impossible to confine our analysis of aphasia to a purely quantitative picture: linguists pay close attention to statistical problems of language, and quantitative linguistics is one of the important aspects of our science. To be able to count it is necessary to know what one is counting; it would be useless to count without defining qualitative characteristics, without a classification of the units and categories to be counted.

The results of the purely quantitative approach to aphasia are at variance with linguistic facts. All of the quasi-proofs used to substantiate the unitary bias are futile because they are based on fictitious rubrics which actually ignore the phonemic, morphologic, and syntactic structure of language. At present, we have a number of objective and careful descriptions of diverse aphasic cases from various linguistic areas. This material unambiguously reveals the existence of qualitatively different, even opposite, types of disturbances. Of course, polarity does not exclude transitional or mixed cases—in this respect, the disorders of language are similar to all other pathological changes.

The frequent occurrence of pure polar types cannot be denied; these fundamental dichotomies enable us to classify the aphasic impairments. Several years ago I had the opportunity to discuss one of them in detail (25). Two different factors, selection and combination, play an essential role in any speech event. If, for instance, I intend to tell something about my father, I have to make a conscious or subconscious choice of one of the possible terms—father, parent, papa, dad, daddy; then, if I want to say that he is in bad shape, again I select one of the suitable words: ill, sick, indisposed, not healthy, ailing. Selections are one aspect of the twofold event, and the combination of the two selected verbal entities, "Father is sick", is its other aspect. The entities among which we make our selection are mutually connected by various forms and degrees of similarity in all its varieties: likeness, similitude, equivalence, resemblance, analogy, diverse grades of specification, contrast. Contrary to selection, which is based on an internal relation, combination involves the external relation of contiguity in its various forms and degrees: neighborhood, proximity, and remoteness, subordination and coordination.

A linguistic reinterpretation of the variegated cases described in the multilingual literature on aphasia, as well as observations made by myself on aphasics of different languages, made it clear to me that we have to deal with two basic types of aphasia. Either the internal relation of similarity and correspondingly the selective ability is impaired or, conversely, the external relation of contiguity and hence the capacity of combination appears to be affected.

After publishing my first outlines of this hitherto overlooked dichotomy (24, 25), I was happy to find support and approval on the part of such experts in the field of aphasia as Luria in Moscow (38, 39), and Wepman (8, 47) and Goodglass (14, 15, 17) in this country. Their observations and also earlier studies, especially Goldstein's (13), prompted me to examine and point out the very close relationship between the dichotomy of selection and combination and the traditional discrimination between two types of aphasia which were known under the somewhat misleading names of "sensory" and "motor". Any terminology is conventional but in this case nomenclature creates an erroneous impression, as if the entire problem lay either in the damaged articulatory motor activities or in the harmed sensory apparatus. This misunderstanding disappears as soon as the term "encoding" is substituted for "motor" and "decoding" for "sensory". In this way occasional symptoms are replaced by far more essential features. The difference between combination and selection disorders closely coincides with the difference between encoding and decoding disturbances. Before discussing the interrelation of these two pairs of syndromes, let us delineate the most salient types of encoding and decoding aphasia.

Among the contributions of neurologists, psychiatrists and psychologists to the study of aphasia, Luria's works seem to be the most instructive, first because he approached the different types of aphasic impairments on several levels, and second because he had the opportunity to work with numerous cases, since a high number of aphasic patients, especially war veterans with brain injuries, were brought together in Moscow. The amount of cases that illustrate his findings is quite impressive. In a book published in 1962 (39) and in a paper for the Ciba Foundation symposium (41), Luria deals with six types of impairments, among them the basic types of encoding disorders, the traditional "Broca's" or "motor" aphasia—in Luria's nomenclature the "efferent" (or "kinetic") type—and the basic type of decoding disorders which carried in these studies the customary label "sensory" aphasia.

Permit me to give a brief answer to the question of what are the main features of efferent aphasia on the various levels of the verbal pattern. Of course, in any given case not all of these symptoms must be present and not all the linguistic levels must necessarily be affected. In some cases the deficit is chiefly or uniquely phonological; in some instances, the losses belong mostly or only to the syntactic level.

In efferent aphasia, words are preserved, especially those which can be independent of the context—mainly substantive nouns, and in particular concrete nouns which carry the main function. On the other hand, the construction of a sentence presents enormous difficulties; in the first place we observe the disappearance of purely grammatical words, namely connectives (conjunctions and prepositions), as well as such strictly grammatical, formal words as pronouns. The more independent the word is and the more it approaches the model of a pure initial word, the more viable it is. Thus nouns are preserved better than verbs, and substantives better than adjectives. The nominative is the only case which survives, and verbs are used in their most nominalized form. Thus, if there is an infinitive in the verbal pattern of the given language, this form shows a higher resistance in efferent aphasia than the finite verbs. The traditional label "telegraphic style" is well suited to the speech of such aphasics. Their utterances tend to be reduced to one-word sentences.

On the phonological level, the phonemes are preserved. The difficuty is not in the phonemes by themselves but in their combinations, the transition from one phoneme to another, the diversity of phonemes within polysyllabic words. Intensive use is made of phonemic assimilation and dissimilation. The more independent a phoneme or distinctive feature is in respect to the context, the greater the probability of its survival. Among the distinctive features, the inherent ones are more resistant than the prosodic, since only the latter involve interphonemic relations within the sequence.

Efferent aphasia is, I repeat, a typical contiguity disorder, and eloquent manifestations of disturbed contiguity are observable on all levels of language. The root, as the lexical and least dependent part of the word, is better preserved than the grammatical suffixes. It is noteworthy that words of the same root but with different suffixes are mutually associated by semantic contiguity, whereas words with a common suffix but different roots display a semantic similarity. Among syntactic relations, "government" is more easily abolished than "agreement" because the latter links the modifier to its initial word not only by contiguity but also by similarity, whereas "government" is confined to pure contiguity. For the efferent type of aphasia with its agrammatism, the best definition was given by the ardent proponent of a scientific approach to aphasia, Hughlings Jackson, one century ago (23). He was the first to recognize that the main deficiency consists in the loss of the ability to propositionize, i.e., to construct a proposition.

The so-called sensory aphasia, acutely analyzed by E. S. Beyn (2), presents an opposite linguistic syndrome. Here the syntactic wholes—sentences —are preserved. The most viable elements are those which serve to construct sentences, the so-called little words, such as connectives, pronouns, etc. Adverbs and adjectives are retained longer than verbs and nouns; the predicate is more stable than the subject. The initial substantive of the sentence presents the greatest difficulty, especially if the patient speaks a language like English or French, where as a rule the subject appears at the beginning of the sentence. This difficulty becomes particularly acute when the subject is a substantive in a nonderived, primary form, i.e., a pure lexical form with a minimal dependence on the context. It is interesting that deverbative and deadjectival nouns are less vulnerable.

If the required word is context-free, the word-finding operation is an impossible task for a patient severely affected by a selection (i.e., similarity) disorder. He is unable to build an equational sentence or to name an object drawn or pointed at; he often is unable to respond to a word by its repetition, although the same word may be pronounced easily within a context. Some patients counter the request to repeat the negation "no" with the unwittingly whimsical statement, "No, I cannot".

Faced with these two types of aphasia, we may ask ourselves why the first of them—the loss of the ability to integrate, to create a context—affects chiefly the encoding process; and why, on the other hand, the inability to analyze a context into its constituents, to separate them, and to operate with those constituents which are not prompted by the context, handicaps first and foremost the decoding process. Before answering these questions, it seems appropriate to discuss the deficits of the latter, the sensory type, on the phonemic level.

Here again the combinations are preserved, but within these combinations some phonemes are simplified, especially those which cannot be predicted from their environment. Certain phonemic distinctions are lost. For linguists this point is clear and, in accord with this linguistic experience, Luria (38, 39) repeatedly points out that in sensory aphasia it is not the physical but the phonemic hearing which is lost. Among psychologists, however, there are still skeptics who see only risky hypotheses in such references to a breakdown in phonemic perception. But without this hypothesis one could not explain why in a language such as Czech or Hungarian, where the contrast of long and short vowels plays a great role both in stressed and unstressed positions, a sensory aphasic may lose the ability to distinguish long and short vowels whether in hearing or in his own speech. There is no question of inability to hear or articulate vowels of longer or shorter duration; what is lost is the distinctive semantic value of the difference between long and short signals in the phonemic code.

The phonological deficits of sensory aphasics reflect the hierarchial structure of the phonemic pattern. A few months ago an important paper (6) was published by the Polish linguist Doroszewski, a remarkable field worker who carefully followed, recorded, and described a typical case of sensory aphasia. In this case report one finds scrupulous observations on disturbances in the relevant Polish distinction between voiced and voiceless consonants. These data are particularly eloquent since the observer had no preconceived opinion and disregarded the principle underlying and explaining the order of these deficits. In the opposition voice-voiceless, the voiced consonants are the so-called "marked" category. Many habitually voiced consonants lost their voicing mark in the speech of the patient, but there was no change at all of habitually voiceless (unmarked) into voiced (marked) phonemes. Besides voicing (+)/voicelessness (−), several other binary oppositions underlie the Polish consonantal system: they mark compactness (+) *versus* diffuseness (−), acuteness (+) *versus* gravity (−), stridency (+) *versus* mellowness (−). It is indeed significant that sensory aphasia manifests a tendency to reduce the recurrence of marks in a phoneme. Thus 91 per cent of the compact (+) consonants, but only 35 per cent of the diffuse (−) consonants, lost their voicing in the speech of the Polish aphasic. Among the diffuse (−) consonants, 57 per cent of the acute (+) ones and only 6 per cent of the grave (−) ones became voiceless. Among the diffuse acute (−+) consonants, 100 per cent of the strident (+) phonemes, but a mere 50 per cent of the mellow (−) ones, changed from voiced to voiceless.

Now let us go back to the question of why the combination disturbances which hamper the construction of a context and any act of integration affect primarily the encoding activity of the patient, whereas selection disturbances strike especially the decoding activity. Both connections, which at first glance seem arbitrary, are in reality well founded. No further explanations are needed for a psychologist like Dr. Osgood, who traced the cardinal difference between the integrating and representational capacities (46).

In the process of encoding, impairments affect the context rather than its constituents, whereas the decoding process presents the inverse relation. Why are the constituents intact in the encoding? Because the speaker makes the selection of the elements before combining them into a whole. The secondary stage, the building of a context, is more susceptible to disruption, while its constituents are much more viable. Therefore, the encoding process succumbs most often to combination disturbances. In decoding operations we have first to grasp the whole: here lies the greater difference between the attitude of listeners and of speakers. The decoder is a probabilist to a much greater extent than the encoder. Thus there are no homonyms for the speaker; when he says "bank" he knows perfectly whether he is speaking about the shore of a river or a financial establishment, whereas the listener, as long as he is not helped by the context, struggles with homonymy and has to use a probability test. The identification of the constituents is the second stage, which can be characterized as a self-identification of the listener with the speaker: the sequential synthesis yields to a simultaneous synthesis, and sequences change, as George Miller (44) would say, into chunks. Naturally, the consequent is shakier than the antecedent and therefore the decoding process is particularly vulnerable to the selection disturbances.

When observers discuss encoding and decoding disorders and prefer to term them as "predominantly encoding" and "predominantly decoding", they are obviously right because there are no purely encoding or purely decoding disorders, only a difference in hierarchy. There is a much lesser dependence of decoding on encoding than vice versa. More or less intact decoding processes are compatible with badly disrupted encodement. An eloquent case was recently presented by Dr. Lenneberg (29); a boy who at eight years was totally speechless but at the same time understood perfectly the language of adults. On the other hand, one could hardly imagine the preservation of a full-fledged encoding capacity despite the atrophy of decoding ability. The active mastery of a language implies its passive knowledge. Each of us knows more languages passively than actively, and the stock of words one understands exceeds the number which one actually uses. The sphere of our decoding action is wider than our encoding activities.

A highly important connection observed is the impairment of internal speech in any serious case of efferent aphasia. Internal speech, a cardinal problem for both linguists and psychologists, was nevertheless somewhat neglected until it became a gratifying topic of modern Russian research. I would like to refer especially to Vygotsky (55), Luria (39), Zhinkin (57), Sokolov (53), and the other authors cited by the latter. In the light of these stimulating studies, the detriment of the internal speech provoked by efferent aphasia is quite understandable. It suffices to confront agrammatism as the pivotal sign of the efferent syndrome with the predicative nature of internal speech and, moreover, to recollect that internal speech is the usual context of our externalized, uttered speech, and that it is the destruction of the contextual frame which characterizes this type of aphasia.

It is equally natural that the sensory type of aphasia entails an incapacity for metalingual operations. The vital ability to translate one verbal sign into another (synonymic or more explicit or, inversely, more elliptic) underlies the development and use of language, but the sensory aphasia which inhibits any intralingual and interlingual translation and any identification of verbal signs abolishes the metalingual function.

Having surveyed the efferent type of combination disorders and the sensory variety of selection disturbances, we may now proceed to the other types of aphasia. It was Luria (35, 39) who singled out most clearly what he called dynamic aphasia. Like efferent aphasia, this type belongs to the combination disorders, but presents no disruption on either the phonemic or the grammatical level. As long as the patient operates with such entirely (both grammatically and lexically) coded units as words, or with such partly (only grammatically) coded units as sentences, there is no trouble. Difficulties begin as soon as speech exceeds the limits of a sentence and the utterance consists of more than one sentence. A combination of sentences which is free of obligatory rules, especially of hierarchical, subordinative rules, is a particularly intricate task for patients with some combination defects, and they fail to execute it, especially to build a monologue, that is, a context which is incumbent on the speaker alone.

The other deficiency of such aphasics is their vanishing capacity for switching from one system of signs to another, for instance, answering a verbal order by a prescribed gesture. According to Luria's definition, what is impaired in such cases is the regulative function of speech (37, 39); as a matter of fact, it is an incapacity to use alternatively two different semiotic codes within the same discourse. In comparison with the efferent type, the dynamic variety is simply a more attenuated form of combination impairment: disintegration in the former type, mere limitation in the latter.

To this dualism of disintegration and limitation we find a correspondence also among the selection disorders. If the disintegration of selection processes is represented by the sensory type, the limitation of these processes appears in the variant described by Luria (39, 41) under the traditional label— semantic aphasia. This type in turn demands a linguistic reinterpretation. In the various forms of selection impairments, the words and their internal structure confront the patient with much greater handicaps than the organization of the sentence. Morphology is more difficult and embarrassing for him than is syntax. The more a word within a sentence depends on the syntactic environment, the higher are its chances of being understood and uttered by a sensory aphasic; in semantic aphasia, the selection disturbance appears to be attenuated. Any grammatical category, and in particular nouns, survives solely in its primary syntactic function. Morphology yields to syntax. Each part of speech is defined by the only syntactic construction assigned to it. Nouns are confined to an adverbal position and are no longer understood when used as adnominal modifiers. Patients suffering from semantic aphasia cannot grasp the difference between phrases such as "wife's brother" and "brother's wife". The predicative function of a noun, especially in clauses without copula, e.g., Russian *lev—zver'*, "[the] lion [is an] animal", puzzles such an aphasic.

The word order in these cases becomes much more uniform and inflexible. Since in English not only aphasic but also normal speech has a rigid word order, let us take an example from a language with freer word order. The basic word order of Russian (subject, predicate, object) admits a stylistic inversion (object, predicate, subject) since the accusative of the object and the nominative of the subject are distinguished by their declensional endings: "Luka pomnit Ol'gu" and "Ol'gu pomnit Luka" both mean "Luke remembers Olga", while "Ol'ga pomnit Luku" and "Luku pomnit Ol'ga" state that Olga remembers Luke. For a Russian with semantic aphasia, any noun which precedes the verb becomes a subject, and any postverbal noun is comprehended as an object notwithstanding the inflectional endings. All such examples reveal a limitation of morphology in favor of a clear-cut and stabilized syntactic pattern.

The two remaining forms of aphasia are perhaps the most complex and notable varieties. One of them, termed by Luria (35, 39) afferent (or kines-thetic) aphasia, evidently belongs to the class of encoding disturbances based on a disruption of the capacity for combination. In contradistinction to the efferent type of combination disorders which affects the phonemic sequences, single phonemes merge in the afferent type. Also, sensory aphasia shows deficits in phonemic distinctions, but there, as we saw, disturbances in phoneme-finding, quite similar to the word-finding difficulties, lead toward an orderly abolition of certain distinctive marks. The number of selections decreases: e.g., in the Polish case cited (6), the presence of the compactness mark in a consonant nearly excludes the voiced-voiceless distinction. Conversely, for afferent aphasics the difficulty consists in the combination of distinctive features into a phoneme. Such a bundle of concurrent features is too complex for these patients, and they implement only one or a few features of the given phoneme with random substitution of its other constituents. The retained features carry the phonemic information, while the substitutes are mere fillers.

This type of aphasia, in both its linguistic and clinical aspects, demands a further, subtler inquiry. However, I would like to refer to an instructive annotated report on a typical case of afferent aphasia, prepared for publication jointly by two Warsaw scholars, a linguist, Halina Mierzejewska, and a psychologist, Mariusz Maruszewski (43). This study makes it clear that there is no constancy in the repertory of preserved features and that terms of any binary opposition are mutually interchangeable: voiced and voiceless, nasal and oral, continuant and discontinuous, strident and mellow, compact and diffuse, acute and grave, sharp and nonsharp (cf. 27).

The combinations impaired are temporal sequences in the efferent type of aphasia and bundles of concurrent features in the afferent type. The relation between combination and selection disorders (or correspondingly between the prevailingly encoding and decoding level of aphasia) coincides with the dichotomy of successivity and simultaneity disturbances. In the afferent type, the correspondence between both dichotomies ceases, since here it is simultaneous combinations that are affected.

The opposite discrepancy between the two dichotomies is manifested in the amnestic type (35, 39). If a patient suffering from amnestic aphasia is asked to point to his eye, he will do it; likewise he will fulfill the request to point to his ear. But when asked, "Show your eye and ear", he will indicate only one of the two named organs, omitting or erroneously identifying the other one. Finally, the proposal that he show his eye, ear, and nose will simply perplex this patient. It is a selection disorder, but in contrast to the sensory type, amnestic aphasia affects only an iterative selection, a selective operation expanded into a sequence. Three different choices have to be made successively by the patient from one and the same series "eye-ear-nose". "John, Peter, and Mary came to Boston" is a sentence with three coordinative nouns. "John sang, Peter played, and Mary danced" is a sentence of three coordinative clauses. The coordinative constructions are the only ones which suffer in the amnestic aphasia. They are the only grammatical sequences deprived of any internal syntactic hierarchy, and therefore the only open groups with freely addible and omissible members. The coordinative words, phrases, or clauses are linked together only by mutual formal similarity. In these groups, similarity relations involve not only the simultaneity axis but also the successivity axis of language. Through such a double play of similarity, the coordinative groups become the maximal impediment for patients with similarity disorders.

Thus three dichotomies underlie the six cardinal types of aphasia: (a) combination, which implies contiguity and affects primarily encodement, *versus* selection, which implies similarity and affects primarily decodement; (b) successivity *versus* simultaneity; and (c) disintegration *versus* limitation. The afferent and amnestic types do not take part in the latter dichotomy. A tentative tabulation of these three dichotomies was proposed in my paper for the Ciba Foundation symposium (26).

When I interpreted and classified on the linguistic level all the instructive material contained in Luria's publications (35-39, 41), the factual testimonies in various European and American works on aphasia, and my own observations, I became interested also in the extant attempts to classify aphasic impairment on yet other levels. I followed Hughlings Jackson's warning against any mixture of different levels in the investigation of aphasia (23) and outlined my typology of aphasic impairment on a purely and strictly linguistic basis. At the same time I realized that a call for autonomy should not be confused with isolation. While autonomy is rewarding, isolation is always harmful. After an autonomous examination of each given level is accomplished, it is useful and even necessary to look for the correlation between the different levels. Thus I asked myself what was done in the intricate questions of brain topography; what functional areas in the cortex were found responsible for the different types of language disorders.

I used the results of this topographic research, in particular Luria's (35, 36, 39) and Pribram's (50) data. After several detailed discussions with the latter at Stanford, a close correspondence between the location of the lesions and the linguistic typology of impairments suggested itself. A tentative topographic analogue to all three linguistic dichotomies may be drafted.

The combination (contiguity) disorders appear to be connected with the more anterior lesions of the cortex, and the selection (similarity) disorders with the more posterior lesions. If we confront the basic varieties of these two kinds of disorders, the efferent type and the sensory type, we learn that the former is associated with anterotemporal and the latter with posterotemporal lesions. There are two types of milder disturbances corresponding to these two types of verbal disintegration: the combination ability under-goes a limitation in the "dynamic" impairments, and the selection ability in the "semantic" impairments. These two attenuated forms of aphasia (mere limitation *versus* disintegration) are connected with the two polar areas: the frontal intrinsic area of the forebrain is responsible for the dynamic impair-ments, and the posterior intrinsic area (the postero-parietal and parieto-oc-cipital sections) for the semantic impairments (36, 38, 39, 50).

In the efferent and dynamic types of combination disorders, the succes-sivity axis of language is affected, whereas the sensory and semantic types of selection disorders affect the simultaneity axis. As to the two transitional types, one of them, afferent aphasia, is a combination disorder which affects the simultaneity axis, while the other, amnestic aphasia, is a selection im-pairment concerned with the successivity axis. These transitional types are linked with more central parts of the cortex—the afferent type with retro-central lesions and the amnestic type with centrotemporal lesions (cf., Luria, 35, 39, and Penfield's views on the interpretive cortex, 48).

Luria's and Pribram's studies and their joint research, both at Stanford University and the Burdenko Institute in Moscow, suggest that the dichoto-my successivity-simultaneity corresponds to the structural difference be-tween the mediobasal and dorsolateral areas of the brain (26, 39, 51). If this cerebral correlate of the linguistic coordinates proves to be valid, then this correspondence opens new prospects to the intricate problem of the interre-lation between our sequential and simultaneous perceptions, in particular between such temporal, chiefly sequential phenomena as speech and music, and such typically spatial, chiefly simultaneous phenomena as perception of visual arts. It seems to me that the dichotomy successivity-simultaneity, which plays such an essential and still unexplored role in language, gives a key to the pending investigation of different sign systems in their interrela-tionships. Perhaps the study of this dualism will throw a new light upon the different functions and functional areas of the brain.

*Magoun:* May I ask you to elaborate the generalization about an impair-ment in mediobasal versus dorsolateral parts of the brain? Could you ampli-fy a little more fully the relationship of the dynamic frontal, semantic parie-tal, amnestic centrotemporal, and sensory posterotemporal foci which were delineated to the mediobasal or dorsolateral parts of the brain?

*Jakobson:* All three types of successivity disorders—the dynamic, efferent, and amnestic types—seem to be localized much deeper and to be connected with the mediobasal area. All these three types affect the sequence, primari-ly the sentence and combination of sentences. If we accept Luria's and Pri-bram's suppositions, then the operations dealing with the time sequence ap-pear to be connected with the mediobasal part of the brain. I confess that I feel impressed by this hypothesis because it throws new light on the dichot-omy of successivity and simultaneity. This dichotomy belongs, as you know, to the burning questions in linguistics, psychology, and many other fields. Anyway, in all its aspects, the dichotomy requires careful examination.

*Wepman:* I have discussed this concept many times with Dr. Jakobson when it was at a different stage of development than it is now. I am most interested in his naming a separate type of aphasia, called amnestic, since I think that all aphasia could probably be described, in one sense, as amnestic, as a loss of memory and the ability to recall. For myself at least, I would need a great deal of proof about the neurophysiological localization of the aphasic types he presents.

*Jakobson:* Luria showed me diverse cases. In his Moscow Institute he works with an impressive number and variety of aphasic patients. The results of their careful examination appear very convincing, as do the numerous and detailed post-mortem data. Many brain pictures are published in his books (35, 39, 40), with a parallel description of the cases. He pays attention to the different aspects of aphasia with particular reference to the changes in speech and to the localization of the brain lesion. Pribram also, when working with Luria, made valuable observations in that area.

I completely agree that the term amnestic is very vague. But the same could be said about most of the terms used. However, I did not want to introduce new labels. Thus comparison of my findings with Luria's work would be facilitated by my use of the same terms he uses.

May I add that I take full responsibility for the linguistic part of the paper presented, for the linguistic interpretation of Luria's and others' clinical testimonies and of my own observations. As to the topographic data, I simply collated Luria's and Pribram's conclusions with my linguistic statements. The correspondence between the linguistic and topographic dichotomies is striking, but I would propose to discuss both aspects independently.

### Discussion

*Geschwind:* Dr. Jakobson has given us a brilliant presentation of the major contrasting types of aphasia. I would like, however, to make some historical corrections. Dr. Jakobson stated that Hughlings Jackson was the founder of the scientific study of aphasia; I do not agree with this view. Jackson did not make the contrast between the two major types of aphasia. Bastian (1) was probably the first to point out on the basis of clinical observation that there were aphasias in which comprehension was impaired. Jackson, in fact, actively opposed the idea that there were such aphasias. In the face of such an error, I find it hard to call Jackson the founder of the scientific study of aphasia. It is interesting that despite his brilliant contributions Bastian was severely criticized by Head (18), in my opinion quite unfairly.

The real founder of the scientific study of aphasia was certainly Wernicke. His classic paper (56) succeeded (where Bastian's earlier paper had failed) in drawing attention to the existence of an aphasia in which the patient did not comprehend and had fluent, paraphasic speech. He contrasted this syndrome with the type of aphasia which Broca had described more than ten years earlier, in which the patient has a paucity of speech and good comprehension. It was Wernicke who really established in the eyes of the world the dichotomy between these two types of aphasia. In addition, there is little question that the greatest single source of contributions to aphasia were the students of Wernicke, among whom are such different figures as Liepmann, Goldstein, Bonhoeffer, Lissauer, and Kleist.

The point has been raised that the words "sensory" and "motor" are confusing as applied to aphasia. I think that these labels have become confusing through loss of contact with the original use of the terms by German neurologists. German neurology went into the ascendancy in part because of the German victory in the Franco-Prussian War, and similarly suffered somewhat from neglect with Germany's defeat in World War I. There was a decline in the interest of American and British neurologists in the German literature, and confusion appeared in the use of the terms sensory and motor which had, in my opinion, been used in a consistent manner by the German authors.

A difficulty arises with the model presented by Professor Jakobson. It suggests that in association with fluent paraphasic speech there must be a disturbance of comprehension, and indeed, it is suggested, also a disturbance of repetition. Conversely, disturbance of comprehension is thought of necessity to entail a disturbance on the expressive side. Yet when we study the cases we can find that these elements may vary independently. Thus, if fluent paraphasic patients with a great flow of speech and good preservation of syntactic structures are considered, one will find that they fall into several groups: (a) some show disturbance of *both* comprehension and repetition; (b) others may show absolutely letter-perfect repetition and yet have absolutely no comprehension; (c) a third group shows marked impairment of repetition but excellent comprehension. This third group has what is called "conduction" aphasia, for which Kurt Goldstein (11-13) used the term "central" aphasia.

One of the odd things about these fluent paraphasic patients is the fact that repetition and comprehension can be so thoroughly dissociated that patients who show the most excellent repetition, even of foreign words in languages unknown to them, may show such a profound loss of comprehension.

*Osgood:* Would you not agree, perhaps, that pure echolalia almost requires lack of comprehension?

*Geschwind:* I would agree that forced echolalia probably does require lack of comprehension.

The second way in which Dr. Jakobson's model presents some difficulties is in its view that disturbance of comprehension (or decoding) necessarily entails a disturbance on the expressive (or encoding) side. A common argument is that for correct expression there must be feedback. The fact is, however, that there are many excellent cases in the literature of isolated comprehension disturbances; I have partially reviewed this problem (9). Dejerine (4) described in detail an extensively studied patient with intact vision who had lost the ability to read, but who could write and had normal language performances otherwise. Many such cases have been described—e.g., Symonds (54), Holmes (20), and many others. I have personally seen three such cases. All these patients could copy words they could not read, so it is obvious that vision was intact. These well-studied individual cases in the literature establish beyond doubt the existence of isolated comprehension disturbances. I might add that one should not be impressed by large numbers of cases. Most of the best papers in the literature have probably been single-case descriptions. Mechanisms often tend to become blurred in the larger series.

Let me cite some further examples of the preservation of normal expression in the face of severe comprehension difficulty. Liepmann (30) and Liepmann & Storch (33) described the first case of pure word-deafness to come to postmortem. Their patient was followed very carefully in life with, among other things, intensive audiometric studies. At necropsy all the peripheral hearing apparatus was shown to be intact by examination of the temporal bones, and the lesion was shown to be a central one. This patient had severe loss of comprehension of spoken language, with otherwise normal hearing and intactness or near intactness of all other aspects of language. There have been other such cases, including a recent excellent study by Hemphill & Stengel (19).

I believe that many of these varying clinical pictures which cannot be accounted for by Dr. Jakobson's model in its present form can be explained by further attention to certain anatomical features which I shall not discuss at present.

One last word is in order on the problem of localization. Dr. Jakobson's diagram of localization was not on a model of a real brain. What comes through, however, is that he and his collaborators have ended up in the same place that Wernicke did in 1874. Various investigators, such as Head (18) and Marie (42) set out to destroy his scheme; they somehow ended by supporting Wernicke's views on localization, although Head at least never admitted to it.

*Jakobson:* I am grateful to the organizers of the Conference for giving me the opportunity to meet Dr. Geschwind for the first time and to open a discussion with him. I am very interested in all that he said, and on many questions we are in agreement.

He may be right in pointing to the weak aspects of Jackson's views, but in some other problems, particularly in his emphasis on the verbal aspects of aphasia (23), Jackson surpassed his contemporaries. I would place him among the precursors of modern linguistics. He launched many ideas which later were developed in the science of language, partly under his influence, partly independently.

Bastian was indeed a very remarkable specialist in the pathology of language, and actually his writings on aphasia and other speech defects should be read much more because they contain many important and still viable thoughts.

I did not say that everybody who uses the terms "motor" and "sensory" interprets them mistakenly, but there still is a danger that some people in some countries, and particularly in America, could misinterpret this terminology. However, I always tend to avoid discussion about terms. The most difficult and thankless task is to propose and promote better terms. My teacher used to say, "Call it what you want. All that matters is to know what you are speaking about."

When the decoding ability is destroyed, the encoding ability may still be preserved if it was strongly developed before the onset of the decoding disturbances, but even then such disturbances usually lead to a deterioration of encoding as well. When decoding is disrupted for a longer period, then encoding has very little chance to remain intact.

*Geschwind:* Dr. Jakobson suggests that comprehension (decoding) disturbances cannot last for a long time without accompanying expressive (encoding) disturbances. Yet Dejerine's patient (4) went over two years without being able to read a word of French. During this time he continued to conduct his business at a very high level, played cards, played musical instruments, and continued to write letters on business affairs. The difficulty in reading persisted the full period. I have personally seen such patients present a stable picture over many months.

*Jakobson:* Dr. Geschwind's example is quite instructive. But problems of reading and writing are not in direct correspondence to the problems of speaking and listening, because reading and writing are secondary habits, superstructures upon speech, and they differ from speech both in their development and in their disturbances. As to spoken language, may I ask whether there are recorded cases of a lengthy sensory breakdown with preservation of intact motor activities?

*Geschwind:* Such stable isolated comprehension disturbances are not restricted to written language. For example, Liepmann's case (30) had stable isolated word-deafness over many months. The one patient I have seen who most closely approximated pure word-deafness, although she did not show as isolated a disturbance as either Liepmann's or Hemphill & Stengel's (19) case, had had a stable disturbance for several months. I do not believe that it really makes a difference whether these isolated disturbances are for visual or spoken language.

*Jakobson:* This mild paraphasia seems to be here a byproduct of decoding disturbances. As Feuchtwanger clearly demonstrated (7), there is neither bilateral nor unilateral implication between aphasia and amusia. When cautiously, perhaps overcautiously, I question the existence of decoding disorders without reverberations on the encoding side, I feel influenced both by the warning of psychologists against the symmetrical model of encoding and decoding aphasia and by the fact that the active mastery of language implies its passive mastery.

*Wepman:* I think we should not forget there is a level of language lower than the cortical one. The example that was given of the echolalic response of a patient can certainly be true, even though the conceptual level is unable to function. The patient is commonly seen who can echo or can repeat anything that is said, and yet has no spontaneous language of his own. Whether or not we ever see pure types, or whether we see what we are looking for, is another problem. Although there is no ideal topographical relationship between the brain and language, the fact that it is even possible to suggest such a relationship using behavioral data is important, for it provides us at least with a take-off point for discussing the issue from a linguistic point of view.

*Geschwind:* From the point of view of localization one fascinating fact is that there is no case on record, to my knowledge, of a child who developed the fluent and paraphasic type of aphasia. The same lesion which in the adult typically produces a fluent paraphasic aphasia produces a loss of speech in the child. For this reason, aphasia is more difficult to localize in children than in adults. Isserlin (21) pointed out, on the basis of studies made in the German army in World War I, that the younger an aphasic was who had a lesion in the posterior speech regions, the less likely he was to become fluent and paraphasic. The fluent aphasias are mostly diseases of relatively old men.

*de Hirsch:* Both the causes and the effects of impaired language development are much more generalized in the child than they are in the adult. Whatever it is that happens to the child involves the developmental process itself. Thus, linguistic difficulties in children differ from those in adults qualitatively rather than quantitatively.

*Geschwind:* I agree; I believe that the difference between the child and the adult is the result of the developmental stage at which the damage occurs.

*Jakobson:* I agree entirely that there are two basically different kinds of repetition: the very low level of repetition—echolalia—must be sharply distinguished from intentional repetition. In sensory aphasia the loss of ability for such repetitions parallels the incapacity for making equational statements. Goldstein (13) fully realized that "repetition is not at all such a simple performance." The collapse of equation is the pivotal problem of sensory aphasia. According to Goldstein, "the patient of the sensory type may not realize that the word presented sometime before is the same when presented a short time later." Word identity does not exist for him, and the word is inseparable from its context. Those linguists who deny the general meaning of a word and operate only with contextual meanings unwittingly describe the language of sensory aphasics.

One can only agree with Dr. Geschwind's request for accurate and exhaustive descriptions of aphasic language. The number of such records is still insufficient. As was recently emphasized by the linguists Ross in the London Ciba Foundation symposium (52) and Ivanov in Moscow (22), we badly need a large collection of aphasic texts, edited, as Ross suggested, with the same care as the works of classical authors. It must be precisely stated in what situations the recorded utterances were produced; texts must be reproduced, transcribed, and annotated with the greatest methodological skill. At present we usually have at our disposal only the answers of the patients to the clinicians' questions. That is a classical example of objects essentially distorted by their observers. In addition to these instructive experiments, the completely free speech of aphasics with their families and conversation of aphasics with one another must be meticulously recorded.

Most of the extant records do not meet the methodological requirements. Only when aphasic speech is recorded with the joint participation of linguists and clinicians will we have well prepared and annotated samples of the various forms of aphasia. The Ciba Foundation symposium (5) advocated the desirability and urgency of an ample anthology of precisely transcribed and annotated aphasic texts supplemented with phonographic records, where all the different types of aphasic impairments would be adequately represented.

As to the cerebral topography, I am afraid that a misunderstanding arose in our discussion. While the efferent type of aphasia is actually related to Broca's area, the dynamic type, according to Luria's (39) and Pribram's (26, 51) conclusions, is linked with injuries in the more frontal portions of the brain, precisely "before Broca's area".

*Osgood:* I would agree that naturalistic studies of aphasics in natural environments would be helpful, but they are hard to interpret because of the multiple determination of their behavior. Perhaps either you, Dr. Jakobson, or Dr. Geschwind in his studies with Davis Howes, have some answer to the question. Word-association shows a very clear split, with two types relating to your distinction between similarity and contiguity. They are the paradigmatic type, in which the association is in the same substitution class, *versus* the sequential type of association. An example of the first type would be table *versus* chair; of the second type, man *versus* walks. Using this basic distinction between the similarity disorder and the contiguity disorder, as carried into this analysis from your earlier writings, I certainly would expect that aphasics who are clearly identified in terms of their spontaneous behavior as having a continuity-type disorder should tend to have great difficulty in association, or tend to give very few sequential types of associates. On the other hand, the aphasic with a similarity disorder should tend to give sequential associates and not the paradigmatic type. This seems to me a straightforward prediction. Are there any data at all on word-association aphasics? Was this part of your program, Dr. Geschwind?

*Geschwind:* Davis Howes and I did not study the problem Dr. Osgood has referred to, and I gather that Dr. Wepman has not done so either. I do not know whether Harold Goodglass has studied it.

*Wepman:* One of the unfortunate things about studies of aphasics is that they have all been studies of aphasia as a generality rather than as individual types of language disturbances. I think it is time in the study of aphasia that we start with peculiar types and generalize from the individual. I have lived through an endless number of sessions with groups of aphasics. Many aphasics do not talk, you know; most of them do not talk as much as we have been talking about them.

We find that when aphasics have some interchange they are inclined to communicate quite well with gestures. They are not inclined to speak very much to each other, and they do not tend to communicate to any extent without gestures.

I am not sure that aphasics in a naturalistic environment would provide very much of a verbal corpus for study. They talk much better to people who are not aphasics than they do to each other. They talk to pictures better than they talk to other people. There seems to be a failure in human interrelationship at the verbal level. Consequently, they will talk in a room by themselves or to a set of pictures better than they will to another person. What then is a naturalistic environment for an aphasic patient?

*Jakobson:* In connection with Dr. Wepman's remarks, may I remind you of Luria's early monograph (34) with the results of his observations on children's habitual responses to words. Are these responses paradigmatic or syntagmatic? Is the stimulus "house" responded to by "cabin" or some other word for a certain kind of house, or perhaps by a mere synonym of "house"? These are paradigmatic responses, whereas syntagmatic responses add to the word "house" some predicate or attribute: "stands", "burns", "broken", "old", "little". This duality corresponds to our observations on similarity *versus* contiguity.

As to Dr. Wepman's important remarks concerning the natural context of aphasic utterances, yes, the ideal would be to have not only tape recordings but also sound films, since gestures may play a considerable role.

In general, in our detailed discussion of aphasia, it is appropriate to recollect a statement of Hughlings Jackson's to the effect that aphasia could be labeled "asemia" because it is not necessarily confined to deficiencies in verbal behavior but can extend to other semiotic activities as well, for example, gestures accompanying speech.

*Geschwind:* I think Jackson was wrong in asserting that aphasia involves not only verbal activity but also involves all symbolic actions and gestures. This view is part of the old concept that aphasia is an aspect of a more generalized disturbance which was given the name "asymbolia". Jackson did not, in fact, make any extensive study of the use of movements by aphasics. The pioneer study in this field was made by Liepmann (32), the same man who five years earlier had initiated the study of apraxia in its modern sense (31). Liepmann showed, and I have been able to confirm (10), that there are some aphasics who show great difficulty with learned limb movements, while others preserve them. Goodglass & Kaplan (16) studied the same problem independently from a different point of view and came up with essentially the same conclusions: aphasics *may* have a disturbance of gesture language but this is not necessarily the case at all.

I can give one very good example from my own experience that aphasia cannot be regarded as a general disturbance of sign activities. This case is very similar to those studied by Liepmann (32). My patient had a dense right hemiplegia together with an aphasia in which he showed a great paucity of speech but produced good single-word responses. He could not carry out simple commands with his left side, e.g., "Point to the floor" or "Make a fist". Yet he could reply to such questions as, "What occupation were you engaged in before you became ill?" with the correct answer, "Retired". When asked if he knew the use of a hammer, he replied, "Nails". He was able to point out when the examiner made a demanded move correctly, having rejected incorrect movements by the examiner. Close consideration of this case shows that the patient could give correct verbal responses (although of only one word) in situations in which he could not make the correct gesture. The reverse is also seen. In any case there is no support for a generalized asymbolia.

*Jakobson:* There is some misunderstanding here. In his works on the affections of speech (23), Jackson never stated that each kind of aphasia is a general deficit in all the semiotic activities. But since verbal behavior is one of the semiotic activities, it is very important to find out in any type of aphasia the relation between the affections of language and the status of all other sign systems used by the patient. Evidently there is an interrelationship between different semiotic patterns, but it does not mean that all these patterns must necessarily be disturbed. I recall, for instance, once more the remarkable observations of Feuchtwanger (7), who described the mutual independence of verbal intonation and musical melody. Either of them can be lost without any harm to the other. Aphasic cases of completely monotonous speech, without any syntactic and emotive intonations but with full mastery of complex musical melodies, and vice versa, were observed and recorded. In the question of verbal problems with respect to other semiotic provinces, I am again for autonomy but against any isolation. When investigating aphasia we must perform an intrinsically linguistic analysis and at the same time pay due attention to the semiotic whole.

*Lindsley:* I wonder sometimes whether we do not pay too much attention to primarily sensory or motor aspects of aphasia. I am thinking here about

attention, or attentional factors; about whether we pay attention to a group
of words that we have said. As an illustration, I noticed Dr. Jakobson made
two statements in his talk, and these were perfectly well made, but he corrected himself and said just the opposite. That means that he somehow was
paying attention to auditory feedback or afterimages of what he had said.
He may have been paying attention to the specific word combinations, the
contiguities, or the sequence when he uttered these phrases, but apparently
they did not satisfy him because he came back and corrected them with the
opposites.

What I am concerned about here is something that Lashley (28) mentioned in the Hixon Symposium some years ago, namely that the use of a
particular word like "right", "rite", or "write", which is used in a variety of
combinations, could only be known after one had uttered a whole sentence,
and literally one had then laid before oneself the auditory feedback or, let us
say, an afterimagery which enabled one to see the context in which these
same sounds had been used, as in "millwright" or the "rite" of ritual, and so
forth. In other words, I am wondering whether the deterioration we are
looking for is one of specific reception as much as it is of the overall attention that one pays not to individual words but to groups of words. I take it
that Luria is interested in something of this sort because he has written to
me about some literature on reticular activation. I suppose he has in mind
attention as well. He made the statement that the only lesions which led to
deterioration of verbal instruction were in the frontal area. I take it that by
"verbal instruction" he means being able to keep in mind attentively, for a
long period, something which has been uttered as a verbal instruction, or
which the individual gives himself as a verbal instruction. So, in relation to
Dr. Jakobson's statement about the role of mediobasal areas, I am really
concerned about whether we know something about mechanisms which
control attention. If nonspecific thalamic nuclei regulate the rhythms of the
brain, and if the rhythms of the brain have anything to do with attention, as
some people, including myself, think, then the dorsomedial and intralami-
nar areas of the thalamus may possibly be concerned with this attentive
role.

I believe that attentional mechanisms ought to be given more consideration when we examine aphasics. I do not know precisely how one goes
about this, but I think the matter of getting at attentional mechanisms and
the auditory afterimagery or the delayed feedback would be a very important part of it.

*Jakobson:* Dr. Lindsley's comments are most relevant. In our own activities, when we are somewhat tired and want to say many things, we can
make aphasia-like mistakes and immediately correct ourselves. Yet we can
concentrate our attention in two different ways—either on the context or on
its constituents. That is the essential difference between us and aphasics.
Aphasics have a unilaterally oriented attention, neglecting either the whole

or the constituents, without being able to be unitarian, as some students of aphasia would like to see them. The clear-cut types of aphasia present the most striking examples of such one-sidedness.

For instance, in Paris Professor J. Alajouanine[*] brought me, instead of the best wines, his most interesting cases of aphasia. There was one remarkable case of sensory aphasia, a French truck driver who had had a traffic accident. His high intelligence was preserved, however, and he was able to help us efficiently in our examination of his case. He understood what we were talking about, tried to inform us, spoke readily, and uttered long sentences. The main difficulty for him was to begin a sentence; its initial word was a serious handicap for him, especially when the sentence was the first in an utterance. Also, when one showed him something, e.g., a pencil, and asked, "What is this?" he could provide a detailed comment without being able to name the thing itself. Or if he was posed the question, "What is a pencil?" he could not build the required equation. How consistently the patient eliminated the initial word of the sentence may be illustrated by the following example. He was writing, and we asked him what he was doing; he answered, "J'écris." Professor Alajouanine took a pen and we asked the patient what he was doing; the patient replied, "Il écrit." Then I started to write and asked him what I was doing, and he was unable to start his reply. Why? Because with autonomous initial words in French—*vous, nous,* etc.—it is possible to build elliptic one-word sentences: "Qui écrit?"—"Vous." On the other hand, such elements as *je, tu, il* are mere preverbal prefixes. We repeated and repeated, in various ways, the same experiments, and we saw that the personal pronoun handicapped the patient only when it was an independent initial word, whereas when functioning as prefix it presented no difficulties.

As to the question of Luria's observations about difficulties in fulfilling instruction, it is merely a variant of dynamic aphasia with the most frontal localization. Luria emphasizes the patient's inability to carry out instructions received. When we analyze all the examples he gives in different studies devoted to the "directive function of speech" (36, 37, 39, 41), we note that the common denominator of all these cases is the impossibility of passing from one system of signs to another. If one says, for instance, "Draw a circle", the patient, who has to switch from verbal activity to another semiotic system—in this case drawing—is embarrassed. We find here various types of intersemiotic relations, such as the transition from gestures to words, from words to gestures, from words to pictures, etc. I think this impairment can be clearly explained as a variant of encoding disturbances.

*Hirsh:* With respect to this linguistic analysis of aphasia, I want to ask whether all the aspects you have described are necessarily language-bound aphasia, in particular some of the deficiencies that you described in the cases of sensory aphasia. In reference to the duration of vowels in Czech

[*] Department of Neurology, La Salpêtrière.

and Hungarian, you mentioned a patient who had difficulty in judging or discriminating the durations of auditory signals when they were not words. I wonder whether this same specificity of the difficulty can be enlarged to other dimensions. Consider the example Dr. Geschwind gave about repetition (p. 79). Is repetition more difficult for whole linguistic units, like words? Would this patient have less difficulty repeating single idiophones, or would the patient, as Dr. Geschwind said, have less difficulty in repeating sounds in a language other than his own? Finally, in the question of sequence, can the patient who has difficulty with verbal sequence demonstrate that he has no difficulty with sequences outside of language?

*Jakobson:* The structure of verbal sequence (immediate constituents and a basically subordinative system) is quite different from other temporal sequences, and therefore verbal sequences naturally confront the patient with specific problems.

In Czech—I take an example from the well-known work of the Prague expert on aphasia, A. Pick (49)—"drāha", with the accent on the first syllable, means "road", "way"; "drahā", with the accent on the second syllable, means "dear" (feminine). The difference between long and short vowels is one of the basic distinctive features in the prosodic structure of Czech or Hungarian, but the distinctive role of this difference can be lost in the language of a native aphasic, and both quoted words become homonyms, although the ability to pronounce vowels of longer and shorter length and to perceive this phonetic difference may be preserved. The Oslo psychiatrist Monrad-Krohn (45) describes the case of a Norwegian woman who during an air attack was wounded in the brain, incurring a very limited aphasia: she lost the ability to distinguish, both when listening and when speaking, the two word intonations which play a significant phonemic role in the Norwegian language. The fact that Norwegian intonations differentiate meanings of words precludes their use for emotive variations of sentences; in German, however, when intonational differences are not utilized for the distinction of words, they assume an emotive function. As soon as Monrad-Krohn's patient ceased to employ word intonations for phonemic purposes, she shifted to an emotive use of intonations. The results were distressing. When she shopped, the Norwegians did not want to sell her anything, suspecting her of being a German, although in fact she knew no German. What was lost was not the Czech vocalic length or the Norwegian pitch, but only a certain linguistic function which these features carry in their given languages. It is important to insist on this point because too often an extrinsically acoustic or articulatory interpretation is erroneously substituted for a thoroughly linguistic, phonemic approach. In any given case one must determine what is deficient in the patient's speech—phonemic distinctions or mere variations (contextual or optional)—and, furthermore, what are his deficits in the perception and reproduction of foreign speech sounds and of nonverbal auditory signals.

# REFERENCES

1. BASTIAN, H. C., On the various forms of loss of speech in cerebral disease. *Brit. For. Med.-Chir. Rev.*, 1869, **43**: 209-236; 470-492.

2. BEYN, E. S., Fundamental laws of lexical and grammatical structure in aphasias. *Vopr. Psixol.*, 1957, **4**: 90 (in Russian).

3. BRAIN, W. R., Statement of the problem. In: *Disorders of Language* (A. V. S. de Reuck and M. O'Connor, Eds.). Churchill, London, 1964: 5-20.

4. DEJERINE, J., Contribution à l'étude anatomo-pathologique et clinique des différentes variétés de cécité verbale. *C. R. Soc. Biol.* (Paris), 1892, **44**: 61-90.

5. DE REUCK, A. V. S., and O'CONNOR, M. (Eds.). *Disorders of Language.* Churchill, London, 1964.

6. DOROSZEWSKI, J., Language as a sign system and the speech processes. *Sprawozd. Prac. Nauk. Wydz. Nauk Spolecz.*, 1963, **6**: 1-16 (in Polish).

7. FEUCHTWANGER, E., Amusie. *Fortschr. Neurol. Psychiat.*, 1932, **4**: 289-305.

8. FILLENBAUM, S., JONES, L. V., and WEPMAN, J. M., Some linguistic features of speech from aphasic patients. *Lang. Speech*, 1961, **4**: 91-108.

9. GESCHWIND, N., The anatomy of acquired disorders of reading. In: *Reading Disability* (J. Money, Ed.). Johns Hopkins Press, Baltimore, 1962: 115-129.

10. ——, Sympathetic dyspraxia. *Trans. Am. Neurol. Ass.*, 1963, **88**: 219-220.

11. GOLDSTEIN, K., Die transkorticalen Aphasien. *Erg. Neurol. Psychiat.*, 1917, **2**: 352-629.

12. ——, Die Lokalisation in der Grosshirnrinde; nach den Erfahrungen am kranken Menschen. In: *Handbuch der Normalen und Pathologischen Physiologie*, Vol X (A. Bethe et al., Eds.). Springer, Berlin, 1927: 600-842.

13. ——, *Language and Language Disturbances; Aphasic Symptom Complexes and Their Significance for Medicine and Theory of Language.* Grune & Stratton, New York, 1948.

14. GOODGLASS, H., and BERKO, J., Agrammatism and inflectional morphology in English. *J. Speech Hear. Res.*, 1960, **3**: 257-267.

15. GOODGLASS, H., and HUNT, J., Grammatical complexity and aphasic speech. *Word*, 1958, **14**: 197-207.

16. GOODGLASS, H., and KAPLAN, E., Disturbance of gesture and pantomime in aphasia. *Brain*, 1963, **86**: 703-720.

17. GOODGLASS, H., and MAYER, J., Agrammatism in aphasia. *J. Speech Hear. Dis.*, 1958, **23**: 99-111.

18. HEAD, H., *Aphasia and Kindred Disorders of Speech.* Macmillan, New York, 1926.

19. HEMPHILL, R. E., and STENGEL, E., A study on pure word-deafness. *J. Neurol. Psychiat.*, 1940, **3**: 251-262.

20. HOLMES, G., Pure word blindness. *Folia Psychiat. Neurol. Neurochir. Neerl.*, 1950, **53**: 279-288.

21. ISSERLIN, M., Aphasie. In: *Handbuch der Neurologie*, Vol. VI (O. Bumke and O. Foerster, Eds.). Springer, Berlin, 1936: 627-806.

22. IVANOV, V. V., Linguistics and investigation of aphasia. In: *Strukturno-Tipologicheskie Issledovanija* (T. N. Moloshnaja, Ed.). Akad. Nauk SSSR, Moscow, 1962: 70-95 (in Russian).

23. JACKSON, J. H., *Selected Writings of John Hughlings Jackson,* Vol. II (J. Taylor, Ed.). Basic Books, New York, 1958.

24. JAKOBSON, R., Aphasia as a linguistic problem. In: *On Expressive Language* (H. Werner, Ed.). Clark Univ. Press, Worcester, 1955: 69-81.

25. ———, Two aspects of language and two types of aphasic disturbances. Part II in: *Fundamentals of Language* (R. Jakobson and M. Halle). Mouton, The Hague, 1956: 53-82.

26. ———, Towards a linguistic typology of aphasic impairments. In: *Disorders of Language* (A. V. S. de Reuck and M. O'Connor, Eds.). Churchill, London, 1964: 21-46.

27. JAKOBSON, R., and HALLE, M., Phonology and phonetics. Part I in: *Fundamentals of Language.* Mouton, The Hague, 1956: 1-51.

28. LASHLEY, K. S., The problem of serial order in behavior. In: *Cerebral Mechanisms in Behavior* (L. A. Jeffress, Ed.). Wiley, New York, 1951: 112-146.

29. LENNEBERG, E. H., Understanding language without ability to speak: a case report. *J. Abnorm. Soc. Psychol.,* 1962, **65**: 419-425.

30. LIEPMANN, H., *Ein Fall von reiner Sprachtaubheit.* Psychiatrische Abhandlungen, Breslau, 1898.

31. ———, Das Krankheitsbild der Apraxie ("motorischen Asymbolie") auf Grund eines Falles von einseitiger Apraxie. *Mschr. Psychiat. Neurol.,* 1900, **8**: 15-44; 102-132; 182-197.

32. ———, Die linke Hemisphäre und das Handeln. *Münch. med. Wschr.,* 1905, **52**: 2322-2326; 2375-2378.

33. LIEPMANN, H., and STORCH, E., Der mikroskopische Gehirnbefund bei dem Fall Gorstelle. *Mschr. Psychiat. Neurol.,* 1902, **11**: 115-120.

34. LURIA, A. R., *Speech Reactions of the Child.* Akad. Kom. Vospitanija im. N. K. Krupskoj, Moscow, 1927 (in Russian).

35. ———, *Traumatic Aphasia: Its Syndromes, Psychopathology and Treatment.* Akad. Med. Nauk USSR, Moscow, 1947 (in Russian).

36. ———, Brain disorders and language analysis. *Lang. Speech,* 1958, **1**: 14-34.

37. ———, The directive function of speech in development and dissolution. *Word,* 1959, **15**: 341-352; 453-464.

38. ———, Disorders of "simultaneous perception" in a case of bilateral occipito-parietal brain injury. *Brain,* 1959, **82**: 437-449.

39. ———, *Higher Cortical Functions in Man and Their Disturbances in Local Brain Lesions.* Moscow Univ. Press, Moscow, 1962 (in Russian).

40. ———, *Human Brain and Mental Processes.* Akad. Pedagog. Nauk RSFSR, Moscow, 1963 (in Russian).

41. ———, Factors and forms of aphasia. In: *Disorders of Language* (A. V. S. de Reuck and M. O'Connor, Eds.). Churchill, London, 1964: 143-167.

42. MARIE, P., and FOIX, C., Les aphasies de guerre. *Rev. Neurol.,* 1917, **31**: 53-87.

43. MARUSZEWSKI, M., and MIERZEJEWSKA, H., The application of linguistic analysis in research on aphasia. *Studia Psychologiczne,* 1964, **5**: 73-103 (in Polish).

44. MILLER, G. A., The magical number seven, plus or minus two: some limits on our capacity for processing information. *Psychol. Rev.*, 1956, **63**: 81-97.

45. MONRAD-KROHN, G. H., Dysprosody or altered "melody of language". *Brain*, 1947, **70**: 405-415.

46. OSGOOD, C. E., Motivational dynamics of language behavior. In: *Nebraska Symposium on Motivation* (M. Jones, Ed.). Univ. of Nebraska Press, Lincoln, 1957: 348-424.

47. OSGOOD, C. E., and MIRON, M. S. (Eds.), *Approaches to the Study of Aphasia*. Univ. of Illinois Press, Urbana, 1963.

48. PENFIELD, W., and ROBERTS, L., *Speech and Brain-Mechanisms*. Princeton Univ. Press, Princeton, 1959.

49. PICK, A., Über Änderungen des Sprachcharakters als Begleiterscheinung aphasischer Störungen. *Zschr. Neurol. Psychiat.*, 1949, **45**: 230-241.

50. PRIBRAM, K. H., The intrinsic systems of the forebrain. In: *Handbook of Physiology; Neurophysiology II* (J. Field, H. W. Magoun and V. E. Hall, Eds.). Am. Physiol. Soc., Washington, D.C., 1960: 1323-1344.

51. ———, A review of theory in physiological psychology. *Ann. Rev. Psychol.*, 1960, **11**: 1-40.

52. ROSS, A. S. C., CLARKE, P. R. F., and HADDOCK, N. L., Edition of text from a dysphasic patient. In: *Disorders of Language* (A. V. S. de Reuck and M. O'Connor, Eds.). Churchill, London, 1964: 299-323.

53. SOKOLOV, A. N., Inquiry into the speech mechanisms of thought. In: *Psixologicheskaja Nauka v SSSR*, Vol. I. Akad. Pedagog. Nauk RSFSR, Moscow, 1959: 488-515 (in Russian).

54. SYMONDS, C., Aphasia. *J. Neurol. Neurosurg. Psychiat.*, 1953, **16**: 1-6.

55. VYGOTSKY L. S., *Thought and Language* (E. Hanfmann and G. Vakar, Eds. and Transl.). M.I.T. Press, Cambridge, 1962.

56. WERNICKE, C., *Der aphasische Symptomencomplex. Eine psychologische Studie auf anatomischer Basis*. Cohn & Weigert, Breslau, 1874.

57. ZHINKIN, N. I., *Mechanisms of Speech*. Akad. Pedagog. Nauk RSFSR, Moscow, 1958 (in Russian).

# AUDITION IN RELATION TO PERCEPTION OF SPEECH

IRA J. HIRSH
Central Institute for the Deaf
St. Louis

We should be able to relate audition to speech perception by first review-ing what we know about audition and then applying the principles that seem relevant to the perception of speech. This approach turns out to be less than satisfactory because the traditional characteristics of the hearing process emphasize auditory dimensions that are not often applicable to spoken stimuli. Just a quarter of a century ago Stevens & Davis (46) re-viewed what was then known about the psychological and physiological as-pects of hearing, but there is no reference to speech in that now classic book. There may have been two reasons for this omission: that not very much was known about the perception of speech, or that nine years earlier Harvey Fletcher (10) had summarized what was known.

If we restrict our attention to the psychological part of the Stevens & Davis review, we note that during the ensuing 25 years not very many new areas have been opened up and, thus, not very many new chapter titles would have to be devised for a revision at the present time. (Of course, there are many new data, and the major exception to that statement has to do with the hearing of speech.)

One other omission or, at most, a thin section in that work (46) has to do with auditory theory. Auditory theory in 1938, and for many of the preced-ing decades, was almost exclusively the theory of pitch perception (2). Some attention was also paid to auditory localization but, in general, auditory theory meant pitch theory. (Note that in the field of vision we have much more specificity in theory: at least visual psychologists refer to their concern with wavelength as color theory.) More recently, as Licklider (32) came to address the subject of auditory theory, he could outline three examples of theory concerning three distinct auditory processes: pitch perception, signal detection, and the perception of speech.

In a different tradition, experimental phonetics evolved from a less tech-nically oriented discipline of linguistics (42, 43); it was not often blessed with the most recent advances in engineering. Good acoustical phonetics was to come later (27). Technical advances touching on phonetics were brought together by Fletcher (10) in 1929, but it must be noted that the

93

primary physical dimensions that were used to describe speech sounds were those measurable by the then available tools of telephone engineering, and these were mainly of technical interest to telephone transmission. Thus, at the same time that the auditory psychologists were discussing the audibility of pure tones, the differential sensitivity for tonal signals that differed in frequency or intensity, the masking of tones by tones, the auditory localization of tones, and so on, telephone engineers were describing speech sounds in terms of their acoustic power and the distribution of that power as a function of frequency. Consequently, we are not surprised by the then prevalent notion that the frequency analysis performed by engineering instruments was somehow related to the kind of analysis that the auditory system must perform for the perception and recognition of speech.

In what follows we shall first review superficially certain features of the auditory process from a traditional point of view. I shall omit any references to the underlying physiological processes or anatomical structures because there are people in this group who could do it better than I; in addition, several theoretical reviews of auditory physiology have recently become available (6, 28, 37, 50; 40).

Then we shall turn our attention to certain acoustical features of speech. I shall not describe phonemes by reference to the various parts and functions of the speech mechanism; this kind of motor description is probably better known anyway and, from the point of view of the listener, it is the available acoustical energy that must be received and processed. In thus neglecting descriptive phonetics, I must remind myself, and you, that recent experiments show that the speech mechanism in the listener is not irrelevant, that the listener typically makes categorical responses, and that these categories seem to be defined by the listener's own speech habits (29).

Next we shall consider certain psychoacoustic studies that have been inspired by the recently acquired knowledge in acoustical phonetics and, finally, we shall examine studies on the intelligibility of speech to listening subjects.

Having reviewed these experimental areas, we will attempt to summarize the present state of the art, though finding that the art thus defined deals in a molecular fashion with speech sounds or, at most, with the recognition of words. Although it is likely that such information on the speech-perception process is necessary to the understanding of the more complex perception of speech as it exists in the context of language, it does not suffice. Extra-acoustical, linguistic and memorial features may be regarded as perhaps outside the domain of audition, and it may be that the learning of vocabulary, of grammatical rules, and of the constraints imposed and used in the comprehension of long segments of language comprise an area that is distinct from the auditory process. But there is increasing evidence that the auditory aspects of such learning and such development are peculiar to the auditory modality and therefore must be treated in a manner distinct from that applicable to written language.

## CLASSICAL DESCRIPTION OF AUDITION

In a pretechnological era such as the middle of the 19th century, natural philosophers were less prone to study the various aspects of nature in a systematic way dictated by a particular model and more likely to focus on particular phenomena and immediate experience. Thus a hundred years ago, when Helmholtz (18) gathered together the facts then known about hearing in the first edition of *Die Lehre von Tonempfindungen* (17), he concentrated on those aspects of auditory experience that could be related to his knowledge of music, physics and physiology. The subject of the book is therefore limited to the words of the English translation, "Sensations of Tone". It is interesting to note that in that great book the two principal contributions to theory under this title have to do with the perception of pitch and the nature of vowels. When Stevens & Davis summarized *Hearing* 75 years later, the field had been considerably broadened.

ABSOLUTE SENSITIVITY. The sensitivity of the auditory system is described in the now familiar audibility curve that shows the threshold of detectability for pure tones to be about constant between frequencies from 500 to 4000 cps at a sound pressure level of about ten decibels above the zero dB reference level of 0.0002 dynes per square centimeter, a pressure equal to two tenths of a billionth of one atmosphere. Below 500 cycles, the threshold rises at about 15 dB per octave; above 4000 cps it rises at a somewhat lower slope. Many details concerning the measurement of the absolute threshold have been worked out since 1938 (19), especially those having to do with the technique of acoustic measurements, psychophysical technique, etc., but the most recent results are not very different.

The lower limit of energies in pure tones that are just barely detected by the auditory system being thus established, the upper limit or ceiling on auditory perception was reported as one of several thresholds of feeling. In this country the early measurements described by Stevens & Davis (46) were amended during World War II, with various aspects of "feeling" being detailed (31). These newer measurements yield a threshold of "tickle" that lies about 10 dB higher than the older measurements, putting an upper boundary on the auditory area of 140 dB sound pressure level, roughly constant throughout the range of audible frequencies.

These two thresholds are mentioned merely to indicate a boundary on what is called the auditory region or the auditory area. It is within this area that one must work to describe auditory signals.

DIFFERENTIAL SENSITIVITY. What next appeared to be of interest—and this, of course, goes back to Fechner's role in the founding of psychophysics—was the differential threshold. This can now be interpreted outside the region of psychological scaling as an attempt to define the grain of the auditory area. A pure tone can be presented with an energy level higher than indicated and with frequencies bounded by this region. But now comes the question, "How can I be sure that tone X will appear to be different from tone Y?" By the use of differential-sensitivity measures we attempt to establish a vertical and a horizontal grain, to indicate how large a change in intensity and in frequency, respectively, one can notice.

In the case of frequency discrimination of pure tones, it appears that the discrimination of frequencies is dependent upon the sensation level, but above a sensation level (level above absolute threshold) of about 30 dB or a little less, the minimum frequency change ($\Delta f$) that can be detected for frequencies below 1000 cps is a constant $\Delta f$ of about 2 or 3 cps. Above 1000 cps, however, it is the relative frequency change that remains constant, the minimum frequency change detectable being somewhere between 0.1 per cent and 0.3 per cent ($\Delta f/f$).

Sensitivity to changes in intensity is not particularly dependent upon the frequency of the pure tone, except at very low sensation levels. Above about 30 dB sensation level, relative differential sensitivity is approximately constant, the minimal detectable change in intensity being represented by a relative change of less than 1 dB.

Within the general area of the pitch and loudness of pure tones, there are several aspects in addition to differential sensitivity that were already well known by 1938. Some of these studies on differential sensitivity gave rise to the argument about the quantal nature of sensitivity to increments. There was also the systematization, chiefly from the work of Stevens (45) himself, of the dimensions of tonal experience and the creation of psychological scales of pitch and of loudness that have been extended in very recent years both with respect to classes of stimuli and underlying rationale.

Note that the area thus defined in terms of extent and grain was an area that dealt only with pure tones. Tone signals provided the base for this description of the auditory process.

In the study of the pitch of complex tones, it had been observed that certain series of filtered clicks, in which the fundamental frequency of repetition did not exist physically in the stimulus, would yet be assigned by listeners a pitch corresponding to that fundamental frequency. This kind of pitch perception, based apparently on the periodicity or repetitiveness of the stimulus series, seemed to break down above 1000 cps. It has already been noted that differential sensitivity for frequency also shifts from a constant $\Delta f$ to a constant relative increment ($\Delta f/f$) at about 1000 cps. Here are the beginnings of what has come to be a duplex theory of pitch perception (29) that utilizes the place principle of Helmholtz (18) (but with a rather different conception of resonance) for higher frequencies, and something like the telephone theory of Gray (13) or the volley theory of Wever (49) at low frequencies (2). The important changes in differential sensitivity since 1938 have less to do with better measurements than with an increase in the number of dimensions along which discrimi-nability is measured.

OTHER AUDITORY DIMENSIONS. In the early years of psychoacoustics, primarily steady-state measurements were supplemented by studies on the role of time on the very dimensions that have been discussed so far. The absolute sensitivity of the auditory system, described by the classical audibility curve, concerns long tones. As these tones are shortened toward the lim-iting case of a very brief acoustic click, there is temporal integration of energy over about 200 msec. for the auditory threshold (31). This is dem-onstrated in a fashion not unlike the Talbot-Plateau law in vision. The same kind of temporal integration also holds for loudness at levels above the absolute threshold.

These basic concerns with sensitivity, both absolute and differential, reflect an approach to the auditory system as one to be described in terms that would predict its functioning. What are the ranges of energy levels and frequencies that will activate the system and, within those ranges, what kinds of steps will define the grain or resolving power of the system?

AUDITORY LOCALIZATION. The remaining psychologically oriented chapters in the Stevens & Davis work (46) deal with less systematic topics representing interesting auditory phenomena. Listeners can tell where a source of sound appears to be located in space; thus the study of auditory localization is in-troduced. The early data for auditory localization are the result of experi-ments with pure tones. The story in 1938 was that the phase relation be-tween the signals at the two ears, as well as the intensity relation, con-trolled the localization or, more precisely, the directionalization of a sound source. Two kinds of experiments contributed to this view: one in which the interaural phase relations and the interaural intensity relations could be manipulated by the experimenter by means of earphones, and a second in which actual sources of sound in space were used. (We should note that the now publicized stereophonic effect was known, had been experi-mented on, and is reported upon by Stevens & Davis.)

To bring the story up to date, we would have to add further experiments that utilize noises and clicks (7); specification of the difference limen for az-imuth with an actual sound source in space (36); specification of the relative roles of time differences and intensity differences, and the change in this re-lation as a function of level (7). One important generalization that seems to emerge from the supplementary work during the past 25 years is that, while the two-ear localizing system is an extremely precise indicator of time differences as small as 10 or 20 microseconds between the signals at the two ears, such temporal precision degenerates rather rapidly as the levels of the signals decrease. We should also note that a time difference between signals

presented to the two ears that is just detectable as a shift in localization is
several orders of magnitude smaller than a discriminable (unfused) time gap
between two signals presented to a single ear.

Another group of phenomena concerns distortion in the auditory system
and the resulting aural harmonics that can be heard when only a pure tone
is introduced as a signal, and the various combination tones about which
Helmholtz (18) had written extensively in 1863. There are also auditory
beats, that is, fluctuations that can be detected when two pure tone stimuli
are close together in frequency and are applied either to the same ear or
one to each ear. Such effects have since become more detailed, but major
changes or explanation have not been forthcoming.

INTERFERENCE EFFECTS. A final set of phenomena concerns the interference
of one sound upon another. The most studied aspect of interference is
masking, the change in the audibility of one sound that is brought about
by the simultaneous presentation of another sound. Stevens & Davis (46)
report mostly the masking of one pure tone by another and the masking of
brief sound impulses by pure tones. The original data of Wegel & Lane
(48) and of Békésy (47) have stood very well over the years but have been
extended, again by different kinds of sounds.

The addition of control to irregular or random noise stimuli has extended
our knowledge of masking and has led to another major part of auditory
theory, that of the critical band (19, 31). This is a narrow band of frequencies within which are found the only ones effective for the masking of a
pure tone lying at the center of the band. This notion, originally proposed
by Fletcher (11) in 1940, has provided not only valuable empirical data (and
some recent amendments and corrections, 41) but also a concept useful for
the formulation of theories of pitch perception and of the physiology of the
cochlea. During the past 25 years the information on the masking of tones
by tones has been enriched by findings on the masking of tones by noise
and by complex tones, of sound impulses by noise, binaural masking (31),
and the masking of speech (33) by a variety of sounds (to be discussed
later). In general, masking increases linearly with masking-noise level, the
particular amounts of masking for different frequencies depending on the
spectrum of the noise.

Another kind of interference occurs when the interfering tone precedes
the tone whose audibility is affected. This phenomenon may be labeled auditory fatigue, auditory adaptation, residual masking, temporary hearing
loss, noise-induced threshold shift, and permanent noise-induced hearing
loss, depending upon the time relations among the stimuli, the durations
and intensities of the interfering stimuli, and the duration of the effects (51).
In 1938 the amount of information on these phenomena was relatively
small; a tremendous amount is now available, ranging from very small time
intervals and detailed laboratory studies to the temporary and permanent
effects of industrial noise in field studies. Interfering tones of any level will

have aftereffects if they are measured soon enough, but the more permanent effects require levels of more than 90 dB.

This summary of the classical 1938 description (46) is probably too brief to do it justice, but it should be noted that when Licklider (31) attempted to review the same area in 1951, he was able to add to the chapter headings in the Stevens & Davis book only one new major section ("Temporal Effects in Hearing", about which I will have more to say presently), a theoretical concept based on the critical band, and a large amount of data obtained by the use of new stimuli. By way of anticipation, I must add that in the same *Handbook of Experimental Psychology* (44) there is, in addition to the Licklider review, an entire new section by Licklider & Miller (33) on the perception of speech.

Let us now give some attention to the acoustical characteristics of speech, the message that the listener will receive.

### ACOUSTICAL CHARACTERISTICS OF SPEECH

When Helmholtz (18) analyzed the vowels a century ago, his investigating instrument was primarily his ear, as has been the case for many experimental phoneticians, some of whom, incidentally, I am sure have presbycusis. For the most part, the basic facts about vowel spectra and vowel production are, by 1863 standards, portrayed correctly, if crudely. Analysis of separate speech sounds was to wait for further developments in experimental phonetics, represented by Scripture in 1902 (42). Scripture shows a concern for more varied kinds of speech sounds, the consonants in particular, though in his book these are not analyzed acoustically but rather according to how they are produced in the mouth.

In 1929, armed with the vacuum tube, some other instruments, and electrical engineering, Fletcher (10) quantified the acoustics of speech in two different ways. First he quantified all speech averaged together: for example, he found for conversational speech a level (about 70 dB) that in fact allows those with normal hearing a fairly decent safety margin, far enough above threshold so all or most of the acoustic energy in speech will be easily detected. Fletcher also analyzed the power in individual speech sounds, telling us, for example, that the vowel sound "aw" in English is about 30 dB more powerful than the consonant sound "th" (unvoiced). He, or some of his colleagues, also studied the distribution of this acoustic power with frequency. The following generalizations can be gained from this early work and subsequent related investigation. The overall sound pressure level of speech, about a meter from the mouth of a talker who is speaking at a conversational level, is approximately 70 dB. Over a long time, with all of the individual speech sounds averaged in continuous speech, the energy is distributed largely in the low frequencies and falls off above 500 cps at about 10 to 12 dB per octave (1). This average spectrum is characteristic of all speech sounds taken together—but we know that the spectra of individual speech sounds are different, and that these spectral differences probably account for at least some of the discriminations made by listeners.

The vowels of English, the subject of most of the acoustical analyses of speech sounds, are different from one another primarily with respect to the position in frequency of each of two regions of reinforced frequencies, harmonics of the fundamental vocal tone that are reinforced by the resonating properties of the vocal tract. There are some individual differences among talkers, both between and within groups taken by sex or by age. Detailed measurements of these formant frequencies (38) and related experimental material are now available in a recent and already classic book by Fant (9).

I cannot emphasize too strongly that even up to the present time acoustic analyzers (people) have tried to find phonetic differences by portraying the spectral characteristics of speech sounds. The case for the vowels is quite clear, and there are also spectral differences among the consonants (16, 24). Phoneticians have known for a long time that there are many more kinds of differences among speech sounds than are given by the acoustic spectrum. The difficulty has been that acoustic analysis and measurement did not lend themselves to many dimensions other than intensity and frequency until quite recently (23), and therefore gave less than satisfactory acoustical correlates of differences that can be described quite well by the phonetician or by the listener.

As has been mentioned many times in this brief review, technical advances have freed us from certain kinds of restrictions. One that should be mentioned here is the acoustic spectrograph (39), which portrays "visible speech" by plotting the frequency dimension on the vertical scale and time on the horizontal scale (Figure 15), making it possible to see how acoustic spectra change as a function of time. A vowel sound, for example, instead of being demonstrated as a spectrum with an envelope showing two humps corresponding to resonances in the vocal tract, will appear on the spectrogram as a series of bars or formants for as long as the vowel exists: the abscissa shows duration.

In the 1930's, when attempts were being made to characterize a phoneme in such a way as to give its acoustical analysis as a function of frequency, the implication was that the information in such a particular sound remained the same forever; in other words, it was a steady-state acoustic analysis. With the aid of such instruments as the sound spectrograph we can note that the information may be given by acoustical dimensions other than the steady-state ones.

Duration was mentioned by Dr. Jakobson as being important in certain languages to distinguish two lengths of vowel; in consonants it is also certainly important. If we look, for example, at the spectrum for the sounds "th" and "s" (Figure 15), we see that the "th" sound is essentially a brief but elongated, thin vertical line, indicating very short duration and a spread of en-

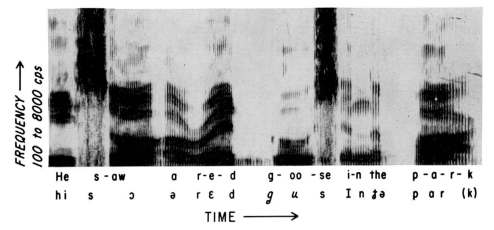

**Figure 15.** Spectrogram of the English sentence "He saw a red goose in the park"; the frequency of the spectrum is shown as the ordinate and time as the abscissa. Intensity is shown by the darkness of the tracings. It is evident that the vowels contain clear resonant peaks or formants, that these formants change as one passes from one vowel to a consonant or to another vowel, and that fricative sounds like "s" contain a continuous spectrum predominantly in the higher frequencies.

ergy throughout frequency, with an emphasis perhaps in the high-frequency region; the "s" sound is made with the tongue roughly in the same place as the "th". Clearly the primary difference between the two sounds is one of duration, an acoustical quality or characteristic that would not be revealed by traditional steady-state analysis.

As you know, there are also transitions. As we move from vowel to consonant, from consonant to other consonants, these transitions or dynamic aspects, changes in tongue position and manner of articulation, appear to be extremely important for the perception of speech. Perhaps the boldest attempt to combine these various features or levels of description (the phonetic or motor, the acoustic, and the auditory) is the system first advanced by Dr. Jakobson and his colleagues at the Massachusetts Institute of Technology, and recently summarized by Jakobson & Halle (26). I have already mentioned the role of spectrum in differentiating speech sounds. To illustrate, the vowels "ah" and "ee" are distinguished by the fact that there is a region of energy reinforcement or resonance corresponding to some cavity sizes and shapes in the vocal tract, that shifts from one vowel to the other. Presumably, then, the recognition of those vowel sounds depends upon the detection of the frequency regions where those resonances occur. But Dr. Jakobson (26) points out that we must specify different characteristics of the spectrum, not just its location in frequency.

Returning to the traditional plot of intensity and frequency, let us look at two fricative consonants. The fricative sound "s", for example, has a spectrum with a bunching of energy in the high-frequency region. The fricative sound "sh" has also a high-frequency resonance, but the spectrum is much broader. The difference between these two spectra is not only the location of the center of the band in frequency, but also how wide the band is. These two sounds can be different with respect to the center frequency and width (23). From acoustic and motor or phonetic points of view, Dr. Jakobson proposes that we can sort out all of the various speech sounds according to the values that we find in each of twelve essentially binary dimensions as distinctive features.

With respect to the spectrum, we must deal with the following binary appositions of four of these distinctive features: compact *versus* diffuse (these two adjectives describe the spectrum but less well the articulation), grave *versus* acute, flat *versus* plain, and sharp *versus* plain. The first two I have already discussed; the compact spectrum is one in which the energy is concentrated in a small frequency region, while the energy of a diffuse spectrum is more spread out over frequency. The third and fourth features, flat *versus* plain and sharp *versus* plain, refer to shifts in formant frequencies. A plain spectrum has a relatively even energy distribution across frequencies; flattening "manifests itself by a downward shift of a set of formants or even of all the formants in the spectrum", and sharpening "manifests itself in a slight rise of the second formant and, to some degree, also of the higher formants" (25). I prefer to call plain spectra "flat"; Dr. Jakobson calls them "plain" by reference to musical terminology, I believe. It is a musical flat as opposed to sharp, where the energy increases with frequency. Except for this lack of correspondence between vocabularies of acoustician and linguist, I think that the identification of these distinctive features is quite clear.

There are other features, however, not so easily related to the spectrum. Talkers use them in making different speech sounds. Some of these correspond to what the phoneticians call "manner of articulation", as opposed to place of articulation. Place of articulation in the vocal tract gives rise to spectral changes, while the manner of articulation produces changes such as the difference between a very short, plosive sound and a continued, fricative sound.

With regard to the sound source, we can describe a sound as voiced or voiceless. Concerning the pattern as a function of time, we can have abrupt, short sounds, discontinuous, as Dr. Jakobson calls them, or prolonged, continuous sounds. My aim here is merely to outline a system in which, unhampered by the limitations of acoustical instruments, are set the variety of dimensions that seem to be available to talkers, that possibly are utilized by listeners, and that will eventually be describable in acoustical terms.

#### AUDITORY PSYCHOPHYSICS SUGGESTED BY SPEECH ANALYSIS

Not only has the psychophysics of tone been enriched by new data, but the technical information on the acoustics of speech has also increased remarkably in the last 25 to 30 years. As a result, the psychophysics of tone has changed, and new dimensions have been explored in auditory psychophysics. Let me mention just a few.

In view of our discussion of the role of spectrum in the discrimination of speech sounds, it is not surprising that recent psychoacoustic literature describes experiments directed at finding difference limina, the differential sensitivity for complex tones and noises that differ with respect to bandwidth (22) and to the center frequency of the band (34). Thus, by using signal-generating machines instead of talkers, one can ask listeners to discriminate between noises different as to their center frequency and/or the bandwidth of the filter through which the noise is passed. The old experiments on frequency discrimination for pure tones have been repeated with complex signals, so as to investigate the listener's ability to detect band frequency changes. Similar experiments have been done with complex tones; these obviously synthesize those auditory dimensions that appear to be relevant for the differentiation of speech sounds that, by acoustic analysis, turn out to be different with respect to spectrum.

More interesting perhaps is an entire area in psychoacoustics that has to do with temporal perception. Certain speech sounds differ from each other with respect to duration, but only recently have we begun to learn something about the differential sensitivity of the auditory system for sounds of different duration. There appear to be important transitions in speech that involve the recognition of changes in frequency or in intensity with time, or even the recognition of the rates at which such changes occur. The very changes that have been found in speech have been successfully synthesized, for example, in the work of the Haskins Laboratories in New York City (30), but such changes in a "pure state" have not received much attention in the psychoacoustic laboratory.

A final example, from a long list of possible ones, illustrates what I consider to be one of the basic dimensions to be described about the auditory process, that is, its temporal resolving power. If two brief clicks are presented sequentially with a time interval between them of less than one millisecond, they blend into a single fused sound and thus define in one way the temporal grain of the auditory system. Another way, which gives about the same results, is to measure the frequency for auditory flutter that barely produces fusion. Such a measurement (31) utilized white noise as a stimulus because of the negligible change in the acoustic spectrum that is brought about by interrupting such a signal. The analogy to the visual flicker fusion frequency is obvious enough, but my guess is that auditory flutter fusion is more relevant to everyday auditory perception than is visual flicker fusion to visual perception. The generalization available is that series of events that are not repeated more rapidly than 1000 times per second at reasonably high or moderate levels will not be heard as single fused images.

Perhaps I should also point out that such temporal fusion is only the beginning of a series of other steps that might be required in consideration of the demands made by speech stimuli. Even if two acoustic events are separated in time sufficiently to be heard as separate, are there not cases where their order of occurrence must also be judged? Such kinds of questions have been the subject of some recent investigations of my own (20), and it turns out that considerably more than one millisecond must separate two such events so that their order of occurrence may be judged correctly. If the listener is to distinguish "mitts" from "mist", then he must be able to recognize the order in which the last two sounds in each of those words occurred.

I would like to mention another extremely interesting and valuable tool, a machine in the Haskins Laboratories (30) which is a reverse spectrograph, that is, sound patterns can be painted on pieces of tape and fed into a machine which will transform them into sound. This is the so-called Pattern Playback. As an example of its use, let us take the syllables "ba" and "wa" as they appear in spectrograms of talkers: for "ba" there is some low-frequency energy, corresponding to the beginning of voicing in the consonant; then the vowel "a", indicated by its first two formants; and last a transition of energy. In the other syllable, one begins with the same distribution of voicing energy for the "wa" sound as for the "ba" sound, and ends at the same place, the two formants corresponding to "a". But the transition in energy from the "w" voicing to the "a" vowel takes place over a longer time. By abstracting artificially these dimensions from such spectrograms and painting them on tapes to be played back to listeners, it can be seen that the recognition or the distinction between "ba" and "wa" in the ears of a listener is determined almost entirely, or principally, by the rate at which the energy changes from one concentration to another, even though the two concentrations in frequency location are identical.

I have oversimplified this somewhat, but not too much, in presenting the point that not only spectrum, not only duration, not only some of these simple, one-dimensional parts of acoustics are important for distinguishing sounds, but that also some sounds change in frequency as a function of time.

## AUDITORY PERCEPTION OF SPEECH

Let me turn briefly to another area of investigation, that in which the stimulus for psychoacoustic experiment is a unit of speech. In the areas that I have already discussed, synthetic sounds were constructed using as guidelines principles in acoustic phonetics that tell something about how words or speech sounds may be different from one another. This is a story that is probably familiar to most of you, going back, again, to Fletcher's work at the Bell Telephone Laboratories (10), where intelligibility tests were conducted by giving lists of words to listeners who had to respond by repeating the words. The early concern with the use of this technique reflected the early acoustic analyses. After presentation of the word lists, the bandwidth of the transmission system was reduced because of the interest in building telephone transmission systems with narrow bandwidths. In order to investigate noise intrusion, experiments were done in which the noise level was raised as a competing background for the speech message.

In general, the early results from the testing of the intelligibility of speech were concerned with the effects of various restrictions on the quality of a speech transmission channel. In fact, so ubiquitous were the concepts of bandwidth and intensity thought to be that French and Steinberg proposed a scheme (32) on the basis of which they could predict the percentage of words of a particular kind that would be transmitted intelligibly through a system, if only the bandwidth and the signal-to-noise ratio in the system were known. Since that time we know something about the effects of changing the kinds of words used, whether sentences or single words (22), and we know something about other kinds of physical changes, distortions, the sort of data that came out of the work at the Psycho-Acoustic Laboratory at Harvard University just before World War II (35).

Still other sources of research on speech perception have turned up many new factors related to intelligibility. The generalizations made available from this work on the physical characteristics of the speech message and its intelligibility may be summarized in the following way. If one begins with an ideal transmission system with low or no noise, uniform gain as a function of frequency, and no internal distortion, one can predict how the intelligibility of speech will be reduced if the noise level is increased, if the bandwidth is decreased, if the amplitude distortion is increased, if the signal level is decreased, if the system is turned on or off at different rates, etc.

But suppose the transmission system remains ideal, there is no noise, the bandwidth is very wide, and there is no distortion. There are other experimental studies that have told us how the intelligibility of speech increases with the use of a second ear; how it increases or decreases under binaural hearing when there is noise (19); how it will change, depending upon the kind of speech items, whether syllables, words, or sentences (21); and, finally, the effect of interference of competing messages, control of attention, and more general psychological factors (3).

The choice of speech material introduces other general considerations: the number of alternatives available to the listener in his response, the frequency of word usage in the language, the influence of the contextual background as, for example, comparing the intelligibility of a word presented in isolation with that of the same word when presented in the context of a sentence. Such factors have also been shown to influence the visual recognition threshold for words and thus are perhaps not logically a part of this exposition on audition.

These linguistic and statistical factors probably represent the point of greatest impact of information theory and information measurement on psychology. Much of the weakness of the earlier positions in this field I believe involve the notion that the information in speech can be derived from the acoustical characteristics of speech. It is somewhat easier now to conceive of the speech information as residing in the set of all possible stimuli, and of the information transmitted as residing in the set of all possible responses available to a listener. In this scheme, then, the acoustical characteristics of the speech sound determine the discriminability and recognizability of these items as alternatives.

### LEVELS OF AUDITORY PERCEPTION

In summation, I should like to introduce, as a vocabulary, four levels of auditory perception: detection, discrimination, recognition or identification, and comprehension or process.

*Detection,* I think, is simple enough and can be quickly disposed of. That is to say, if one is to recognize speech, if one is to discriminate differences among speech sounds, then the acoustic energy in those speech sounds must lie above the threshold of hearing. If the threshold is defective, as in cases of hearing loss, then the acoustic levels must be raised for similar kinds of discrimination or detection to be observed. There are kinds of hearing loss, however, in which the frequency characteristic of the audiogram is only one aspect of the auditory defect, as indicated by a difficulty in the understanding of speech greater than would be predicted by the elevated thresholds alone. Also, deaf children (especially with hearing aids) provide some good examples of the audibility of speech power concentrated in the low frequencies, but not enough acoustic energy outside of that restricted band of frequencies is available to permit other than mere detection of speech sounds. Some of us believe that when the role of non-spectral cues in speech is better understood, even such low-frequency hearing can be exploited for more discrimination and perception through the auditory channel than has been possible up to now.

There is a stage of *discrimination*—molecular discrimination for our purposes—among the phonemes that is not very well understood. Some of the preceding discussion indicates the kind of studies that are necessary before one can spell out the various psychoacoustic abilities or tasks which will predict that all of the phonemes are distinguishable one from the other. That is why I asked Dr. Jakobson about some of the dimensions, i.e., whether there is a perceptual deficiency restricted to the language setting in some of the aphasic patients he described, or whether that deficiency may be shown with synthetic sounds outside of the context of language. At the present time, in certain areas of clinical practice such as audiology and otology, speech discrimination is defined in terms of a score that represents the percentage of words a listener can repeat correctly when they are presented at a suitably high level. It should be clear that these kinds of tests involve more than phonemic discrimination. The listener's task is not only to judge that one of two speech sounds is different from the other, but to repeat the item and thus demonstrate a degree of recognition and of speaking or, in some cases, of writing. At the moment, there is much discussion about the kinds of auditory pathology that lead to reduction in speech discrimination, but most of it stems from correlational studies in which the two variables are this rather complex score of speech recognition, on the one hand, and not very well substantiated diagnostic categories, on the other. It is my personal opinion that detailed molecular studies (8, 30) of the kind I suggest here are required for an understanding of the bases of speech discrimination.

At a third level of *recognition* or *identification*, we add something about memory to the requirements of speech discrimination. This involves storage of words or phonemes that serve as a reservoir against which incoming auditory patterns may be compared for a recognition purpose. Here we encounter problems and rules in psycholinguistics. It is certainly true that the probability of a correct word response is not only a function of the audibility and the discriminability of the phonemes involved; it is also a function of those many factors that control such response probabilities in hearing as well as in the visual recognition of words. It is clear that the intelligibility of a word is higher when that word appears in a sentence (35). If the test vocabulary is known to the listener, the probability of a correct word identification is higher, as it is if the size of the list is smaller. The role of word frequency in general language or of the emotional content of a word is not as clear in auditory word recognition as it has been in studies on the tachistoscopic recognition of words through vision. I used to believe this indicated that auditory stimuli were more stimulus-bound but, as more evidence is produced on the roles of extra-stimulus factors on auditory recognition of words, I am beginning to abandon that position.

The distinction between discrimination and identification is perhaps artificial and has certainly been oversimplified. In testing an adult for auditory recognition we usually present a word and ask him to repeat it. It is this particular stimulus-response sequence that characterizes most of our studies on speech intelligibility. The number of alternatives and of responses can be manipulated and fixed by the experimenter, or the choice may be free and thus depend in complex ways on speech and language learning.

There are other procedures, used particularly with children, that may help to separate these various psychological processes. If a very young child is suspected of having a hearing or language deficiency, we may very well want to know, for example, whether he can distinguish the word "baby" from the word "shoe". He does not use these words, as far as we know, and cannot recognize them; that is, he cannot give a repeating response. In an experimental session, we may begin to teach these words in the following way: after having made some measurements of the child's auditory sensitivity, we present the word "shoe" at a suitably high level and, at the same time, point to or give the child a shoe. We can do the same for the word "baby", and on subsequent trials we can observe whether the child reliably reaches for one or the other object lying on a table. It is of less concern here that we are teaching the meaning of these words (we could, for example, choose entirely arbitrary stimulus associations) than that he is demonstrating an auditory ability to distinguish between these two sounds. Perhaps he is only showing that he can distinguish one syllable from two syllables, and that in itself is an interesting piece of information. The words "shoe" and "baby" are followed by other pairs of words that have the same number of syllables. This is a simpler task because it demonstrates phonemic discrimination in almost the pure state.

Finally, what I mean by *comprehension* or *information processing* is recognition as described already, but sustained over a period of time. My concept of recognition in the previous section was again quite molecular, having to do with units no larger than a word. In this case I mean to complicate recognition by introducing a time span within which perceived words must be stored to establish the context that was considered important in the discussion of Dr. Jakobson's presentation. There are listeners who can recognize single words but who still complain that they fail in auditory perception in conversation. It is clear that more complexity characterizes language comprehension than any of the processes discussed up to now. We have noted that the intelligibility of words is different when they appear as members of a large sample of contextual language. But what kinds of abilities are implied in the requirement that the statistical and contextual aspects of language be available to the listener? There is recent work on sequential probabilities among words in which the fact that only a subclass is likely to follow the members of another subclass is treated as if such statistical properties were properties of the language system itself. They may be, but if they are demonstrated in the behavior of talkers and listeners, we must know something about how the sequential probabilities develop in the talking and listening habits of such persons. The phenomena themselves are just becoming clear, but the underlying mechanisms or psychological processes remain a task for the future.

How wide a time gap must the listener carry in order to let the influence of immediately past words come to bear upon words that are about to be heard? How many previous words are stored in a running, listening memory in order to permit a listener to engage in efficient language communication? If a listener is free of difficulties in speaking or in auditory discrimination and perception, what will be the effect of a specific memory deficiency on his communicative behavior? How does the rate of talking influence the storage time? When do the words succeed each other too rapidly to be separately identified and stored, and when are they spoken too slowly to be associated together in a sequential context? Here is a series of questions about temporal matters that affect what I think I mean by language comprehension.

I have chosen to indicate something beyond auditory perception, which I think is what this conference is interested in. I say "beyond" to imply the kind of free space that I feel we enter when we leave the safe experimental base for these generalizations about the processes involved in auditory perception. And I shall just leave this dangling behind me.

### Discussion

*Hardy:* Dr. Hirsh has led us through a masterful review and discussion of relations, both major and minor, between audition and the perception of speech. There is no need to reemphasize the points he made very clearly. I should like to restate two or three of them for the sake of extension.

It turns out that hearing, in the sense of "the receiving function in language communication", involves much more than the ear and, indeed, much more than the entire VIIIth nerve system. At stake here are some implications of motor activities in terms of habituated listening, which commonly begins to emerge developmentally by the fourth year of life in the child's experience of what has been termed "auditory self-monitoring". These habits, which are innate in egocentric speech in childhood and, therefore, involved in what is often called inner speech or inner language, clearly contribute to the categorical responses Dr. Hirsh referred to, and are indeed often defined by one's own speech habits. Some quite recent experimental work by Chase and his associates (4) with the use of delayed side tone emphasizes some of the controlling features of categorical responses, even at the proprioceptive level.

A principal point, as has been described, is the importance to the listener of what might be called the connective tissue of speech—transitional events, rates of change, changes in duration, abrupt and gradual starts, all the dynamics of active speech in communication which can scarcely be found in the traditional concept of a phoneme. Relative to some of these aspects of what Dr. Hirsh has called temporal perception ("the recognition of changes in frequency or in intensity with time, or even the recognition of the rates at which such changes occur"), we all have had experiences with dialectal variants or, perhaps, with trying to interpret the speech of deaf persons. These variants elude us for a while until our auditory scanning system becomes adequately tuned to help us process the information and make useful patterns from it. In what passes for dialects of English, the verbal exchange between, say, the Cockney of Whitehall and the farmer of Northumberland never does seem quite to achieve auditory recognition and linguistic comprehension.

Dr. Hirsh has emphasized the concept of temporal resolving power, which must surely underlie some of the developmental errors of infantile speech and their extension into a disorder often referred to as "infantile per-severation". Even in later life the common substitution in lalling of "w" for "r" apparently reflects auditory monitoring gone awry from the negative re-inforcement of motor performance. Correction in these instances can usual-ly be achieved only by helping the subject to learn an entirely new set of relations between auditory monitoring and motor expression.

Perhaps it might be useful to redefine the phoneme in terms of the learned grouping of various spectral and transitional phenomena, in support of which there are considerable experimental data. This approach would go far to emphasize the differences between sensory-neural and conductive losses of auditory sensitivity relative to the intelligibility of the incoming acoustic information. It would also emphasize important differences be-tween what nowadays is sometimes called hypoacusis and dysacusis relative to phonetic instability and phonetic variability. If there were time, it might be interesting to try to define a connection between attention and the ca-pacity of some given central nervous system of an "interfered with" child or adult in order to undertake this learned grouping of acoustic phenomena.

I suspect we may all agree heartily with Dr. Hirsh's final warning about temporal matters that affect language comprehension, on which we still have little information. Our group* has been working for several years on some of the topics or questions that were mentioned. We are largely moti-vated by an attempt to try to find out some of the why's and wherefore's of the impairments of pre-school age children who cannot readily learn lan-guage. Some of them have no apparent sensory defects; others have these in combination with problems of attention and memory which interfere more or less seriously with their learning of verbal-symbolic behavior. To this end we have thought in terms of a model into which one might fit various kinds of experimental learning tasks relative to audition, to auding (more about this later on), and to responding to acoustic stimuli.

I think Figure 16 might illustrate some of these ideas and follow through in extension of Dr. Hirsh's exposition. Relative to some of his latterly stated ideas about possibly productive ways of working with children who have the kind of problems described, one may begin with input of acoustic stim-uli and then think of a feedback system which can be related anatomically, physiologically, behaviorally, and in several other ways. First we think of conductive and transducing operations; these include the functions of the middle ear and probably extend through the activity of the cochlear duct to the level of the shearing action of the hair cells. Then there are coding operations, the level of impressing information within the neural structure.

* This is a current research project supported by the National Institute of Neurological Dis-eases and Blindness, Grant No. NB-3887: *Delayed Language Development: Auditory Input Factors.* Principal investigators are William G. Hardy, Miriam P. Hardy and Harriet L. Haskins.

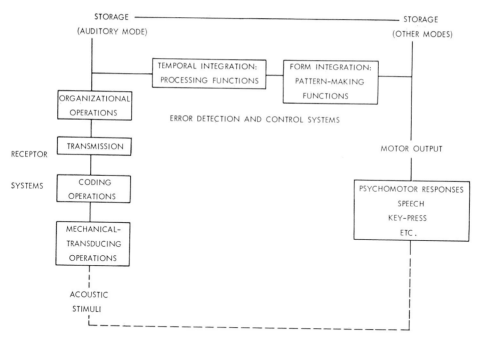

**Figure 16.** Model of central system control of sensory information and relations between acoustic stimuli and psychomotor responses. See text.

Next is the complex of transmissive activity through several synapses; and, finally, organizational operations involving the corticothalamic tracts, by which I believe I mean just about what Dr. Hirsh meant in his discussion of recognition.

Then we go into storage. I am not sure that we could use any directional arrows there because it is difficult to determine in many of these activities—rapid in time—which way the arrow should point. We move then across into integrative activities which can be thought of in two stages, simply as an extension in time, of processing and pattern-making. It is a kind of recognition along a time axis, involving more and more information. This is what I mean by auding, a kind of mind-managerial activity as a necessary stage in ordered, integrated understanding prior to linguistic conceptualization and formulation.

There is another storage function whereby current activity is probably related to previous experience. The first storage function, on the left in Figure 16, relates more directly to auditory experiences; on the right of the figure, it relates to every experience which may be part of the set of both talker and listener. We move down into motor activities—responses—which might be speech, or a key-press, or anything of the sort. If it is speech, it may then serve to close a biosocial feedback loop. This is simply a model to use for designing various studies with children who have learning disorders. It works quite well. Perhaps it serves to emphasize graphically something that is commonly overlooked: that hearing—in the broadest sense of the understanding of acoustic input, particularly linguistic input—also involves the concept of auding, of brain-management of the molecular detail; if hearing did not encompass this, we could not do "it".

We seem to inherit many problems from the language with which pathologies or developmental deviations are characterized concerning time and place, focus, locus, and symptoms. It might be somewhat more objective, certainly it could be more operational, to describe errors or deficits in detection (sensitivity), discrimination, recognition, processing, and so forth. This might promote better professional communication about both normal and abnormal function of hearing and the brain's management of acoustic information.

It is just possible that many of our clinical problems are in a way semanto-iatrogenic. In chronic states, which are brought about by endogenous or exogeneous factors, better progress might be expected in work with subjects who cannot readily receive and convey language if our nomenclature were centered, not on historical etiology or pathology, but on operational descriptions of impairments of function. Such a descriptive approach might possibly promote a better use of the answers to the questions which lead us "beyond auditory perception".

*Denes:* My first comment concerns Harvey Fletcher's book (12). This is in many respects an excellent book indeed. I would not agree with Dr. Hirsh, however, that Fletcher gave little attention to the acoustic properties of consonants. On the contrary, he gave detailed spectral characteristics for all English phonemes, but unfortunately without explaining how he defined the boundaries of the speech wave segments that he associated with a particular phoneme and whose acoustic characteristics he measured. As you know, the problem of segmentation is by no means a simple one and is, if anything, more involved for consonants than for vowels. The plosive consonants provide a particularly good example of the difficulties of segmentation: probably their most obvious acoustic feature is the complete silence that occurs while the flow of air from the lungs is stopped. It is not immediately apparent which speech wave segments were measured by Fletcher in order to arrive at the acoustic characteristics of plosives, all of which are given in his book. On a more general level, by giving a description of the acoustic features of speech sounds without raising and discussing the problem of segmentation, he encouraged phoneticians to believe that one can segment a speech wave into a sequence of discrete units, with each segment corresponding to a particular phoneme. He even encouraged the idea that these acoustic segments and the phonemes were identities instead of just loose statistical correlations. These mistaken views are being abandoned only very slowly under the influence of work such as that done at the Haskins Laboratories (5).

I would like to comment also on "distinctive features". As far as I understand it, distinctive features are a subclass of phonemes and are therefore units of linguistic organization. Yet Dr. Hirsh described them with reference to spectrum, which is clearly in the acoustic domain. I think there is a logical inconsistency when linguistic categories are described in terms of acoustic features. It is unfortunate that Dr. Jakobson could not stay for this session. That is a question I ask him almost every time I see him, and after listening to his reply I am satisfied that I understand how he reconciles an acoustic definition of an essentially linguistic event. But a few days later all my doubts are back again.

One last point. In discussing speech perception, Dr. Hirsh postulated a hierarchy of four distinct steps: detection, discrimination, recognition, and comprehension. I wonder whether the second step, discrimination, is in fact possible without memory, which he said was part of only the third step.

*Hirsh:* First, with regard to distinctive features, it is my understanding that they comprise the linguistic level of discourse, but I think it is true that Dr. Jakobson himself, and his colleagues Halle and Fant, for example, are interested in finding correlates of these distinctive features at three other levels of discourse: they would like to find acoustical correlates for them; they would like to define articulatory correlates, that is, to describe these features in terms of movement and position of the speech mechanism; and they would also like to describe psychological correlates, in the sense of the responses of listeners.* I also have discussed this with Dr. Jakobson; he does not use the word "correlates" as much as I do. He speaks about these features as existing at those three levels, but they are really linguistic.

*Denes:* That is just the trouble. He gives them acoustic names, such as compact, diffuse, and so on.

*Hirsh:* Only some of them receive acoustic names; others have resisted acoustic analysis and are given articulatory labels.

*Denes:* An articulatory name for a linguistic feature is just as bad and often gives rise to confusion. The voiced-voiceless distinction, for example, is a linguistic feature that has acquired an articulatory name. As a result, many a phonetician has difficulty in dealing with sounds such as the last phoneme in the word "eyes" which, from the linguistic point of view, is voiced but which is often pronounced without vocal cord vibration.

*Hirsh:* Your objection to this level of discrimination with respect to phonemes is an excellent one. I described it as a necessary level in building the hierarchy you mention, but I also immediately indicated that most often it was inferred from tests called speech discrimination, in which the listeners had to discriminate and to recognize.

I would like, particularly for clinical purposes, to be able to test phonemic discrimination but, as Dr. Denes said, we really cannot do that without

---

* *Editor's note:* In fact, Fant in his *Acoustic Theory of Speech Production* (9) devotes a final chapter to a discussion of the acoustic correlates of distinctive features. A very considerable part of Halle's book *The Sound Pattern of Russian* (14) is dedicated to the same task, as will be the case with Halle & Chomsky's *The Sound Pattern of English* (15), now in preparation.

studying phonemes and involving memory for phonemes. What I would like to do is isolate some of the acoustical cues that have been shown to be important and test for discrimination along the dimensions of those cues, and for the ability of a listener to judge the rate of frequency change, using purely synthetic sounds, for example. Here I think I would be, if not testing phonemic discrimination, at least testing discriminations along dimensions that are relevant to phoneme distinction.

## REFERENCES

1. BENSON, R. W., and HIRSH, I. J., Some variables in audio spectrometry. *J. Acoust. Soc. Am.*, 1953, **25**: 499-505.
2. BORING, E. G., *Sensation and Perception in the History of Experimental Psychology*. Appleton-Century, New York, 1942.
3. BROADBENT, D. E., *Perception and Communication*. Pergamon, London, 1958.
4. CHASE, R. A., Information system analysis of the organization of motor activity. In: *Psychopathology of Perception* (P. H. Hoch and J. Zubin, Eds.). Grune & Stratton, New York, 1965.
5. COOPER, F. S., DELATTRE, P. C., LIBERMAN, A. M., BORST, J. M., and GERSTMAN, L. J., Some experiments on the perception of synthetic speech sounds. *J. Acoust. Soc. Am.*, 1952, **24**: 597-606.
6. DAVIS, H., Peripheral coding of auditory information. In: *Sensory Communication* (W. A. Rosenblith, Ed.). Wiley, New York, 1961: 119-141.
7. DEATHERAGE, B. H., and HIRSH, I. J., Auditory localization of clicks. *J. Acoust. Soc. Am.*, 1959, **31**: 486-492.
8. FAIRBANKS, G., Test of phonemic differentiation: the rhyme test. *J. Acoust. Soc. Am.*, 1958, **30**: 596-600.
9. FANT, G. M., *Acoustic Theory of Speech Production*. Mouton, The Hague, 1960.
10. FLETCHER, H., *Speech and Hearing*. Van Nostrand, New York, 1929.
11. ———, Auditory patterns. *Revs. Mod. Physics*, 1940, **12**: 47-65.
12. ———, *Speech and Hearing in Communication*. Van Nostrand, New York, 1953.
13. GRAY, A. A., On a modification of the Helmholtz theory of hearing. *J. Anat. Physiol.*, 1900, **34**: 324-350.
14. HALLE, M., *The Sound Pattern of Russian; a Linguistic and Acoustical Investigation*. Mouton, The Hague, 1959.
15. HALLE, M., and CHOMSKY, N., *The Sound Pattern of English* (in press).
16. HALLE, M., HUGHES, G. W., and RADLEY, J.-P. A., Acoustic properties of stop consonants. *J. Acoust. Soc. Am.*, 1957, **29**: 107-116.
17. HELMHOLTZ, H. L. F., *Die Lehre von den Tonempfindungen als physiologische Grundlage für die Theorie der Musik* (1st ed.). Vieweg, Brunswick, 1863.
18. ———, *On the Sensations of Tone as a Physiological Basis for the Theory of Music* (J. Ellis, Transl.). Dover, New York, 1954.
19. HIRSH, I J., *The Measurement of Hearing*. McGraw-Hill, New York, 1952.

20. Hirsh, I. J., Auditory perception of temporal order. *J Acoust. Soc. Am.*, 1959, **31**: 759-767.

21. Hirsh, I. J., Reynolds, E. G., and Joseph, M., Intelligibility of different speech materials. *J. Acoust. Soc. Am.*, 1954, **26**: 530-538.

22. House, A. S., and Stevens, K. N., Auditory testing of a simplified description of vowel articulation. *J. Acoust. Soc. Am.*, 1955, **27**: 882-887.

23. Huggins, W. H., System-function analysis of speech sounds. *J. Acoust. Soc. Am.*, 1950, **22**: 765-767.

24. Hughes, G. W., and Halle, M., Spectral properties of fricative consonants. *J. Acoust. Soc. Am.*, 1956, **28**: 303-310.

25. Jakobson, R., Fant, C. G. M., and Halle, M., *Preliminaries to Speech Analysis*. TR 13, Acoustics Laboratory, M.I.T., Cambridge, 1952.

26. Jakobson, R., and Halle, M., *Fundamentals of Language*. Mouton, The Hague, 1956.

27. Joos, M., Acoustic phonetics. *Language*, 1948, **24**: Supp. 23.

28. Katsuki, Y., Neural mechanism of auditory sensation in cats. In: *Sensory Communication* (W. A. Rosenblith, Ed.). Wiley, New York, 1961: 561-583.

29. Liberman, A. M., Cooper, F. S., Harris, K. S., and MacNeilage, P. F., A motor theory of speech perception. In: *Speech Communication Seminar, Proceedings*, Vol. II. Speech Transmission Laboratory, Royal Institute of Technology, Stockholm, 1963: D3.

30. Liberman, A. M., Ingemann, F., Lisker, L., Delattre, P., and Cooper, F. S., Minimal rules for synthesizing speech. *J. Acoust. Soc. Am.*, 1959, **31**: 1490-1499.

31. Licklider, J. C. R., Basic correlates of the auditory stimulus. In: *Handbook of Experimental Psychology* (S. S. Stevens, Ed.). Wiley, New York, 1951: 985-1039.

32. ———, Three auditory theories. In: *Psychology: A Study of a Science*, Vol. I (S. Koch, Ed.). McGraw-Hill, New York, 1959: 41-144.

33. Licklider, J. C. R., and Miller, G. A., The perception of speech. In: *Handbook of Experimental Psychology* (S. S. Stevens, Ed.). Wiley, New York, 1951: 1040-1074.

34. Michaels, R. M., Frequency difference limens for narrow bands of noise. *J. Acoust. Soc. Am.*, 1957, **29**: 520-522.

35. Miller, G. A., *Language and Communication*. McGraw-Hill, New York, 1951.

36. Mills, A. W., On the minimum audible angle. *J. Acoust. Soc. Am.*, 1958, **30**: 237-246.

37. Neff, W. D., Neural mechanisms of auditory discrimination. In: *Sensory Communication* (W. A. Rosenblith, Ed.). Wiley, New York, 1961: 259-278.

38. Peterson, G. E., and Barney, H. L., Control methods used in a study of the vowels. *J. Acoust. Soc. Am.*, 1952, **24**: 175-184.

39. Potter, R. K., Kopp, A. G., and Green, H. C., *Visible Speech*. Van Nostrand, New York, 1947.

40. Rosenblith, W. A. (Ed.). *Sensory Communication*. Wiley, New York, 1961.

41. SCHARF, B., Complex sounds and critical bands. *Psychol. Bull.*, 1961, **58**: 205-217.

42. SCRIPTURE, E. W., *Elements of Experimental Phonetics.* Scribners, New York, 1902.

43. STETSON, R. H., *Motor Phonetics; a Study of Speech Movements in Action* (2nd ed.). North-Holland, Amsterdam, 1951.

44. STEVENS, S. S. (Ed.). *Handbook of Experimental Psychology.* Wiley, New York, 1951.

45. ————, The psychophysics of sensory function. In: *Sensory Communication* (W. A. Rosenblith, Ed.). Wiley, New York, 1961: 1-33.

46. STEVENS, S. S., and DAVIS, H., *Hearing; Its Psychology and Physiology.* Wiley, New York, 1938.

47. VON BÉKÉSY, G., *Experiments in Hearing* (E. G. Wever, Transl. and Ed.). McGraw-Hill, New York, 1960.

48. WEGEL, R. L., and LANE, C. E., The auditory masking of one pure tone by another and its probable relation to the dynamics of the inner ear. *Phys. Rev.*, 1924, **23**: 266-285.

49. WEVER, E. G., and BRAY, C. W., Present possibilities of auditory theory. *Psychol. Rev.*, 1930, **37**: 365-380.

50. WOOLSEY, C. N., Organization of cortical auditory system. In: *Sensory Communication* (W. A. Rosenblith, Ed.). Wiley, New York, 1961: 235-257.

51. ZWISLOCKI, J., Relation of adaptation to fatigue, masking and recruitment. In: *Proceedings of the Fifth Congress of the International Society of Audiology.* Bonn, 1960: 279-285.

# SPEECH DISORDERS IN CHILDHOOD[*]

JULIÁN DE AJURIAGUERRA
University of Geneva
Switzerland

The study of childhood speech disorders has only recently been undertaken. Much the same approach was used at first in this new field as had been used previously in the study of adult speech disorders, and there was an initial tendency to consider the speech disorders of childhood as miniature aphasias. But it is clear that there are certain characteristics peculiar to the state of childhood itself which involve linguistic behavior as well as physiology.

As the scope of this paper will not enable us to handle the entire field of speech pathology, we will limit consideration to those problems which, in our opinion, deserve thought and discussion. These problems appear to us to reflect the multidimensional approach of the clinician and the current dynamic trends based on genetic psychology, which attempt to deduce from functional disintegrations or non-integrations (in speech) some understanding which could aid in comprehending the process itself. All this means that we are a long way from a thorough technical grasp of the problem, but this is understandable in view of the difficulties of working with variables which are all too often affected by individual differences.

Speech, like any other mental phenomenon, requires certain basic equipment. Even before reaching the functional stage, it is modified and enriched by external influences, but we cannot really speak of it as being an active entity until it becomes functional, and develops as a result of this. The overall effect of external influences is quite different when there is not enough sensory input, and the completely matured cerebral mechanism functions differently according to whether its deficiencies are of recent or early origin. The mechanisms of the mind maintain a certain rigidity, but there is also a certain flexibility in their general arrangement, as well as a special capacity, based at least in part on the temporal development of the brain, to

---

[*] Dr. de Ajuriaguerra made his presentation in French at the Conference. MM. A. Hooton and F. Guignard in Switzerland and Mrs. Ann Kempe Lodwig and Dr. E. C. Carterette in Los Angeles translated his paper.

adapt to certain circumstances. We thus concur with Vygotsky's idea (57) that the relationship between thoughts and words is a dynamic, constantly changing one which can only be understood by relating it to the overall development of the mind (in which we include affective organization).

### The Dynamics of the Physiopathology of Speech in Children

Penfield & Roberts (39) have recently studied the cerebral mechanisms of speech, and we shall therefore not broach the subject in this paper. On the basis of our clinical and anatomical work with children we are concerned with two questions: Are there areas of the brain which may be considered innate speech centers? And if they exist, are these functional zones localized at an early age in a so-called dominant hemisphere?

A refutation of the existence of innate speech centers is deduced from Pierre Marie's (32) assertion that aphasia does not result from lesions of the left hemisphere in children under three years of age. Recent personal observations and findings in the literature (9, 10, 14, 16, 27) led us to conclude that that view cannot be completely accepted. Although we cannot reject totally Marie's basic premise of the absence of preformed speech centers, the study of cases published by several authors and by ourselves clearly brings out certain new facts.

Even though aphasia is encountered much more frequently in adults than in children, it is nevertheless found in childhood more often than earlier authors believed. The severity of childhood aphasia is proportional to the extent of the lesions associated with it, and is particularly severe when the lesions are bilateral. Although it cannot be asserted, as some authors would have it, that childhood aphasia regresses rapidly, the cases we studied for a period of several years nevertheless showed that the regression was more pronounced in children than in adults. However, in the children studied, the lesions were rather extensive though predominantly unilateral. The speech defects due to congenital unilateral lesions of the left hemisphere, described in cases of infantile hemiplegias, do not appear to us to be sufficiently substantiated. Furthermore, we do not know the anatomical basis on which audimutitas develops.

Once we accept the theory that lesions in certain areas of the adult brain result in speech disorders, the study of pathology in children shows that (a) these areas are meaningless unless there is also the capacity to communicate —in fact, afferent and efferent nerve disorders, either sensory or motor, can disturb the organization of speech even in the absence of an anatomically localized cerebral lesion; (b) there are no preformed centers but rather preformed mechanisms which take shape as the capacity to communicate develops; (c) hemispheric dominance is much more labile in children than in adults.

Even if there is perfect cerebral organization and the peripheral organs are adequate, speech can develop only through creative communication. It is therefore possible to say that speech is not a function resulting entirely from the activity of an innate mechanism, but rather a mode of relating which is created by communication based upon a preformed cerebral organization without which speech could not exist. We do not wish to imply by this that we deny the importance of cerebral organization: speech has as its starting point a more or less localized cerebral organization from which it develops as a creative process with its own dynamics and with the learning of a prescribed code.

### SPEECH DISORDERS RESULTING FROM LESIONS IN THE ORGANS WHICH SEND OR RECEIVE MESSAGES

Learning to speak is dependent upon the mechanism of sending and receiving messages. But just as one cannot say that the hands are the instruments of musicianship merely because the pianist plays with them, or that knees are the instruments of faith because one kneels in prayer, so neither can one say that the peripheral apparatus of articulation and hearing are the "organs" of speech. In fact, there are specific means of communication among the deaf, and we know that persons whose larynges have been removed can acquire an esophageal voice. Peripheral organs allow a certain form of communication possible only through the sensory-motor circuit which, by its actualization, initiates the verbal relationship. Moreover, according to Vygotsky (57), the manner in which the structures of thought develop make it possible to use speech as a logical and analytical instrument of thought.

We should like to present some empirical findings which we have studied from different angles. They fall within the framework of message transmission, namely the problem of audimutitas and dysphasia in children.

The few children who fail to acquire speech in spite of sufficient intelligence and adequate hearing are generally known as hearing mutes or audimutes. Classically, two apparently opposed forms of audimutitas may be distinguished: audimutitas of expression, known also by several other names, which is characterized by seriously deficient linguistic expression in children of normal or subnormal intelligence, and congenital word deafness, characterized by failure to understand speech and disordered verbal expression in children whose intelligence and hearing may be relatively normal.

We feel this classification is too schematic, for although in congenital word deafness there is difficulty in comprehension and in verbal expression, expressive audimutes are not exempt from functional disorders of hearing or of understanding. At first we were inclined to accept this two-fold classification, i.e., audimutitas of expression and of comprehension, but it became apparent later that it failed to correspond to the observed facts. It is indeed inappropriate in certain cases, since the absence of conscious verbal expression leads ultimately to disturbances in comprehension; it is altogether insufficient in other cases since non-comprehension of speech may take on forms fundamentally different from each other. Consequently, we classified our observations (1) according to a number of salient factors. In one group we placed children with normal auditory perception but with serious difficulties in praxic organization (performance of complex motor tasks); in a second group we placed children presenting complex problems of auditory perception.

In studying motor organization in our dyspraxic audimute children (Group I), we demonstrated that in no case could the disorders be correlated with a simple motor disturbance such as paralysis. We found a general motor disorganization such as a generalized or a buccolinguofacial dyspraxia. Moreover, there is in this form of disorganization a disturbance of temporal and/or spatial organization. In one sub-group, both temporal and spatial organizations were impaired. In another sub-group, although the Bender and Kohs tests were more or less normal, only the dominant temporal organization was affected: there were serial disorganization, difficulty in following a prescribed rhythm, and loss of rhythmic form as soon as it was set to time and included as many as three elements.

The children in Group II suffered from what is called congenital word deafness. As pointed out by Worster-Drought (59), it is not appropriate in their case to speak of auditory agnosia, much too broad a term for children not totally incapable of distinguishing sounds. The term "verbal agnosia" is equally unsuitable since some children with congenital word deafness have difficulties involving sounds other than those of the spoken word. For these reasons, Allen chose the term "congenital auditory imperception". Without doubt these children have difficulty with auditory perception; they seem to live in a world of sound which never takes on meaning. They are not simple cases of impaired hearing (hypoacousis): the available audiometric records are seldom in agreement (as was observed by Mme. Borel-Maisonny, who studied our cases); the vocal curves are paradoxical; the phonetic audiogram (discrimination for vowels and consonants without lip-reading) shows superior intelligibility for consonants and a total or partial unintelligibility for vowels—the subject is never able to distinguish one vowel from another. When it is possible to perform a pure-tone audiogram, the resulting curve is U- or V-shaped with a more or less large "opening" but always with a sharp dip in the center. The children we have studied are more disturbed by hearing differently than by not hearing at all. Their emotional attitude toward the world of sound is one of defense and rejection; this is why their behavior relative to speech is so strongly negative and their retaining so difficult.

The staff of the Geneva medico-pedagogical service is engaged in the study of the organization of speech and its developmental variables in a population of dysphasic patients (4), i.e., children having difficulties in integrating speech but without sensory or phonatory defects, who are able, although with difficulty, to communicate verbally, and whose mental level is considered normal. These dysphasic children are characterized by disturbances of audioverbal perception of ideational structure in both spontaneous narrative and in attempts to deal with prescribed material, of the phonetic quality of verbal expression, and by errors in the synonym test (analogy relation). A test of useful vocabulary and a naming test were successfully completed by twenty per cent of the cases.

The study is of a qualitative nature, with the staff trying to form groups of patients showing correlations between verbal organization and attitude. It was thus possible to demonstrate two extremes, taciturn types and chatterers. The taciturn patients, so called because they are reserved in their speech, are characterized by the simplicity of their sentences, by narrative which is rather enumerative and descriptive, by homogeneity between their comprehension of speech and their own speech, and by the paucity of variation in their verbal performance. By contrast, the chatterers construct complicated sentences with little regard for syntax; their narrative extends beyond mere enumeration, they pay less attention to chronological order, their narrative is less coherent, with comprehension and production much further apart, and their performance is variable. The prosodic features are some of the aspects affected in our dysphasic patients; moreover, it appears that delivery is most affected in the taciturn subjects, who are unable to reproduce the tonal element they hear, whereas understanding is most affected in the prolific talkers, who fail to differentiate the intonations of the therapist.

At first glance it would appear that the chatterers approach the metonymic extreme described by Jakobson (22, 23). In fact, context is important for these patients; connecting particles (prepositions, conjunctions, adverbs) are used more often, stereotyped phrases and even clichés are frequent, and there are more obvious difficulties in comprehension than for the taciturn group. It should be pointed out in this respect that chatterers prattle on, whereas the taciturn dysphasics are listeners. We have observed, however, that chatterers are as disordered as taciturn patients with respect to sentence structure, and that they may also show aggrammatism and telegraphic style. Moreover, all the children in our study have difficulties with phonetics. It has been further observed that chatterers do as well (or as poorly) as the taciturn patients on the synonym test. Furthermore, analysis of replies to the substantive naming test shows that the same child might apparently answer either by contiguity or by similarity. We may find in the same child disorders of combination and contexture and of selection and substitution. Certain similarity and contiguity disorders may appear in both types of patient, or both in the same patient. Many of our patients presented a clinical picture which constitutes a synthesis of the two groups described by Dr. Jakobson (23) or of the three groups described by Luria (28).

It seems appropriate to ask to what extent these dynamic disorders of speech development are comparable to adult aphasias, and to what extent is it justifiable to speak of retarded development, thus making it possible to relate these disorders to stages in the normal development of children's speech.

Miller & Ervin (35) point out that dialogue may be said to exist as soon as a formal grammatical system begins to take shape. Although our dysphasic children have no coherent formal system—the rules of their speech are extremely variable, with no possibility of analysis and correction—they are capable of receptive communication. These children continue to imitate adult phrases without understanding the grammatical functions of the parts of speech. When a normal child acquires useable syntax by osmosis, he may come to integrate by successive segregations the variable system of morphemes. For example, a child hears, "tomorrow I shall eat", and at another time, "today I eat", and finally he perceives that the morpheme "shall" belongs with the word "tomorrow"; in this way he learns the temporal value of the morpheme. But with dysphasic children, problems in parsing are very persistent, since it is so difficult for them to integrate grammatical notions precisely because of their inability to analyse. Parsing often requires the isolation of marker words. It must be emphasized that it is precisely these words which are phonetically most subject to problems of verbal perception of grammatical elements, simply because they are variable and often barely audible. Still, all our patients presented perceptive disorders, making it difficult to compare their parsing ability with that of normal speakers.

In addition, it is difficult to distinguish clearly, as has been done with adults, the so-called aphasic disorders (characterized by difficulties in abstract thought and the loss of value concepts) from disorders resulting from afferent and efferent disturbances such as adult anarthria. Malmberg (31) draws attention to the fact that external disturbances may sometimes (to the extent that they imply a hindrance to articulation or to perception) result in a speech disorder resembling aphasic phenomena even though it has a different origin. While we recognize the existence of speech disorders due to the impairment of articulation and phonation, or to conditions specific for hypoacusia, we believe that both audimutes and dysphasics, regardless of whether the cause for their condition is peripheral or central, present disorders of a general nature which cannot be explained solely by the converse assumption of afferent or efferent disturbances.

Of the forty subjects included in our first study, we have reexamined 17 between several months and two years later (5). Most of these, but not all, have followed a program of reeducation. All the subjects have progressed as far as their ability to communicate is concerned, but the dysphasic characteristics remain. Although the majority of our cases showed progress in verbal comprehension, narrative, and syntax, many of them showed practically no improvement in audioverbal perception. Verbal style remained generally the same, although there was a levelling trend in that the chatterers were better organized, i.e., had "cooled off", whereas the taciturn subjects had "warmed up". Communication therefore improved in both conditions, becoming more controlled in the chatterers and more fluent in the taciturn subjects. Nevertheless, we have the impression that our subjects risk being left with a particular kind of personal code and that their symbolism will remain highly idiosyncratic, quite removed from the common code which language represents. Certain individuals will, perhaps, use simpler codes of fewer nuances, while others will remain confined to a symbolism much too idiosyncratic to permit normal communication.

It is clear that a certain level of intelligence is necessary for the acquisition of speech (33). However, some mentally deficient individuals have a higher potential for communication than our dysphasics, even though the performance of these mentally deficient patients may be on a lower level. They may have a kind of verbal "know-how" such that their "verbal clichés" fit together coherently, assuming a conversational form corresponding to their mental age. In this respect, when the mental deficiency is sufficiently homogeneous, the level of speech is very similar to the levels of children's speech. However, our dysphasics, either because they cannot sufficiently apprehend data supplied them or because they cannot integrate these data, are incapable of arranging facts or retaining images; they solve their speech problems either by limiting themselves strictly to concrete facts or by a method of successive abstractions having neither the cohesion nor the flexibility of normal narrative.

When retested, all of our intellectually gifted dysphasics (general intelligence was evaluated by a battery of tests) showed marked improvement in their speech. These facts lead us to believe that the mentally retarded organize their speech according to their level of intelligence, whereas our dysphasics reorganize by means of variables which would be interesting to define better. All our patients with well developed intellectual ability made progress in their speech, but a certain number of patients with lesser ability improved equally well. The question remains as to whether the progress observed in speech may be attributed to a modification or to a different utilization of the symbolic figurative representation—particularly in its anticipatory aspect—which is greatly impaired in our patients.

### SPEECH DISORDERS AND INTELLECTUAL DEVELOPMENT

Numerous psychopathologists have studied the problem of the relationship between speech and thought, particularly with respect to aphasia. Similar problems have been considered by linguists as well. De Saussure

(13) has said that the awareness of relationships is scarcely possible without language. And as Jakobson (22) said, language is in fact a tool shaped and manipulated according to the concept to be expressed.

Following Vygotsky, Luria (29) describes the various stages which characterize the progressive development of the regulatory action of speech; he stresses the abstracting and regulating function of speech that allows the formation of systems which react to abstract qualities. According to Luria, it is because of speech that a stimulus is not simply a signal for man but rather an element of general information from its onset: reactions do not depend on the physical qualities of the stimulus; rather, they derive from the system in which the stimulus is integrated. Thus speech, which reflects objective reality, influences directly the shaping of complex human activities. The second signal system introduces a new principle in higher nervous activity. In this respect the Geneva school of genetic psychology is far less positive. Thus for Piaget (41) the development of thought and the acquisition of speech both imply symbolic representation, although the second cannot be considered a mere causal result of the first since both are integral parts of a process which is far more general than the structure of symbolic function. At the Bonn Psychology Congress, Inhelder (19) defended the concept that speech is a necessary but nevertheless insufficient condition for the development of class and relational concepts. Piaget (21) has recently given an excellent analysis of this proposition. It is clear from the work of these two authors that the syntax and semantics of speech comprise structures of classification, such as substantives and adjectives, and serial structures suggested by the comparative. It is equally clear that, as speech is a grouping of symbols and signs, it facilitates and accelerates symbolic representation. It is also true that, speech being at once the cause and effect of socialization, it contributes to the formation as well as to the stabilization of conceptual systems of communication. But, although language plays a role in the attainment of these conceptual systems, it does not of itself appear to be a sufficient factor for the production of operations constituting logical classifications. Recently, Sinclair and Inhelder (19) have shown that, although there is a reciprocal relationship between developmental processes of spontaneous speech in a given context and operational processes, it does not follow that teaching a child certain precise terms accelerates the acquisition of a concept. The child who is still unprepared to integrate a concept rejects the suggestions of the expert, and only the child who is ready to grasp the concept feels the need for the relevant terms; such a child attains a better articulation of the operational problem.

This presentation can now be resumed from the point of view of the pathological conditions of deaf-mutes and dysphasics.

The analysis of the intellectual transactions of deaf-mutes has been thoroughly studied by Oléron (37), Vincent (56) and Affolter (cf. 41). In his first studies, Oléron acknowledged that the deaf tend to maintain intellectual functioning on what he calls a perceptual level as opposed to a conceptual one: the data perceived are not subordinate to the more abstract principle which encompasses them, and this explains the difficulty of considering separately those aspects which are neither immediately given nor intuitively perceived. Later, in 1952, on the basis of a study on the use of relations—relations of size, of weight, of speed, of assimilation of the laws of temporal series or of problems in double alternation—Oléron (36) conceded that speech does not play as important a role as some authors had thought in the execution of certain tasks. Nevertheless, he stressed the lack of flexibility in the thinking of these subjects. Piaget (41) cites Affolter on deaf-mutes between five and seven years of age being capable of mastering basic operations such as classification, serialization, etc. The question remains open, however, as to whether or not deaf-mutes are slow to acquire notions of conservation.

Several particularly interesting facts were observed by the staff of the Geneva medico-pedagogical service in the study of dysphasic children. The results of the Wechsler Intelligence Scale for Children (WISC) test on these patients show the percentage index of the norms to be $\frac{2}{5}$ for the Full Scale I.Q. and $\frac{4}{5}$ for the Performance I.Q. A ratio of slightly more than $\frac{1}{3}$ was recorded for Verbal I.Q., and this is noteworthy in subjects with speech disorders. Comparative analysis of the results of the WISC test shows that certain verbal tests such as comprehension of similarities (Part II) constitute adequate indices of intelligence in spite of speech impairment, whereas other tests such as vocabulary, arithmetic, similarities (Part I), and number repetition, are the subtests most regularly failed at all levels and consequently are those most sensitive to a speech deficit. This distinction between the verbal subtests of the WISC does not become entirely clear until after the age of seven. The bipolar distribution of verbal tests can be explained as follows: in the tests of comprehension and of similarities (Part II) the formal aspect of the question is not essential—key words may be ignored and, to a certain extent, the order of presentation of the data may also be ignored—whereas key elements of the message are few and for this reason are easily retained and manipulated even by subjects whose vocabulary is limited. In the second category of subtests the tasks involve seeking out and defining specific words, an exercise dependent upon the ability to integrate each element of the message whose semantic value is indissolubly linked to the order in which the elements occur in the context; this is a verbal situation supplying a maximum of information with a minimum of redundancy. Here the selection of key elements of the message can be accomplished only by taking into account the other elements which specify the essential ones and shade their meaning.

Examination of these children by means of the Piaget-Inhelder tests brings out the fact that half the subjects, in spite of verbal deficiencies, are able to achieve normal or even superior results because performance flexibility is possible despite poor verbal formulation. Properly speaking, there is therefore no delay in the elaboration of operative thought and, more specifically, in the development of conceptual thought. But 85 per cent, or almost the entire population of subjects tested, gave inferior performances on tasks of spatial representation and figurative anticipation. Learning methods and reasoning processes vary according to the subjects: one group resorts to the concrete means of communication represented by purposeful action or gesticulation. In a second group are those who, despite their verbal deficiency, choose a verbal means of learning about the experimental reality. Whereas some of them try to express themselves in what is often very rudimentary speech, others speak profusely and spontaneously without worrying about being understood. Finally, a third group is made up of subjects who express themselves equally by manipulatory or verbal means— these, in general, are the most intelligent subjects of our population.

One of our questions was whether these children would still succeed in organizing a system of comprehension both sufficiently structured and flexible for the achievement of an acceptable level of logical thought. When 17 subjects were retested several months to two years after their first examination, it was noted that they still showed the same characteristics, although far less pronounced, in dealing with the tests involving a proper grasp of language. Two of these children, now 13 years old, have still not attained a formal structure of speech; for the time being there is nothing to indicate that they will not succeed in this, although with a certain delay. However, it may be predicted that when they do succeed, their language structure will be highly idiosyncratic.

Certain authors consider that language plays a major role in the interpretation of the world of objects, that it acts as a mediator in the formation of an intellectual system to deal with objects. It is true that because of language objects are not only the objects of perception; they take on value, have a name, and this name has special qualities aside from those attached to the perception itself. Language opens up an entire field of possibilities: it is an affirmation of the world of objects and an affirmation of self in relation to them, but it does not create the process of relating. According to Piaget (41), this process is enriched in the course of its development through the contribution of language; prior to speech, the process consists of a kind of "logic of action" before finally breaking through to a formal logic which develops beyond this more primitive form.

Thought and language are covariables, more or less independent at the beginning of organization, becoming more interdependent and unified at the age of transition to the period when concrete operations are performed. But it cannot be said that this stage is a consequence of thought and speech; all that we can say is that logical thought finds its expression in, but is distinct from, organized speech with which it coexists and codevelops. Although it is true, as Piaget (41) has said, that the great general structures of the intellect extend beyond language and cannot be formulated in terms of everyday speech, it is just as true that the flexibility of thought that is to be formulated, such as in normal communication, becomes possible only through the development of speech. From this point of view we agree with Vygotsky (57) that the structure of language does not mirror the structure of thought, and thought is not expressed simply by language but finds in language its reality and its form. For some authors, language involves structures isomorphic to the structures of logic. As for language in its development, we can say that in its actualization as a real and natural means of communication it is both within and beyond the boundaries of thought. Language is sometimes an instrument and sometimes, as in poetry, a creation.

### Social and Emotional Implications of Speech Disorders in Childhood

Speech is created by a relationship, and speaking is an activity implying complicity between speaker and hearer. Learning to speak, Rostand (43) said, is learning to play a series of roles; it is assuming a series of behaviors. A subject deprived of perceptual stimulation will not learn to speak; partial deprivation, such as that resulting from hospitalism, induces retarded organization of speech (14, 53). It is hardly surprising that a deficient verbal supply should hinder speech organization, but research on early frustrations points up the fact that the lack of warm emotional ties between mother and child during the pre-verbal stage may subsequently disturb later verbal and extra-verbal means of communication. Moreover, a certain number of simple delays in the development of speech can be made up rapidly when the children are placed in a social context outside their families. This may be explained either by the family's poverty of vocabulary or by its excessive demands in terms of the child's level of maturity.

Numerous works, in particular the studies by Day (10) and, more recently, by Luria & Yudovich (30) on twins, have shown the importance of interpersonal factors in the development of speech. Luria, using an excellent method, studied a pair of twins retarded in their speech: theirs was the so-called autonomous speech—an extremely limited vocabulary, a language composed of sounds (onomatopoeia), of words related to immediate activity and accompanied by intense gesticulation. By studying ordinary activities—games, the capacity to judge, to engage in abstract thought, to classify, to find opposites—Luria demonstrated that these subjects presented important disorders in those activities as well as in speech. He then separated the two children and arranged for one to be reeducated. As a consequence of separation, progress was noted in the twins' better comprehension of the speech of others, both of them listening willingly and participating in conversations. As described by Luria, the record is fascinating; it shows, in fact, the importance of the twin situation in retarded speech development and, moreover, demonstrates the existence of variations in the children's intellectual structure. Luria attributes these latter modifications to their acquisition and utilization of the conventional linguistic system resulting from their separation. In our opinion, this assertion has not been satisfactorily demonstrated. Before being separated, these children had not achieved more than "autonomous" language, but neither had they attained more than "autonomous" activity: their separation marked not only the opportunity to speak with classification possible but also the opportunity to classify with speech possible. The changes took place not only in relation to the acquisition and utilization of conventional speech but also to the acquisition or utilization of a conventional symbolic system with which language is most importantly involved.

Vygotsky (57) quite rightly insists on the fact that adult speech, with its shaded meanings, influences childhood conceptualization and guides the process of generalization in children. Having no precise notions of the etiological factors which may play a part in dysphasia, we tried to evaluate the influence of the family environment, and were struck by the insufficient linguistic background of our subjects. Moreover, in 22.5 per cent of the cases we have found a twin situation or a similar relationship, i.e., either true twins or siblings of very nearly the same age living symbiotically apart from the family and the outside world. We can only report these facts, without saying that they are the only causes, but it is clear that a situation like that is of little benefit; in order to engage in processes of reciprocal socialization, one must acquire a certain distance with respect to others, from the emotional point of view as well as from the point of view of language and intellect.

Words, Merleau-Ponty (34) has said, far from being mere signs for objects and meanings, actually dwell in things and convey meanings. Benveniste (7) also remarked that language supplies the instrument of discourse in which personality is expressed and created, reaches out to another, and is made known to him. Pichon's (42) "appetitive function" of language depends on the developing personality of the speaker and also on the role language plays in interpersonal communication. Indeed, language as a means of communication implies an agreement which can be used by the speaker in the form of an appeal or an attack, but it can also be reflected by another in the form of gratification or punishment. Before being expressed, language is already experienced as a particular emotion in which others are implicated. Lacan (26) said that there is no word without a response, even if it encounters only silence, so long as there is a listener. Moreover, presence is in itself communication. Language may also be used as a camouflage, and silence, in certain instances, may have a propositional value. Thus Freud could speak of "negation through speech".

It is obvious that where there is no investment in persons or objects, language fails to develop because there is no need to communicate; this is clearly shown in certain cases of infantile autism or infantile psychosis (3). The speaker takes up a position and is at one and the same time himself and others by a feedback effect, but dialogue is possible only if a certain distance is maintained between the speaker and the person with whom he identifies himself. In effect, when language is overinvested, it lacks flexibility and is characterized by obsession or a leaning toward abstract discourse. The majority of our dysphasic patients suffered from an emotional disorder early in life, some of them because there was no need to establish a relationship, others because failure to reorganize verbal perception resulted in altered ways of relating.

### GENERAL PROBLEMS ASSOCIATED WITH THE DISORDERS OF SPEECH DEVELOPMENT

Most of the disorders of speech development in children cannot be attributed to a single cause. Whatever disorganizes speech development acts on the developing personality and disturbs its overall organization, for there is an internal coherence in infantile organization, both in the longitudinal sense of development and in the structures existing at any given time. Even if there is only a single point of impact, the disorganization of this plastic function must involve more than a single system. The symptom itself may be regarded as a sign; with respect to the individual, however, it has no significance in the disorganization except in relation to the developmental level: it constitutes the "face" of a disordered whole.

Disorganization is not a phenomenon of "something missing" but rather, in children, it is a new means of adapting to a deficit, more or less valid when judged in terms of efficiency. The disorganizing impact cannot be considered to constitute in itself the cause of disorganization. The genesis of the disorder does not depend solely on the impact as such but on the stage of development at which it occurs, on the previous organization of a given system, and on the correlation of this system with other systems.

Let us take stuttering as an example. Stuttering is a condition attributed variously (2) to disorders of special organs (motor, phonatory, respiratory, etc.), to disturbances related to hemispheric dominance (9, 10, 16, 18), to faulty feedback mechanisms in speech control circuits, to emotional disturbances, etc. In our opinion, none of these hypotheses can be applied to all cases of stuttering; all we can say is that stuttering has all the earmarks of disorganization involving an external relationship, that something or someone is always involved with the stutterer's world, and that the disorder cannot be understood except on the basis of the relationship. Stuttering is a form of maladaptation as regards speech implementation within the framework of a communicative relationship. It may be considered inadequate timing of the communication process, which is comprised of a preformulated-thought phase, a nascent-word phase, an ordered verbal-expression phase, and finally a phonic-expression phase. This means that stuttering cannot be understood only as the activity of a disordered static anatomical system, nor merely as a lack; any factor that causes mistiming of the phases in the thought-language process may induce it.

This disorder, which occurs at rather well-defined stages in the development of language, and more frequently in boys than in girls, appears during a certain phase of development for various reasons or for an accumulation of reasons, although it has but one equivalent symptomatology. While a large number of factors may go into the behavior of stuttering and are responsible for its "shape", this condition may not be considered merely the sum total of those factors. Whereas it is initially an unstable condition, it later takes on a new form disconnected from the initial causes and is conditioned in the manner of a closed system; in its new structure, stuttering may often resist so-called causal treatment. What we have stated here with reference to stuttering may also be applied to other speech disorders, even to those caused by lesions. It should be taken into account in any attempt to understand and treat them.


### Discussion

*de Hirsch:* I cannot attempt to do justice to the richness of Dr. Ajuriaguerra's paper. It rests on a lifetime of highly original clinical observations, on a whole philosophy of verbal communication. It takes into account neurological, linguistic and affective aspects of children's language and the highly complex dynamic interaction between them.

Dr. Ajuriaguerra points out that children suffering from expressive aphasia are characterized by a generalized and basic difficulty in motor organization which frequently goes hand in hand with spatial, temporal and visuo-motor disturbances. It seems to me that we see in many of these cases more or less subtle forms of ideo-motor apraxia, that is to say, difficulty with conceptualizing the total motor Gestalt (11). Not all of these children's articulatory troubles are related to motor clumsiness, but rather to a more basic difficulty in mobilizing the expressive units of their language.

The children in the second group, who suffer from what Worster-Drought & Allen (60) in the early thirties called "congenital auditory imperception", are described by Dr. Ajuriaguerra primarily in terms of their inability to receive, to respond, and to orient themselves in a world of verbal symbols. I have not, however, found in the European literature a discussion of disturbances in "auding"—disturbances of perception, processing, pattern-making, and retention—as they have been elaborated by the Hardys at Johns Hopkins (17).

We do not make quite as sharp a distinction between decoding and encoding disorders in terms of symptomatology as does Dr. Ajuriaguerra, and we find diffuse and subtle deviations in nonverbal areas in the receptive group nearly as frequently as in the expressive one.

My associate, Mrs. Jansky (24), tested twelve children, six suffering from acquired and six from congenital word-deafness, on 14 verbal and 14 nonverbal tasks. She found that all these children deviated significantly from matched controls on a number of nonverbal performances. These deviations were in gross and fine motor coordination, visuo-motor and spatial organization, and auditory and visual figure-ground discrimination, which I feel to be of great significance in terms of aphasic children's difficulties (12). The children investigated also differed from normals on behavioral categories, such as perseveration, impulsiveness, distractibility and rigidity. Clinically striking was their disorientation, not only in space and time but also in defining themselves and their relationship to people, perhaps because the messages they received, both nonverbal and verbal, were often severely distorted. We were also impressed with these children's degree of disorganization, which can be observed on many levels of integration: motor, perceptual and behavioral. We feel, with Bender (6), that children in both the expressive and receptive groups show marked fluidity and plasticity. Their perceptual experiences are so diffuse and unstable that any slight change in configuration can throw them off. Words, whether spoken or printed, never become familiar, never acquire a physiognomy, as it were. All of this makes learning of any kind a precarious undertaking. However, their difficulty with response to and production of sharply delineated perceptual-motor Gestalten showed not only in the verbal but often also in the nonverbal area.

The group of dysphasics studied by Dr. Ajuriaguerra and his coworkers in Geneva is of particular interest to us. The attempt to correlate these children's verbal organization with personality attitudes and the division between what he calls "taciturns" and "chatterers" make fascinating reading, though I am far from understanding the implications. Nor am I qualified to discuss the way the "chatterers" approach Dr. Jakobson's "metonomique" pole (23). An important aspect of the Geneva findings are the rhythmic disturbances in their group, which resemble those we find in dyslexic children. Except for Wootton Masland's study (58), the prosodic and melodic aspects of dysphasic disorders unfortunately have been neglected in this country, at least as far as children's language disabilities are concerned.

Dr. Ajuriaguerra's remarks concerning the syntactical difficulties of dysphasic youngsters are important. The normal child uses correct grammatical forms long before he understands the logical operations which they represent; by a process of analysis, he slowly arrives at an insight into the grammatical structure of his language. The dysphasic child finds it difficult to integrate grammatical rules since he has problems in abstracting the underlying linguistic relationships (45).

Like Dr. Ajuriaguerra, we have found tremendous variability in the level of communicative effectiveness in the cases we have followed over several years. Some of the children have made little progress, although I am convinced that one of them, at least, is very bright, and her gestures seem to reveal a relatively differentiated level of inner language. The communicative tools of some others are crude, sentence development remains primitive and they continue to have severe difficulties with differentiation and integration. A few are doing surprisingly well. The trouble is, we do not know what accounts for the differences in outcome, although it seems to us that the timing of the original insult is at least one factor. The younger the organism, the more plastic it is and the more available are other pathways.

Much of what Dr. Ajuriaguerra says about dysphasics' performance on the WISC, their deficits on subtests like vocabulary, arithmetic, similarities, as well as their severe difficulties with spatial organization, has been confirmed by observations in this country. To my knowledge, relatively little work has been done here with the Piaget and Inhelder tests (19, 20), and it would be most desirable to learn more about them. What we need are not quantitative evaluations of these childrens' performance, but insight into the way they arrive at their solutions, ways which are probably entirely their own. Only through careful qualitative and step-by-step analysis of their performance will we learn more about the underlying condition.

The time is too short to discuss Dr. Ajuriaguerra's exposition of the relationship between thought and speech. In this he sides with Piaget (40, 41) as against Luria (30). To his quote from Vygotsky (57), "The structure of language does not simply mirror the structure of thought . . . it does not merely find expression in speech; it finds in it its reality and form," I should like to add another quote from the same chapter: "The relationship of thought to word is not a thing but is a process. . . . In that process the relation of thought to word undergoes changes which themselves may be regarded as development in the functional sense." And Vygotsky heads his chapter on thought and language with a verse by Mandelstam: "I have forgotten the word I intended to say, and my thought, unembodied, returns to the realm of shadows."

The idea of studying interpersonal aspects of language by way of the communicative patterns of twins, as used lately by Day (10), is an ingenious one. I, myself, remember working with five-year-old twins who had an entirely idiosyncratic language of their own, an abbreviated code, much of it nonverbal, which served their purposes very well indeed. These twins, children of two physicians from quite discrepant backgrounds, grew up on the grounds of a mental hospital; they were even more resistant than are other twins to entering into communication with a world that was very weird indeed.

Freud (15) says that in schizophrenia the word loses its function of representing the concrete world; the word is no longer a means but becomes an end in itself. Schilder (44) points out that in schizophrenic individuals the signal is identified with the referent; thus, words acquire magic power.

We emphatically agree with Dr. Ajuriaguerra when he points out that developmental language disorders are rarely, if ever, related to a single causative factor. In children, moreover, communicative difficulties result in new forms of adaptation which in turn modify the original state of the organism. Elaborating on his comments, I would say: there is the young organism with its constitutional strengths and weaknesses, including its linguistic endowment; there is the adjustment the organism makes to its original deficit or trauma—in analytical terms, the defensive system it develops in response to the original situation; there is finally the emotional and environmental climate in which it makes its adaptation and which in turn changes its response to its deficit. All developmental language disorders have to be viewed in the framework of all three.

It was a fortunate idea of Dr. Ajuriaguerra to take stuttering as an example of the interaction between specific and interpersonal aspects in language disturbances. My interpretation of the stuttering syndrome is closer to his than to that of my American colleagues, and I would like to say a few words about it. Stuttering, in my opinion, (and in Wyatt's, 61) starts between the age of two and four, when the young child passes from a more primitive to a more highly integrated stage of linguistic organization. He struggles with the syntactical complexities of his language at a time in his life when his neurophysiological development lags behind his intellectual and emotional need to express himself on a relatively differentiated level. Moreover, as often as not, he is at that time being separated from his mother or a new sibling is threatening his place in the family. It is at this point when two crises, the neurophysiological-linguistic and the emotional, coincide, that stuttering first becomes apparent. A similar emotional crisis a year later, when the child has integrated the new linguistic forms, will not result in stuttering, although once stuttering has become a part of the child's adaptive pattern and has been integrated into the ego's defensive system, it is usually self-perpetuating. Thus the stuttering symptom is an excellent demonstration of Dr. Ajuriaguerra's thesis of the intricate relationship between neurophysiological, linguistic, and affective aspects of developmental language disorders.

*Sheehan:* I would like to make some comments on the problem of stuttering. I found Dr. Ajuriaguerra's paper very intriguing, and most American speech pathologists working with stuttering both in the clinical setting and in research would agree with the bulk of his statements. That is, he emphasized social and interpersonal factors; moreover, he appeared to suggest that what we call stuttering may be a term that covers a whole group of disorders, and that it is not necessary to assume that all cases of stuttering have a common origin. He also observed that stuttering begins in childhood, and that there is a predominance of males over females who stutter. Both of these statements apply to stuttering in every culture in which it has been observed, and that includes about all cultures throughout the world, even the North American Indians.

Dr. Ajuriaguerra also referred to the role of feedback in relation to stut-

tering. I would like to mention what is to me a very interesting set of circumstances. Work by Shane (46), by Cherry & Sayers (8) and by Johnson
(25) has shown that if a stutterer reading aloud is subjected to a masking
noise, he becomes quite fluent. He loses auditory feedback from his own
speech process, though proprioceptor feedback may still be available to
him. Moreover, he usually is no longer communicating; the social communication context mentioned by Dr. Ajuriaguerra is missing, and possibly the
removal of this social context accounts for his fluency. On the other hand, a
kind of stuttering in the speech of normal speakers can be produced by
subjecting them to delayed auditory feedback.

I think these facts together are rather intriguing: by changing the monitoring situation, by changing what is fed in through the ears, fluency in
stutterers and something that at least simulates stuttering in normal speakers (48) can be produced.

*Hardy:* One comment on that: if the feedback delay increment is about
two and one-half times the amount required for normal interference, another time pattern is superimposed. This method works just as smoothly,
that is, the stutterer will shorten his phrases within the lag and stop and
listen, and he can keep going this way for half an hour.

*Hirsh:* Would you want to add disruption in the feedback loop to the list
of causes for stuttering?

*Sheehan:* I am not sure that it is an originating cause, though something
of the kind appears to be a mediatory process. Since the experience of stuttering is unpleasant, the stutterer tends to repress the experience, to cut off
the feedback which would normally be available. Many stutterers do not
know what they are doing, clinically. A stutterer can be placed in front of a
mirror, and he will be amazed at what he is doing. It is also fascinating to
observe that a stutterer talking before a mirror, with a group around him,
will speak much, much more fluently. There seems to be a heightening of
visual feedback, with a concurrent self-corrective or control mechanism operating. The effect on stuttering of increased visual feedback, as well as of
altered auditory feedback, is certainly promising for future investigation.

*Wepman:* Before we become too involved, I would like to mention that
we tried an experiment with auditory feedback on aphasics, in which
what they heard was masked either directly or by very delayed auditory
feedback. It did not in the least improve their ability to talk.

*Geschwind:* It has been claimed that left-handers predominate among
stutterers; is that a fact? As I understand it, only seven or eight per cent of
the population of stutterers are left-handed.

*Sheehan:* I would expect the figures to be about the same for stutterers
as for the general population. There is really not much of a correlation between left-handedness and stuttering. What is reported in the literature
seems to be artifacts, i.e., the earlier studies report a relationship, while the
better controlled, more recent studies report none.

*Ajuriaguerra:* We have studied children grouped as normals, dyslexics, and stutterers; a clear right dominance was found in 18 per cent of the normals, but only in 10 per cent of the dyslexics and in 9 per cent of the stutterers.

*Sheehan:* I believe some American speech pathologists would be inclined to question that stuttering may originate through disturbances in the dominant hemisphere. The cerebral dominance theory is one of the early formulations on the etiology of stuttering. Since speech musculature is paired, it was held that stuttering probably resulted from a failure of a unilateral dominant gradient to regulate the timing and synergy of impulses coming to the paired speech musculature from opposite hemispheres. As Van Riper (55) expressed it, if one masseter received a volley of impulses somewhat before the other, the person trying to speak a word would be like a man trying to lift a loaded wheelbarrow by one handle. The interference with cerebral dominance was thought by Travis (54) and Orton (38) to result from competition between cortical impulses, or perhaps between cortical and thalamic levels. After early promise and many spurious positive results, this admirably testable theory was found wanting. The research related to the theory has proven so sterile that what was once a river of effort has dwindled to a trickle. Today the cerebral dominance theory of stuttering is largely unsupported in research literature, and as far as American speech pathologists are concerned, it is a discarded theory. Although some relationship between handedness and speech is fairly well established from studies on aphasia, the relationship between handedness and stuttering is itself open to question. The better and more recent research on that question has followed the course research sometimes follows, that is, the better controlled the study, the less likelihood of a positive result.

*Osgood:* Which implies there is no phenomenon to be measured.

*Sheehan:* Yes, it implies that. The literature on stuttering is full of assertions about lack of cerebral dominance in stutterers and of the presence of neurotic tendencies to stutter. The available evidence seems to suggest that stutterers are people who have learned a particular behavior pattern. They do not seem to differ in their case histories with reference to brain damage or to personality patterns. There is very little support for neurotic interpretations of stuttering; there is a great deal of support for stuttering as a learned process (25, 47, 48, 50, 55).

Whether what we classify as stuttering is really a single disorder, or whether this term covers an entire group of disorders is still an open question (51). Research is needed on possible subtypes, either psychological or physiological, within the stuttering group (49, 51). Stutterers are individuals who show wide variations in almost any measurement to which they are subjected. For example, on the basis of case history and other personality assessment measures such as Rorschach, TAT, MMPI, stutterers do not follow a common pattern but range over every category of clinical nosology, save possibly that of the sociopathic personality. Some stutterers are normal–clinically normal–and well-adjusted to an astonishing degree. Some are hysteric, some compulsive, some brilliant, some mentally deficient, some psychotic, some failures, and some outstanding successes in business or professional fields. As a conflict, stuttering appears to be quite role-specific, in that the differences, such as they are, revolve around the speaker role and the listener relationship.

In a real sense, a stutterer is a stutterer only when he speaks; the ancient joke, "Do you stutter?–Only when I speak" has some basic truth to it. In stuttering there is a highly specific conditioning to the self in the speaker role. Stuttering is a self-role conflict\* (52).

*Wepman:* That joke has another version: "Only when I speak to him." When the stutterer speaks to himself, he does not stutter.

*Sheehan:* That is right; the speaker-listener relationship is highly important. But the stutterer tends to stutter most when speaking as himself; his difficulty is related to his feelings about himself. When he takes on a role as another person, he may not stutter. Some stutterers can take part in plays, speaking fluently in the role of someone else, though they still stutter in everyday life when speaking as themselves.

*Roberts:* I certainly agree that there is a multiplicity of causes for stuttering. On the other hand, the causes are often found in relation to definite brain injuries. Relief from stuttering can be seen, for example, in epileptic patients following removal of specific cortical areas; this results in marked improvement in speech in a year's time, with complete disappearance of stuttering.

*Geschwind:* All the developmental disturbances of language, whether they are low-level like stuttering or high-level like the childhood dyslexias, are much more prevalent in boys than in girls. A four-to-one boy-to-girl ratio has been found wherever the matter has been studied. I suspect that most of this male predominance is related to factors neither cultural nor learned. I must hasten to add that I strongly believe that the stutterer can learn to control his stuttering; the fact that one can learn to eliminate stuttering does not prove that it was originally a learned phenomenon.

*Ajuriaguerra:* The theme running through these comments is that one cannot find a uniform explanation for stuttering. In this connection, three points have been mentioned: first, that there is a variety of conditions under which stuttering can be shown not to occur; these include the feedback examples given by Dr. Sheehan and such activities as singing and story-telling when the story is well known. Second, the predominance of stuttering found in boys over girls may be ascribed to maturational problems or to the boys' higher aggresivity; I doubt any theory will cover all the kinds of cases found. Finally, stuttering does have a tendency to appear

---

\* Sheehan, J. G., *Stuttering Treated as a Conflict of Role.* Paper read at the American Speech and Hearing Association meeting, New York City, 1958.

at around five years of age, when speech is being established; even this does not help us find a uniform explanation. No matter what the cause, whether emotional or connected with retardation of speech or with cerebral dominance, stuttering can assume a completely autonomous function. Even when there is an emotional basis, stuttering becomes so autonomous that psychotherapy may not be an effective remedy.

*Von Leden:* Dr. Ajuriaguerra made the statement that there are no preformed centers for language processes. He indicated that the centers came to life during the process of speaking. I wonder whether he has any definite information on which he bases that statement. Is this not somewhat like saying a car develops an engine or motor while it is running? While it seems unquestionable that the peripheral and the central centers develop together, I would be very anxious to hear what scientific information Dr. Ajuriaguerra has to indicate that no specific center is present in the infant.

*Osgood:* And if there were no specific centers, one would expect that the loci of lesions that produce aphasic defects would be broader and less specific in children than in adults. Is this correct? Does it make much difference where the lesion is located?

*Geschwind:* If there are no preformed centers, it is hard to see how every child eventually develops his centers in the same place. I think that the centers must be preformed in at least some way. There is, however, a hierarchy of preformation. Thus, if the centers in the left hemisphere are destroyed in childhood, there is something in the right hemisphere, also preformed but previously kept from acting, which can then take over.

*Ajuriaguerra:* We did not mean preformed centers in the brain but rather centers that are innately structured. It is agreed that the brain is organized at birth in such a way that these centers will be formed by developing speech function; these centers will be formed in the same place in the brains of a variety of different individuals, but the organization that results from speech function development may take place in one or another hemisphere. The true aphasia that results from brain damage in the child almost always involves a bilateral lesion.

*Osgood:* I wonder about what we observe in the very young child as language disturbance; to what extent is it a function of a very broad set of capabilities—perception, audition, discrimination, motor control—involving therefore little of a detailed linguistic nature? Thus a wide variety of causes might produce disturbances which would be called aphasic in studying a young child. To what extent are we dealing with a problem of locus or of a definition of aphasia?

## REFERENCES

1. AJURIAGUERRA, J. DE, BOREL MAISONNY, S., DIATKINE, R., NARLIAN, S., and STAMBAK, M., Le groupe des audimutités. *Psychiat. Enfant*, 1958, 1: 7-62.

2. AJURIAGUERRA, J. DE, DIATKINE, R., DE GOBINEAU, H., NARLIAN, S., and STAM-
   BAK, M., Le bégaiement. Trouble de la réalisation du langage dans le
   cadre d'une pathologie de la relation. *Presse Méd.*, 1958, **66**: 953-956;
   1037-1040.

3. AJURIAGUERRA, J. DE, DIATKINE, R., and KALMANSON, D., Les troubles du
   développement du langage au cours des états psychotiques précoces.
   *Psychiat. Enfant*, 1959, **2**: 1-65.

4. AJURIAGUERRA, J. DE, GUIGNARD, F., JAEGGI, A., KOCHER, F., MAQUARD, M.,
   PAUNIER, A., QUINODOZ, D., and SIOTIS, E., Organisation psychologique
   et troubles du développement du langage. Étude d'un groupe d'enfants
   dysphasiques. In: *Problèmes de Psycho-Linguistique* (J. de Ajuriaguerra,
   F. Bresson et al., Eds.). Presses Univ. de France, Paris, 1963: 109-142.

5. AJURIAGUERRA, J. DE, GUIGNARD, F., JAEGGI, A., KOCHER, F., MAQUARD, M.,
   ROTH, S., and SIOTIS, E., *L'Evolution de l'Organisation Psychologique
   chez les Enfants Dysphasiques*. (In press)

6. BENDER, L., The concept of plasticity from a neurological and psychiatric
   point of view. *Am. J. Orthopsychiat.*, 1963, **33**: 305.

7. BENVENISTE, E., Remarques sur la fonction du langage dans la découverte
   Freudienne. *Psychanalyse*, 1956, **1**: 3-16.

8. CHERRY, C., and SAYERS, B. M., Experiments upon the total inhibition of
   stammering by external control, and some clinical results. *J. Psychosom.
   Res.*, 1956, **1**: 233-246.

9. CLARK, M. M., *Left-Handedness. Laterality Characteristics and Their Educational Implications* (Publ. Scottish Council Res. Educ., Vol. 39). Univ.
   of London Press, London, 1957.

10. DAY, E. J., The development of language in twins. I. A comparison of twins
    and single children. *Child Dev.*, 1932, **3**: 179-199.

11. DE HIRSCH, K., Gestalt psychology as applied to language disturbances. *J.
    Nerv. Ment. Dis.*, 1954, **120**: 257-261.

12. ———, Tests designed to discover potential reading difficulties at the six-year-
    old level. *Am. J. Orthopsychiat.*, 1957, **27**: 566-576.

13. DE SAUSSURE, F., *Course in General Linguistics* (W. Baskin, Transl.). Philo-
    sophical Library, New York, 1959.

14. FREUD, A., and BURLINGHAM, D., *Infants Without Families*. International
    Univ. Press, New York, 1944.

15. FREUD, S., A metapsychological supplement to the theory of dreams. In:
    *The Standard Edition of the Complete Works of Sigmund Freud*, Vol.
    14 (J. Strachey, Ed.). Hogarth, London, 1953: 222-235.

16. GUTTMANN, E., Aphasia in children. *Brain*, 1942, **65**: 205-219.

17. HARDY, W. G., Dyslexia in relation to diagnostic methodology in hearing and
    speech disorders. In: *Reading Disability: Progress and Research Needs
    in Dyslexia* (J. Money, Ed.). Johns Hopkins Press, Baltimore, 1962:
    171-177.

18. HÉCAEN, H., and AJURIAGUERRA, J. DE, *Les Gauchers. Prévalence Manuelle et
    Dominance Cérébrale*. Presses Univ. de France, Paris, 1963.

19. INHELDER, B., Les opérations de classification dans la formation des concepts.
    In: *Proceedings of the Sixteenth International Congress on Psychology*.
    Acta Psychologica, Amsterdam, 1961 (Vol. 19): 656-663.

20. INHELDER, B., Contribution des études génétiques à l'examen des fonctions intellectuelles des enfants présentant des troubles du language. In: *European Congress on Infantile Paedopsychiatry*. Rome, 1963 (in press).

21. INHELDER, B., and PIAGET, J., *La Genése des Structures Logiques Élémentaires*. Delachaux & Niestlé, Paris, 1959.

22. JAKOBSON, R., *Essais de Linguistique Générale*. Editions de Minuit, Paris, 1963.

23. JAKOBSON, R., and HALLE, M., *Fundamentals of Language*. Mouton, The Hague, 1956.

24. JANSKY, J., *Congenitally Word-Deaf Children*. Thesis, City College of New York, 1960.

25. JOHNSON, W., *The Onset of Stuttering; Research Findings and Implications*. Univ. of Minnesota Press, Minneapolis, 1959.

26. LACAN, J., Fonction et champ de la parole et du langage en psychanalyse. *Psychanalyse*, 1956, **7**: 81-166.

27. LEFÈVRE, A. B., Contribuição para o estudo da psicopatologia da afasia em crianças. *Arq. Neuro-Psiquiat.*, 1950, **8**: 345-393.

28. LURIA, A. R., Brain disorders and language analysis. *Lang. Speech*, 1958, **1**: 14-34.

29. ———, *The Role of Speech in the Regulation of Normal and Abnormal Behavior* (J. Tizard, Ed.). Pergamon, New York, 1961.

30. LURIA, A. R., and YUDOVICH, F. I., *Speech and the Development of Mental Processes in the Child* (O. Kovasc and J. Simon, Transl.; J. Simon, Ed.). Staples, London, 1959.

31. MALMBERG, B., Opposition et identité. *J. Franç. Oto. Rhi. Laryngol.*, 1959, **1**: 65-83.

32. MARIE, P., Existe-t-il chez l'homme des centres préformés ou innés du langage? In: *Travaux et Mémoires*, Masson, Paris, 1926: 115-140.

33. MATTHEWS, J., Speech problems of the mentally retarded. In: *Handbook of Speech Pathology* (L. E. Travis, Ed.). Appleton-Century-Crofts, New York, 1957: 531-551.

34. MERLEAU-PONTY, M., *Signes*. Gallimard, Paris, 1960.

35. MILLER, W., and ERVIN, S., The development of grammar in child language. *Monog. Soc. Res. Child Dev.*, 1964, **29**: 9-34.

36. OLÉRON, P., Le rôle du langage dans le développement mental; contribution tirée de la psychologie de l'enfant sourd-muet. *Enfance*, 1952, **5**: 120-137.

37. ———, *Recherches sur le Développement Mental des Sourds-Muets*. Centre National de la Recherche Scientifique, Paris, 1957.

38. ORTON, S. T., and TRAVIS, L. E., Studies in stuttering. IV. Studies of action currents in stutterers. *Arch. Neurol. Psychiat.*, 1929, **21**: 61-68.

39. PENFIELD, W., and ROBERTS, L., *Speech and Brain-Mechanisms*. Princeton Univ. Press, Princeton, 1959.

40. PIAGET, J., *The Language and Thought of the Child* (3rd ed.). Humanities Press, New York, 1959.

41. ———, Le langage et les opérations intellectuelles. In: *Problèmes de Psycho-Linguistique* (J. de Ajuriaguerra, F. Bresson et al., Eds.). Presses Univ. de France, Paris, 1963: 51-72.

42. PICHON, E., *Le Développement Psychique de l'Enfant et de l'Adolescent*. Masson, Paris, 1936.

43. ROSTAND, F., *Grammaire et Affectivité*. Vrin, Paris, 1951.

44. SCHILDER, P., *Mind: Perception and Thought in Their Constructive Aspects*. Columbia Univ. Press, New York, 1942.

45. ———, Congenital alexia and its relation to optic perception. *J. Genet. Psychol.*, 1944, **65**: 67-88.

46. SHANE, M. L. S., Effect on stuttering of alteration in auditory feedback. In: *Stuttering in Children and Adults* (W. Johnson, Ed.). Univ. of Minnesota Press, Minneapolis, 1955: 286-297.

47. SHEEHAN, J. G., The modification of stuttering through non-reinforcement. *J. Abnorm. Soc. Psychol.*, 1951, **46**: 51-63.

48. ———, Conflict theory of stuttering. In: *Stuttering: a Symposium* (J. Eisenson, Ed.). Harper, New York, 1958: 121-166.

49. ———, Projective studies of stuttering. *J. Speech Hear. Dis.*, 1958, **23**: 18-25.

50. ———, Theory and treatment of stuttering as an approach-avoidance conflict. In: *Psychopathology; a Source Book* (C. F. Reed, I. E. Alexander and S. S. Tomkins, Eds.). Harvard Univ. Press, Cambridge, 1958: 303-325.

51. ———, *Research Frontiers in Stuttering*. Purdue Speech Clinic, January 1961: 1-15 (private circulation).

52. ——— (Ed.), *Stuttering and its Treatment*. Harper & Row, New York (in press).

53. SPITZ, R. A., Hospitalism; an inquiry into the genesis of psychiatric conditions in early childhood. *Psychoan. Study Child*, 1945, **1**: 53-74.

54. TRAVIS, L. E. (Ed.), *Handbook of Speech Pathology*. Appleton-Century-Crofts, New York, 1957.

55. VAN RIPER, C., *Speech Correction; Principles and Methods*. Prentice-Hall, New York, 1939.

56. VINCENT, M., Sur le rôle du langage à un niveau élémentaire de pensée abstraite. *Enfance*, 1957, **4**: 443-464.

57. VYGOTSKY, L. S., *Thought and Language* (E. Hanfmann and G. Vakar, Eds. and Transl.). M.I.T. Press, Cambridge, 1962.

58. WOOTTON MASLAND, M., Some aberrations of language function in children. In: *Seventh International Congress of Neurology* (Abstracts of Papers Presented). Exc. Med. Found., Amsterdam, 1961: 49-50.

59. WORSTER-DROUGHT, C., Congenital auditory imperception (congenital word-deafness) and its relation to idioglossia and allied defects. *Med. Press*, 1943, **210**: 411-417.

60. WORSTER-DROUGHT, C., and ALLEN, E. M., Congenital auditory imperception (congenital word-deafness): with report of a case. *J. Neurol. Psychopath.*, 1929, **9**: 193-208.

61. WYATT, G. L., and HERZAN, H. M., Therapy with stuttering children and their mothers. *Am. J. Orthopsychiat.*, 1962, **32**: 645-659.

# STUDIES IN APHASIA: A PSYCHOLINGUISTIC METHOD AND CASE STUDY*†

JOSEPH M. WEPMAN   and   LYLE V. JONES
University of Chicago       University of North Carolina
Chicago                    Chapel Hill

I have spoken many times about aphasia and its many phases. At this session I want to limit my remarks to a psycholinguistic method or, rather, to various methods that lead to a psycholinguistic evaluation of aphasic speech.

Had it not been for the fact that a great majority, I am afraid, of our patients did not succeed in completely overcoming their problems, we probably would not have sought other ways of understanding them than the methods we had during World War II. But we had so many failures, so many patients who did not improve, and neurological diagnostic terminology did not explain why. The essential factor was that we could not use profitably the kind of analysis of language disabilities which back in those days we had as our inheritance from neurology. Thus it became necessary to search for other ways to study the problems of our patients, to see if we could devise better means for understanding their language difficulties.

When I say "we", I mean the team developed at the University of Chicago, which has now been expanded to the University of North Carolina. Dr. Lyle Jones, now head of the Psychometric Laboratory at North Carolina, and I started to work on psycholinguistic evaluations of aphasia some ten years ago (21). We are still engaged in it together.

Some years ago we used to speak of the brain as a black box, borrowing the term from McCulloch. I think that it is an improper term today. In the time that has gone by, the box has become translucent rather than black. We can draw a better analogy perhaps from our present knowledge of the moon: we know something of its face, we can even describe parts of it, but its greater part is on the dark side, so we know very little about it. Sometimes we talk about aphasia in meetings like this as if we understood it completely. And at other times, at least in private conversations, we are inclined to talk as if we did not understand it at all. I think probably some-

---
* Studies partially supported by grants MH-01876 and M-10006 of the National Institute of Mental Health, Department of Health, Education and Welfare.
† Presented at the Conference by Dr. Wepman.

where between the two lies the state of our knowledge. We have seen many patients with many problems. We have talked about a number of language disorders, some of which I believe are aphasic and others which are not. We subtend a great deal under the name and under the term "aphasia"; there is even an Academy of Aphasia. But only a few years ago did we begin to explore the possibility of a loss of linguistic processes as a result of impairment.

The clinical evaluation of language impairment in adult aphasia has been until recently almost exclusively an assessment of stimulus-response behavior based on a pass/fail scoring of individual items. A patient's ability to speak, read, write or spell in response to given specific stimuli which differed in both type and degree of difficulty provided a protocol reflecting the language deficit. Such methods were used by Head (10), Weisenburg & McBride (20), Eisenson (2), Halstead & Wepman (9), and Schuell (18), among others. More recently, interest has developed in evaluating the underlying processes of the language deficits. The work of Goodglass & Berko (7) and Goodglass & Mayer (8) are illustrations of research into grammatical language disturbances in certain types of aphasia, while Geschwind (5) has reported extensively on many underlying temporal and linguistic features of aphasic speech. Interest in the linguistic processes was emphasized in the work of Jakobson (13) and Luria (16), and we have stressed it in our research for the past several years (3, 15, 21, 22). It is now almost as commonplace to read of aphasia as a psycholinguistic disorder as a neurological one.

### Psycholinguistic Methods

Our interest in psycholinguistic analysis of aphasic language was stimulated by some of the early experimentation in the standardization of items for the Language Modalities Test for Aphasia (22). Here it was noted that a useful distinction could be made between responses to visual and auditory stimuli, that a tremendous amount of information was obscured by the pass/fail dichotomy, and that often a real difference appeared in many patients between their ability to respond to specific stimuli and their ability to communicate in a relatively unstructured situation. This led not only to a consideration of a differential, psycholinguistically based scoring of responses to specific items, but also to an evaluation of the free speech of patients according to their vocabulary and ability to use it.

The Language Modalities Test for Aphasia (22) in its final form took both methods into account. Instead of a pass/fail method of scoring in the analysis of specific responses to given visual and auditory stimuli, a scale of errors was derived which provided a psycholinguistic evaluation of each response. Differential scoring of items was related to the modalities of input, and items were provided for an evaluation of free speech.

Several factor analyses and analyses of variance were made of the

TABLE 6

LANGUAGE MODALITIES TEST FOR APHASIA SCORING SUMMARY

| | Visual Stimuli | | | | | | | | | | | | Auditory Stimuli | | | | | | | | | | | |
|---|---|---|---|---|---|---|---|---|---|---|---|---|---|---|---|---|---|---|---|---|---|---|---|---|
| | Oral responses | | | | | | Graphic responses | | | | | | Oral responses | | | | | | Graphic responses | | | | | |
| Scale value (s.v.)* | 1 | 2 | 3 | 4 | 5 | 6 | 1 | 2 | 3 | 4 | 5 | 6 | 1 | 2 | 3 | 4 | 5 | 6 | 1 | 2 | 3 | 4 | 5 | 6 |
| Stimulus type | | | | | | | | | | | | | | | | | | | | | | | | |
| Pictures | | | | 3 | 1 | 2 | | | 2 | 3 | 1 | | | | | | | | | | | | | |
| Words | 3 | | | 3 | | | | | | | | | 3 | | | | 1 | 2 | 2 | 1 | | 3 | | |
| Numbers | 4 | | | 2 | | | | | | | | | 1 | | | 4 | | 1 | | | | | | |
| Sentences | 1 | | 2 | 3 | | | | | | | | | 2 | | | 1 | 3 | | | | | | | |

* Scoring categories (s.v.) for all oral and graphic responses:
  1: correct response
  2: phonemic or orthographic response
  3: syntactic errors
  4: semantic errors
  5: jargon or illegible
  6: no response

specific response scores of over 150 subjects. Before doing these analyses, a method had to be developed for quantifying the observed qualitative differences. A spoken word response, for example, might be wrong in a variety of ways: the response might, 2, differ from the correct word only because of inadequate articulation; 3, be the correct word response except for tense, gender or other syntactic form; 4, be a totally different word; 5, be unintelligible jargon; 6, be no response at all; and 1, of course, be right! To quantify such differences, a scaling method devised by R. A. Fisher (4) was adapted, so that each qualitative response category was assigned a number to represent the extent of error (1); the scale developed has been described elsewhere in detail (23). The six categories found useful (Nos. 1-6 above) characterized each response in psycholinguistic terms.

Table 6 shows the scoring of a patient by means of the six-point scale. This differential, scaled scoring method permits an analysis of language impairment in terms of the type of errors most commonly made, taking into account differences between responses to visual and auditory stimuli in written or spoken responses. The protocol depicts the specific language errors of the subject. In the case shown, for example, it is obvious that the subject not only makes many errors but also that in naming pictures he is equally likely to use an incorrect word (scale value 4), lapse into jargon (s.v. 5) or make no response at all (s.v. 6). When words were presented visually, however, at least half the time he substituted another word for the right one (s.v. 4). Numbers were easier for him; he read four correctly (s.v. 1) and misread only two (s.v. 4). In reading sentences he was correct only once (s.v. 1), twice made syntactic errors (s.v. 3), and three times used incorrect words (s.v. 4). On the other hand, in response to auditory stimuli, he gave many more correct responses (the task is simply one of repetition), otherwise he lapsed into jargon, or gave no response. Only to number stimuli did he repeat the wrong number more often than the right one. He showed a similar distribution of responses in writing; when asked to write the names of pictures, he often misnamed and wrote illegibly. He retained some skill in writing words, for most errors were incorrect substitutions.

It became apparent in reviewing literally hundreds of such protocols that a useful differentiation of aphasic patients might be made on this psycholinguistic scale. Furthermore, through the determination of the major types of errors, therapy for a patient could be directed at his peculiar linguistic problem.

While experimenting with methods of evaluating the responses to specific stimuli along the two major input modalities, it became evident that some patients were talking better in free speech than in direct response to the stimuli. This led to the addition of pictures about various subjects to the test. The patient was asked to respond by telling a story about a picture. Protocols of subjects showed some marked differences in linguistic ability. For example, one of the pictures shows a poker game in progress, and the free speech responses of different patients illustrate the differences in their relatively spontaneous speech:

Subject #207:

> "Well, I would say . . . ah . . . prak . . . ah . . . parkenkawr . . . dray men are spey. They are the ticks and the, ticks . . . five tars . . . in that what I'm wrong."

Subject #208:

> "Ah . . . the wish . . . uh . . . oh . . . the men are . . . uh . . . ins . . . enjoying a new game . . . ah . . . that's . . . I can't tell you that, doggone . . . I can't tell you the name of the doggone thing. It's uh . . . that's ridiculous. See, I never, I never, played that. I never played the . . . that kind of thing . . . ah . . . they were, they were, they were playing with a well . . . they were round things . . . oh wait a minute . . . no . . . I can't they're playing with . . . well, I can't tell you the name of the darn things."

Subject #212:

> "Cards . . . It's a 'cards' . . . four men . . . game . . . money . . . table . . . money and cigarettes . . . everything . . . fun cards. That's all . . . cards money . . . fun."

It is evident from the three responses to the same stimulus that each of the subjects possessed a different degree of capability in linguistic function. Patient #207 used many neologisms, substituting for most of the nominal parts of speech either jargon or neologistic expressions; without knowing the stimulus, the listener or reader is unable to identify the subject matter from the context. Patient #208 illustrates the type of aphasia wherein the syntax of the language is relatively intact but semantic ability is nearly absent, while Patient #212 can use meaningful words, but does not use most of the interstitial syntactic words of the language.

This difference in spontaneous language led us to a more explicit study of the retained and distorted language of those aphasic patients who might be classified as "talking aphasics"—patients who were able to use words but had lost some of the linguistic processes necessary for a full exposition of thought or idea.

To identify the linguistic disturbances in aphasia, the semiotic classification of language proposed by Charles Morris (17) seemed most appropriate. He suggested three basic properties of signs and their relationships to objects, interpreters and each other. These properties he called the "semantical", which is the relation of signs to objects or events; the "syntactical", the relation of signs to signs; and the "pragmatical", the relation of signs to interpreters.

In our psycholinguistic analyses we found disturbances in the ability to use words having the semantical property (semantic aphasia); disturbances in the use of grammar, either in the highly frequent words of syntactic expression or in the inflections of words for syntactic purposes (syntactic aphasia); disturbances in the ability to interpret the relationship between sign and referent, the pragmatical property (pragmatic aphasia).

Semantic aphasia resembles Jackson's (12) propositionalizing disability in part, but is probably much closer to Luria's (16) "loss of the ability to communicate ideas" and to Dr. Jakobson's (13) description of the "similarity" disorder in language usage. Such patients are well described in Dr. Jakobson's recent exposition, in which he pointed out that the repertory of phonemes and words goes on, but morphology appears to be radically subdued by syntax. Their words tend to be limited to the more frequently used words of the language (21). Notably, there is a retention of some grammatical form and function.

In the opposite type of impairment, syntactic aphasia, the ability to nominate, propositionalize, communicate ideas, and decode may well be relatively intact. Grammar, both in use of words for grammatical purpose and in the form of inflectional endings, tense or gender, suffers most radically, as Goodglass and others (7, 8) have pointed out. As Luria (16) suggests, these are often "telegraphic" speakers, dropping from their speech the interstitial matrix of language. Dr. Jakobson (13; personal communication) speaks of the disorder as a loss of the ability to encode or to combine, a contiguity disorder in his terms, where normal word selection is retained.

The third disturbance of a linguistic nature is in what Morris (17) called the pragmatical property, or the relationship of sign to its interpreters. This is a much less widely discussed disability. In many ways patients with this affliction show parts of the classical receptive disorder: they fail to retain a good working relationship between their verbal efforts and the stimuli shown them. While not unlike the semantic aphasic in many ways, their disability seems much more one of controlling their verbal efforts. Luria (16) describes a similar condition in his "breakdown of the regulatory functions of speech connections". In pragmatic aphasia there appears to be a

TABLE 7

COMPARISON OF THE DEVELOPMENT OF LANGUAGE AND THE FIVE APHASIAS

| Stages of Development | Stages of Aphasia |
| --- | --- |
| Speechlessness | Global |
| Babbling—cooing | Jargon |
| Fortuitous speech | Pragmatic |
| Substantive symbols | Semantic |
| Grammar | Syntactic |

disruption of the ability to obtain meaning from a stimulus and use it as a basis for orderly symbol formulation. Many words and frequent neologisms apparently unrelated to the stimulating situation are commonly found. The meaning of an utterance to the listener is typically severely disturbed. Clinically, patients of this type seem to retain all the phonological properties of language; they speak with good intonational patterns and there is a ready flow of words, but with no apparent self-criticism. In reviewing such patients, Dr. Jakobson* pointed out that the loss of delimitation between morphology and syntax favors neology.

These three psycholinguistic types of aphasic impairment, together with two other types not so classified, have an interesting parallel in the five stages of the development of language in children (Table 7). The hypothesis that aphasia might be viewed as a regressive psycholinguistic process phenomenon was considered in our discussion of this parallel categorization of speech development and aphasic types (24).

Viewed in retrospect, it seems that we identified, from clinical observation and from aphasia tests, three specific linguistic processes that could be differentially impaired. For confirmation of these we turned to a more elaborate design for the exploration of the impairment. It is with these methods that the remainder of this paper is concerned.

As I remarked at the beginning, we began research in aphasia in an attempt to answer some questions about patients whose conditions did not improve. Patients in the global category, i.e., without speech, presented the greatest difficulty. We began to explore in therapy the notion of whether one could move a patient progressively from a global aphasic state through jargon aphasia, where only phonemes without meaning were expected of him; then through a pragmatic state where the phonemes become joined into words, even though inappropriate; to the semantic, and finally the syntactic states. This would take the place of the usual and often unsuccessful approach of trying to move the patient from his global disability directly to the semantic state. Usually, it is attempted to make every aphasic a meaningful speaker. We raised the question, which has no answer at the moment, of whether this movement may be too great for a patient with severe

---

* Personal communication, 1963.

damage; perhaps he should move up through each stage. Dr. Lenneberg said earlier that a patient who had lost childhood speech always went through all the recovery stages.

*Lenneberg:* That is not exactly what I said. This course is seen only in very young children, whereas later on we do see aphasic symptoms. There is a difference.

*Wepman:* I accept the correction. It was in very young children who had lost their speech that we observed an upward movement through every stage. At the present time we are trying to find out whether this is true in the adult aphasic. We found by accident that when a patient was at the pragmatic level he did move up through the pragmatic, semantic and syntactic steps. This can be demonstrated more specifically in a particular case study that will be presented after the analytic method has been detailed.

We began to study the process by first categorizing the words of an individual's speech production according to their frequency of occurrence as measured by the Thorndike-Lorge word count (19). We studied the 900 most frequent words of the language in relationship to a particular patient's ability to speak. We found what we thought was an interesting result that in a way reduced the idea of anomia to a frequency notion rather than to a nominal notion. The research set out to analyze the verbatim verbal product of a series of unselected aphasic adults; to assure somewhat standard conditions of stimulation, each patient's response to 20 cards of the Thematic Apperception Test (TAT) was transcribed verbatim, and each word was classified into a part-of-speech category. The speech of one subject could then be contrasted with that of another, as well as with normal unimpaired speech, according to the relative use of the different parts of speech.

The usefulness of such a language analysis was shown in 1956 in a comparison made between a single normal speaker and an aphasic patient (21). At that time a simplified linguistic analysis was used, comparing the frequency of five parts of speech: nouns, verbs, descriptive modifiers, pronouns, and other. Figure 17 shows the comparison that can be made; the purpose of the analysis at the time was to explore the concept of anomia. As shown in the figure, the aphasic subject's speech was not entirely devoid of nouns; those retained, however, tended to occur only among the most frequently used words of the Thorndike-Lorge list. A similar distribution was found in the use of verbs, although with less consistency. Descriptive modifiers (which then included both adjectives and adverbs) showed considerable variance from the normal speaker, high frequency words being used too often, and low frequency words being used too seldom. It was concluded from this analysis that the speech of a so-called anomic patient might well be characterized by the loss of all but the most general (and hence most frequent) words of the language, rather than by a loss of nouns only as the terms implies.

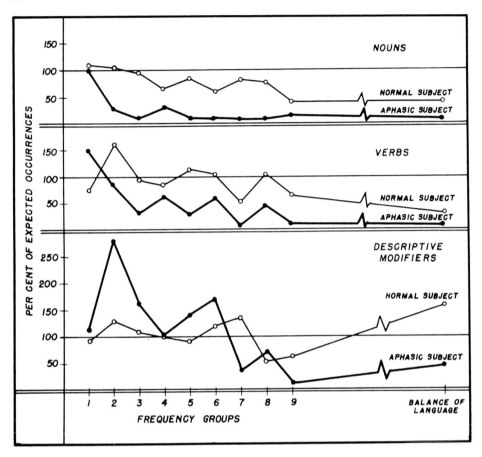

**Figure 17.** Relative frequencies of occurrences of nouns, verbs and modifiers in the speech of normal and aphasic speakers. (From Wepman, Bock, Jones & Van Pelt, 21.)

The method, while considered suitable for this purpose, failed to use a tremendous amount of information by collapsing the modifiers and listing all other parts of speech as a single category. It was this experience that led to the more definitive grammatical analysis of the present study as a necessary next step. Our aim was to develop a more complete method of analyzing basic speech and comparing it with the frequency of use by normal and other aphasic speakers—in the previous study the comparison had been with the Thorndike-Lorge (19) frequency counts of written language.

To provide a base for these comparisons, two essential steps needed to be taken prior to the investigation: first, a classification of parts of speech which could be used with relative reliability in the analysis of spoken language (14); second, the development of a computer program which would permit automated relative frequency analysis of the verbal corpus. The new grammatical system seeks to avoid inconsistency and arbitrariness and to portray in somewhat more refined terms the structures of the English language. It provides an ease of classification not possible with classical English grammar. Thus, the more consistently a given word is included in only one class, the less relative unreliability will appear. This is essential in the analysis of aphasic speech since, as has been shown, context provides few clues for the additional values of meaning or use of the words in question. In most cases such consistency coincides with grammatical criteria. To classify within a single part of speech the various uses of "where", "why", "when", and "how", for example, not only simplifies classification, but also serves to give a more consistent grammatical picture of their function than does the traditional classification system.

Since a major purpose of the system was to provide a base for statistical evaluation of speech, an attempt was made to avoid establishment of classes which would include an insignificant proportion of word occurrences in the speech to be analyzed. Consequently, words with idiosyncratic syntactic behavior were included in the class where they best fit, even if they did not fit there very well, unless they were of high enough frequency to merit a separate class. Fourteen categories were found necessary to describe the part-of-speech usage (14). Below are shown these categories with a brief description of the meaning ascribed to each.

## Part-of-Speech Categories

1. Noun: differs little from conventional classification, except that numerals are listed as quantifiers, and certain "nominal" uses of adjectives are listed in Category 3.

2. Verb: differs little from conventional classification, except that auxiliaries have been classified separately (see Category 9).

3. Adjective: differs from classical usage in that it does not include demonstrative or pronomial possessives, both of which are classified as pronouns; nor does it include numerals or numerical expressions.

4. Adverb: this class, which is the most heterogeneous in classical classification, has been reduced by those adverbs derived from adjectives, which are classed with the latter. Also excluded are all adverbially used prepositions and post-verbal particles, which have been listed separately (Category 8).

5. Pronoun: all personal pronouns in all of their uses, including the possessive, the reflexive, and the demonstrative. A number of words traditionally classed as pronouns have been treated otherwise (see Relative and Quantifier Categories, Nos. 6 and 10).

6. Relative: all forms which may introduce both subordinate and interrogative constructions.

7. Article: includes only "the", "a", and "an".

8. Indefinite: all combinations of "some", "no", "every", or "any", with "one", "body", "thing", "where", or "place", each of which may be followed by "else".

9. Auxiliary: all verbs which may introduce questions, which cannot be preceded by "to" and must be followed by another verbal form in a declarative sentence.

10. Quantifier: all words which may be used independently or as nominal modifiers to indicate number.

11. Prepositions: all prepositions in all their uses, even when not accompanied by a noun phrase or when used as an accompanying particle of a verb. For convenience, the word "to", wherever it may be used, is included.

12. Conjunction: includes words which are traditionally known as coordinate and subordinate conjunctions.

13. Interjection: all interjections; includes "no" except when used as a quantifier, and also "yes".

14. Unclassified: a word is considered unclassifiable if it could belong to more than one of the categories above and the context is insufficient to determine which.

One major problem in this type of classification which needed to be solved before it could be used, was the question of inflected endings. To consider as a distinct word each inflected form would inflate considerably the apparent number of different words appearing in a given transcript. The procedures employed in the present study demand identification of all inflected forms, collapsing them into their uninflected base. Currently, inflectional forms remain differentially coded, so that information regarding form of inflection is retained. Only the base form, however, is considered in developing word counts.

A computer program for the Univac 1105 has recently been completed at the University of North Carolina. It will accept English texts and perform a partial grammatical classification based upon the categories shown in Table 6. Stored within the computer is a dictionary of the 402 words which occur with high frequency in the TAT protocols of normal speakers; these are words which are unambiguous with respect to grammatical class. Evidence from a preliminary analysis of 27 of 56 normal speakers shows that the list of 402 words accounts for an average of more than 83 per cent of word occurrences. (The most frequently appearing 34 words account for some 50 per cent of all word occurrences!) It is proposed to use the computer program for the original grammatical classification of the bulk of words, employing post-editing to handle the remainder. In the original stage of the research, each word of each record was coded manually for part of speech after reducing the words of the text to their base forms.

Currently, then the precedure is: (a) to record the subject's stories to 20 TAT cards, (b) to reduce each inflected form to its base, retaining the inflection itself as a separate record through differential coding, (c) to punch each word on an IBM card (approximately seven words can be punched on a single card), (d) to store the data from the IBM card on a magnetic tape, (e) to feed the tape to the computer to obtain original, dictionary stored classification and the relative frequency of each word, and (f) to classify every word not classified by the computer by dictionary look-up procedures and by referring to the text for context. The computer produces

### VERBS USED 334 TIMES        1207 PER 10,000

|     |             |         |    |       |    |     |        |
|-----|-------------|---------|----|-------|----|-----|--------|
| 1   | ACT         | V USED  | 1  | TIMES | 3  | PER | 10,000 |
| 2   | BECOME      | V USED  | 4  | TIMES | 14 | PER | 10,000 |
| 3   | BET         | V USED  | 1  | TIMES | 3  | PER | 10,000 |
| 4   | COME        | V USED  | 3  | TIMES | 10 | PER | 10,000 |
| 5   | COMFORT     | V USED  | 3  | TIMES | 10 | PER | 10,000 |
| 6   | CONCENTRATE | V USED  | 1  | TIMES | 3  | PER | 10,000 |
| 7   | COVER       | V USED  | 1  | TIMES | 3  | PER | 10,000 |
| 8   | CRY         | V USED  | 3  | TIMES | 10 | PER | 10,000 |
| 9   | DAYDREAM    | V USED  | 3  | TIMES | 10 | PER | 10,000 |
| 10  | DEBATE      | V USED  | 1  | TIMES | 3  | PER | 10,000 |
| 11  | DIE         | V USED  | 1  | TIMES | 3  | PER | 10,000 |
| 12  | DREAM       | V USED  | 4  | TIMES | 14 | PER | 10,000 |
| 13  | DROWN       | V USED  | 1  | TIMES | 3  | PER | 10,000 |
| 14  | FIGHT       | V USED  | 1  | TIMES | 3  | PER | 10,000 |
| 15  | FIGURE      | V USED  | 1  | TIMES | 3  | PER | 10,000 |
| 16  | FIND        | V USED  | 3  | TIMES | 10 | PER | 10,000 |
| 17  | FINISH      | V USED  | 1  | TIMES | 3  | PER | 10,000 |
| 18  | FOLLOW      | V USED  | 1  | TIMES | 3  | PER | 10,000 |
| 19  | GAZE        | V USED  | 1  | TIMES | 3  | PER | 10,000 |
| 20  | GET         | V USED  | 14 | TIMES | 50 | PER | 10,000 |
| 21  | GO          | V USED  | 5  | TIMES | 18 | PER | 10,000 |
| 22  | GOOF        | V USED  | 1  | TIMES | 3  | PER | 10,000 |
| 23  | GOT         | V USED  | 1  | TIMES | 3  | PER | 10,000 |
| 24  | GUESS       | V USED  | 17 | TIMES | 61 | PER | 10,000 |
| 25  | HAPPEN      | V USED  | 2  | TIMES | 7  | PER | 10,000 |
| 26  | HOLD        | V USED  | 1  | TIMES | 3  | PER | 10,000 |
| 27  | HOPE        | V USED  | 1  | TIMES | 3  | PER | 10,000 |
| 28  | IMAGINE     | V USED  | 4  | TIMES | 14 | PER | 10,000 |
| 29  | JUMP        | V USED  | 3  | TIMES | 10 | PER | 10,000 |

Figure 18. Typical computer print-out for TAT protocols, showing relative frequency of each word as a part of speech.

a print-out showing each word listed alphabetically by part of speech and the relative frequency of that word (Figure 18).

At the present time, such print-outs have been completed for all 14 categories for 56 unimpaired speakers. This selected population was stratified in the following ways: by age (groups under-60, 60-70, 70-80, 80-90); by socioeconomic/education levels (groups with less than an eighth-grade education and common labor work record, with a high school education and white-collar work record, and college graduates working in the professions); and by sex. Data from this normal sampling, it is felt, will provide a merged base for a frequency count by part of speech for normal speakers. At the same time, individual records can be compared with any particular pathological subject.

The data are still in the process of being analyzed and are not yet published. Some 38 records of aphasic subjects have also been studied to date.

These results will also be reported in the future both separately and in relation to the normal model.

## A Case Study

Among the aphasic subjects is one whose language has been studied during the process of recovery from aphasia. This case is presented here both as an illustration of the application of the present method of grammatical analysis and as a demonstration of the method when employed on a single subject over a period of time.

The patient had suffered a spontaneous hemorrhage; he was 49 at the time of the first test, which was done three months after the insult. The second test was made a month later.

I will not attempt to give my conception of what TAT Card 2 says. If you are not familiar with it, you will have difficulty figuring out what the subject meant when he said:

> "Well, all I know is somebody is clipping the kreples and some why, someone here on the kureping arm, why I don't know."

We counted the number of times there were word-finding difficulties. Then we presented the same test to him a month later. The next quote shows how he responded to the same card:

> "Well, this is a, is a, woman . . . young girl, and she's got two . . . ah watching a, a man and what looks to be a . . . somebody older, watching they make a, young doing of . . . trying to one on the . . . Jesus, that darn word. On the young . . . I can say it but I can't say it. That these are people use in the . . . I can see it but I can't say it. I don't know why the girl's looking in the other direction, but the . . . are watching the man using the . . . and of course is nice tall and that sort of thing. Well, what else can there be?"

You notice how the semantic difficulty is resolving itself as the patient goes through the stages of recovery.

> "Here's a . . . a girl . . . who . . . who apparently goes to . . . we'll say will go to college or high school, we'll say high school, and um her father or brother are working on the fields, the farmer's field, the farming fields. And ah she is working with this man, this . . . field this horse is plow a field, but the girl isn't interested in working at the fields. She's not interested as much as the other people who may be her sister or her mother . . ."

You will also notice that occasional syntactic defects occur in the speech. The three dots represent pauses; the period represents the transcriber's idea of when a sentence started or was completed.

*de Hirsch:* Do you take the meaning unit?

*Wepman:* The meaning unit would be an acceptable notion if we could figure out the meaning, but when one has "clipping the kreples" it is not always possible. This is the last response, a year after the insult:

> "As I recall it, I was supposed to tell a story about a girl who was watching her father and mother in the fields, and the father is driving the horse,

the plow at the field, and the mother was working her husband while the daughter was going away to school . . . the daughter was feeling a little embarrassed because she was doing nothing physically while his father and mother are in the field."

Notice there still is a syntactic defect: "the father is driving the horse, the plow at the field, and the mother was working her husband", which is something mothers frequently do, but I do not believe he meant it that way. However, it is also quite evident that the patient had recovered considerably over a year's time.

This patient's eight successive TAT protocols, obtained over a 14-month period, were made part of the present research and are shown in graphic form in Figure 19. In the figure, the abscissa represents the percentage of total word production for each of 13 parts of speech. The leftmost part of the graphs presents on the ordinate the eight successive TAT protocols. For comparison, the same categories are shown for two normal controls (subjects #305 and #005) who were matched with the patient for age, sex and socioeconomic status. The right-hand points in each graph give the same data (means) for 27 unselected normal subjects.

In the first graph, note the very wide discrepancy between the first TAT protocol and the following seven in all parts of speech. The tendency for verbs, adjectives and adverbs is to remain relatively constant and surprisingly similar to the verb and adverb percentages of the matched and unmatched normals; while the adjective category eventually becomes equal to the two matched normals, none of the three categories are in keeping

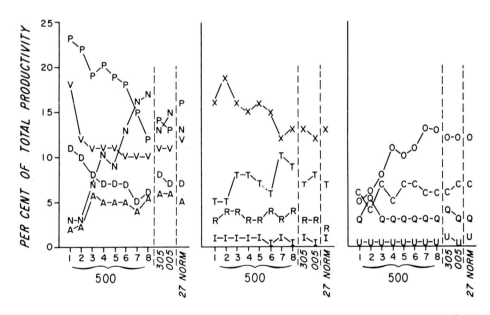

Figure 19. A longitudinal study of eight successive TAT protocols of a single subject compared with two matched normals (Subjects 305 and 005) and the means of 27 unselected normal speakers.

with the unmatched group. The noun and pronoun categories seem to illustrate best of all the patient's changing verbal ability; note the progressively falling curve of the pronouns and the rising curve of the nouns: as the patient recovers, the percentage of pronouns steadily decreases and that of nouns increases just as steadily.

The middle graph in Figure 19 shows how comparatively stable the relatives, articles, indefinites and auxiliaries are. The auxiliaries decline steadily from over-use to a close approximation of the normal speaker's values. Articles vary considerably, going from under-use to slight over-use, while the relative and indefinite categories remain constant and are about as frequent in the aphasic's speech as in that of the controls.

In the rightmost graph, the behavior of the preposition is especially instructive: beginning with marked under-use, there is a steady increase until the patient's frequency of use shows a close approximation to that of both the unselected and the control normals.

This single subject's record has been demonstrated for the purpose of illustrating the method. The change with time provides the examiner with an interesting and useful way of discovering in which of the categories improvement has taken place. He may discover where concentrated therapeutic attention is or is not needed. Both applications seem appropriate for therapeutic ends as well as for insights into language structure.

*Hirsh:* The course of recovery did not seem to retrace the normal steps of language.

*Wepman:* True, or so it seems, except in one factor. The patient was at first unable to make pragmatic use of language; he had many neologisms; at that time, he was using words, but not very meaningful ones. He then shifted to the semantic type of aphasia, where he used many words but not complete sentences; he had difficulty with the substantive parts of language, making occasional syntactic errors. If the normal development follows that pattern, then, in that sense, he did follow it.

*Hirsh:* There is no pattern, for example, between lexical words and functional words. Taking them as dichotomous, one has prepositions increasing and pronouns decreasing in the same period of time; also, nouns go up and verbs descend. I should have thought that in some of the classifications that Dr. Jakobson advanced, one or the other of the general classes would be marked by a general trend in one direction.

*Wepman:* If we had examined this patient at the fifth month instead of at the third month, he would have looked better from that viewpoint; we would have found no change in verbs and a shift in nouns. Nouns and pronouns balance each other. The noun-pronoun ratio, in fact, appears to be a very interesting finding for the aging process, judging from this particular analysis, for we found that it always equals one in every sentence. Wherever there is no noun, there is a pronoun.

We then wanted to explore other ways of presenting the data. Two se-

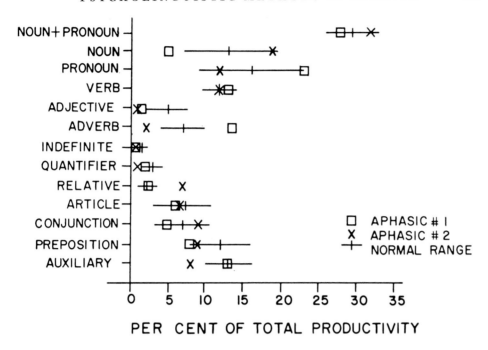

**Figure 20.** Comparison of two aphasic subjects and the mean and variability of 27 normal speakers. The variability of normal subjects is indicated by two standard deviations above and below the mean.

lected subjects have been compared to illustrate different types of aphasia using our psycholinguistic analysis. Figure 20 shows the distribution of parts of speech in 12 categories for the two subjects when compared with the mean response pattern of 27 normal subjects. The two aphasics show a remarkably different distribution in their use of grammatical properties, while at the same time they are remarkably alike in certain categories. The differences lie in their use of nouns, pronouns, adverbs, relatives, conjunctions, and auxiliaries; the similarities appear in such categories as verbs, adjectives, indefinites, quantifiers, articles, and prepositions. Most often both patients were within the normal range, but in notable exceptions they were not. Note the marked under-use of nouns by one subject, while in that category the other subject was at the extreme upper end of the normal distribution. In adjective usage, both subjects fall below the range of the normal population, while in adverbs one is far above and the other far below. In only two other categories were there discrepancies from the normal range. The same subject was well above normal in use of relatives and somewhat below in use of auxiliaries.

The import of such analyses has not yet been fully assessed. That aphasics can be classified by these means, however, seems amply demonstrated; that aphasia is more than a single process disturbance seems equally well shown.

We have reviewed evidence which supports the dichotomy that Dr. Jakobson and others have expressed between the use of common function words and of substantive words. However, certain grammatical categories do not fit the scheme, contrary to what one would expect.

## SUMMARY

Psycholinguistic methods for analysing the verbal output of adult aphasics have been presented. The use of differential linguistic analysis of stimulus-response evaluations and the more elaborate study of the relative frequency of the various parts of speech have been detailed. Both seem to provide more information concerning aphasia than any other method available for the study of impaired language structure.

One of the by-products of the project has been the completion of a computer method of grammatical analysis permitting the study of a fairly large sample of normal speech. This will result in a lexicon for normal language usage in terms of relative frequency of word occurrences in relation to specific but generalized stimuli, the pictures of the Thematic Apperception Test. At present further work is contemplated using the computer dictionary for the analysis of other pathological, language-impaired groups such as adult schizophrenics and children with speech problems. Another study is planned on free speech obtained in the absence of specific stimuli. Finally, it is expected that a complete list of the relative frequency for each word occurrence will be prepared. Linguistic analysis is no longer merely a potential in the investigation of aphasia: it is a reality. It has been shown to be of value both as a clinical tool and as a means of studying the normal language structure.

### Discussion

*Geschwind:* Dr. Jakobson strongly criticized the usefulness of certain studies of aphasia which incorporated quantitative approaches. I think it should be obvious that the work summarized by Dr. Wepman deserves no such criticism and, indeed, represents an important advance. The paper on anomia by Wepman, Bock, Jones & Van Pelt (21) was, in fact, the pioneer work in the study of quantitative approaches to aphasia, and its importance extends beyond the new ground it opened.

First I should like to present a little glossary which may be of use to some of you. It is very striking that nearly all serious students of aphasia have come up with certain broad classifications which, despite differences in nomenclature, are clearly consonant. I do not mean to suggest that major contributions have not been made by these different students, but that certain underlying agreements may be obscured by nomenclatural differences.

Thus Dr. Wepman's pragmatic aphasia corresponds in its general description to what was described by Wernicke (25) and classically called Wernicke's aphasia or sensory aphasia; Head (10) called it syntactic aphasia; an aphasic of this type is fluent and has many paraphasias in his speech. Dr. Wepman's second group, semantic aphasia, is generally equivalent to the classic, anomic, amnestic, or amnesic aphasia, where the main difficulty is word finding: there are few neologisms and good preservation of all other aspects of speech; it is not equivalent to Head's semantic aphasia. These two groups together correspond generally to what Dr. Jakobson calls similarity disorders. Dr. Wepman's third classification is syntactic aphasia: it corresponds broadly to the classic Broca's, motor, or expressive aphasia; Head called it verbal aphasia, while Dr. Jakobson calls it contiguity disorder. These terms are all summarized in Table 8. I would note two things: Head is often regarded, and indeed regarded himself, as an anti-localizer; despite this he did in fact localize these aphasias and accepted the classical localizations! The localizations which Dr. Jakobson accepts are also perfectly consistent with classical views.

Table 8 is not exhaustive. It includes only the major groups of aphasic disturbances. It does not include Head's semantic aphasia, which is perhaps not really an aphasic disorder. Neither does it include—although these are all indeed aphasic disturbances—the nearly isolated language disturbances such as word-deafness (which was not described by Wernicke and is not equivalent to Wernicke's aphasia, as is often mistakenly stated), word-blindness with or without agraphia, conduction aphasia (which is equivalent to the central aphasia of Kurt Goldstein), and the isolated agraphias. I would stress that it is necessary to avoid the confusion that may result from the fact that the same authors have used the same term in different senses. Dr. Wepman, would you agree with this tabulation?

*Wepman:* No; I would not go along with using pragmatic aphasia as a

TABLE 8

NOMENCLATURE OF THE APHASIAS

| Classical | Wepman | Jakobson | Head |
|---|---|---|---|
| Broca's<br>Motor<br>Expressive<br>Anterior | Syntactic | Contiguity | Verbal |
| Posterior<br>　Wernicke's<br>　　sensory | Pragmatic | Similarity | Syntactic |
| Anomic<br>Amnesic<br>Amnestic | Semantic | Similarity | Nominal |

term representing Wernicke's. In my opinion, pragmatic aphasia is much closer to the actual description made by Luria (according to Dr. Jakobson) of regulatory dysfunction.

*Geschwind:* The patients you describe are, I believe, fluent and paraphasic.

*Wepman:* They are fluent; they have many neologisms; I would not say they do not have difficulty in articulation, because they do. They are not typical of Wernicke's aphasia. This may be a real heresy: I do not believe Wernicke described aphasia when he talked about Wernicke's aphasia.

*Geschwind:* I do not understand why Dr. Wepman should feel that what Wernicke described was not aphasia. The speech of the first patient in Wernicke's monograph (25) was fluent with many paraphasic errors.

Dr. Wepman spoke of five different types of aphasia as stages in the recovery process. It appears to me, however, that his patient did not really go through those different types; the patient he describes had, I believe, fundamentally a fluent type of aphasia at all times. I do not think that the fluent aphasics recover in the same way as the nonfluent. They are, in general, two distinct groups.

There is another reason why I do not believe these five types can be taken as stages of recovery. The evidence from the literature makes it overwhelmingly clear that localizations are different for different kinds of aphasia. There is, as far as I know, no case in which a fluent aphasia resulted from a lesion in Broca's area. It is hard to see how disturbances with different localizations could possibly be different stages in the recovery process.

Evidence for the difference in localization comes from another source. Consider Dr. Wepman's series: global, jargon, pragmatic, semantic, and syntactic. In our experience, the groups he calls syntactic and global usually have hemiplegias; by contrast, the groups he calls pragmatic and semantic do not have hemiplegias. This clearly must result from anatomical difference in location of lesion and argues against these forms being on a continuum.

Let me add quickly that I am not arguing against Dr. Wepman's regression hypothesis *in toto*. There is certainly a possibility that different parts of the speech system mature at different times in childhood. A posterior lesion might give one kind of regression, an anterior lesion a different kind. I would like to emphasize that the points related to the stages of aphasia and nomenclature made up only small parts of Dr. Wepman's talk, and I wish to reiterate my agreement with most of his presentation.

I should like to turn now to some work done by Dr. Davis Howes and myself, which is in many ways complementary to the work of Drs. Wepman and Jones. Despite our differences in approach, there have been some remarkable areas of convergence and very few major areas of disagreement. This is encouraging to me, and I hope to Dr. Wepman as well. I want

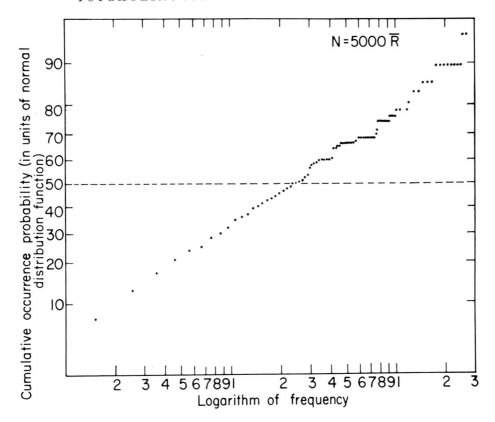

**Figure 21.** Graph of word-frequency distribution for 5000 consecutive spoken words of a normal subject. $\overline{R}$ indicates that words immediately repeated are excluded from the count. The frequencies of words are plotted on a logarithmic scale on the abscissa; the left-hand scale corresponds to words which occur one to ten times; the middle scale numbers should be multiplied by ten to correspond to frequencies of 20 to 100; the right end of the scale corresponds to frequencies of 200 and 300. The dashed line indicates the 50 per cent point; it corresponds to an abscissal value of about 24, i.e., 50 per cent of the sample is made up of words each of which occurred 24 times or less in the sample. The logarithmic value at this point is log 24/5000, i.e., −2.32. This value is the mean µ of the distribution. In aphasics the curve is of the same form but shifted to the right, which corresponds to smaller absolute values of µ (see Figure 22).

to stress that most of the work I shall present is an extension of certain types of investigations originally carried out on normals by Dr. Howes, sometimes in collaboration with others.*

Dr. Howes began by studying the problem of word-frequency distributions in normal people. Professor G. K. Zipf (26), who worked at Harvard, had investigated this problem and had shown that, to a first approximation, if one ranked the words of a text in order of frequency of occurrence, the product (frequency × rank order) was approximately constant. Howes

---

* Dr. Howes (11) has reviewed extensively the results in the study of aphasics, with more complete documentation and many graphs.

approached this somewhat differently; Figure 21 shows the type of function that he developed. Word frequency is plotted on the abscissa; on the ordinate the fraction of the sample made up of words having a given frequency or less is shown cumulatively. Thus, for example, one particular point on the curve will represent the total fraction of the sample made up of words which occur five or fewer times in the sample. The ordinate is in units of the normal distribution function, while the abscissa is in units not of frequency but of the logarithm of frequency. If this form of plotting is used, the curve is linear, which shows that the word-frequency distributions curve approximates closely a logarithmic normal curve, i.e., the logarithms of the frequencies of words have a normal distribution. The upper right-hand part of the curve is not linear; I shall not discuss the reasons at this time. This curve has two parameters: one is the mean $\mu$, roughly the point at which the curve crosses the 50 per cent line, and the other is the standard deviation $\sigma$, which is roughly equivalent to the slope of the curve.

Essentially the same form of the curve is obtained for aphasics, i.e., they too show a log-normal distribution of word frequencies. While the shape of the curve is preserved, the parameters (the mean and standard deviation) do tend to change.

*Osgood:* How do you obtain the data? What kind of listing procedure do you use?

*Geschwind:* The recording procedure is fairly straightforward: our technicians talk to the patients, and at least 5000 words per patient are collected. The ideal recording situation is one in which the listener turns on the tape recorder and the patient starts talking. Ideally, the listener says nothing; in practice there is usually need to speak. We accept no protocol unless the patient has produced at least ten times as many words as the listener. We try to make our method as near what one might call naturalistic as possible, and try to use exactly the same technique in recording for both patients and normals.

The possession of large texts changes many preconceived ideas. We have been struck by the number of aphasics from whom we have obtained 5000 words, many more than I would have predicted clinically. Obviously, there are some patients to whom this technique is not applicable.

We have made word-frequency distribution curves for several bilingual patients in both their languages. Although the curves show a shift away from normal, it is remarkable how similar they have been for our patients in the two languages. There are many bilingual patients who, if tested clinically, would appear to perform much better in one of their languages. Some have insisted that they were very poor in their first language, yet when a native speaker is provided and a large body of words is recorded, the patient is found to be much better in the first language than he thought he was before he had the chance for some practice. We wonder now

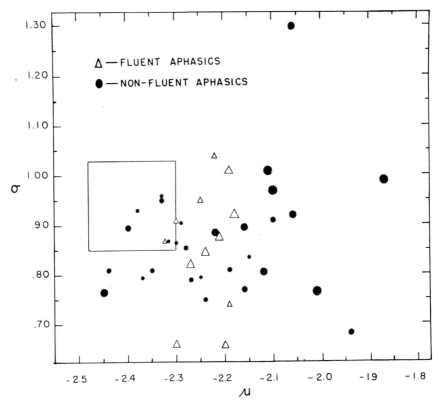

**Figure 22.** Parameters of the word-frequency distribution, μ (mean log frequency: see Figure 21), and σ (standard deviation of log frequency, i.e., the reciprocal of the slope of the word-frequency curve). The inner square indicates the range in which normal values of μ and σ fall. The sizes of the circles and triangles correspond to degrees of severity, the largest representing the most severely impaired patients. Note that for fluent aphasics μ generally is shifted to the range −2.3 to −2.2. More severely affected nonfluent aphasics generally show the greatest deviation in parameter values from normal. (From Howes, 11.)

whether the differences in bilinguals are as profound as they are usually assumed to be. Only after an adequate practice period in each language can valid judgments be made about potential performance in it.

*Osgood:* To what extent is the slope or the mean a sensitive index of individual differences?

*Geschwind:* Dr. Osgood's question is essentially whether our measures of the parameters would be very sensitive to differences in the performance of our bilinguals in their two languages. I suspect that there could be significant differences in performance in the two languages that this technique would not pick up. It would certainly pick up any large difference.

Figure 22 shows the distribution of means and standard deviations of the word-frequency curves for normals and aphasics. The normal values all lie within the small square. The parameters of the aphasics, as can be seen, may be grossly different from normal. We have separated fluent and nonfluent aphasics (we often call these "jargon" and "standard", respectively; they correspond generally to the posterior and anterior groups of Table 8). Notice that the fluent patients show little change in their means, which lie only slightly away from the normal range. It is striking, in fact, that regardless of degree of severity the deviation of the mean from the normal is of the same order of magnitude in these patients. By contrast, the nonfluent group shows large changes in the means, which run more or less parallel to degree of functional impairment.

We have also measured rates of speech, i.e., words per minute, in our aphasics. In normals the rate of speech remains remarkably constant over long periods of speaking. We were surprised to discover that the same was true for the aphasics. It is often stated that aphasics fatigue rapidly; we have shown that in a free situation without stress an aphasic can speak for well over an hour with very little change in his rate. This was true even of our slowest patient, who spoke only ten words per minute, approximately one tenth of the normal rate. On the basis of these findings, I believe that when one speaks of the ready fatigability of aphasics, one is really talking about a different set of phenomena, such as susceptibility to emotional stress.

While our nonfluent aphasics spoke slowly, some of our fluent ones actually had supernormal rates of speech. These patients slowed down as they improved, in contrast to the nonfluent ones who spoke more rapidly with improvement. It has occasionally been suggested that fluent aphasics appear to be speaking more rapidly than normal only because people do not understand them (just as many Americans think that Frenchmen speak very fast), but our data show that some of these patients do have supernormal rates.

*Osgood:* How do you define words?

*Geschwind:* We found that if more than one observer is asked to judge a tape recording, there is a very high rate of agreement as to whether an utterance is a word or part of a word. The number of disagreements is small because even in the worst patients the number of neologisms is small. There may be an occasional problem as to what is a word, not great enough to affect our measurements significantly.

*Denes:* Another problem which I found frequently when analyzing normal speech is what to do about incomplete words and about the grunt "er" or "uh" which occurs with such great frequency in normal conversation.

*Geschwind:* We have made tabulations in which we measured grunts and fragments and made our calculations with or without them. This did not produce a major change.

*Wepman:* Did you include partial words as whole words? How did you handle a word's different forms—"hat" and "hats", for instance?

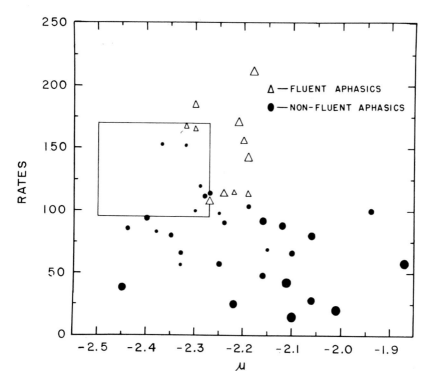

**Figure 23.** Rates of speech (in words per minute) plotted against the word-frequency parameter $\mu$. The inner rectangle indicates the region of normal values. Note that fluent aphasics have rates ranging from normal to super-normal. Among nonfluent aphasics, rate, $\mu$ and severity vary together. (From Howes, 11.)

*Geschwind:* We counted partial words as whole words. "Hat" and "hats" were treated as separate words. We have made calculations treating all the forms of a word as the same word rather than as different ones, but again the effects are not great. Similarly, it makes little difference whether "New York" is counted as one word or two.

*Denes:* A more serious question is whether words like "we're" or "I've" are one or two words.

*Geschwind:* They are one word for us.

*Wepman:* For us they are two.

*Osgood:* Is this kind of measure insensitive?

*Geschwind:* As you can see, the types of measures Dr. Howes has used do show major shifts in parameters. In addition, the measures clearly separate the nonfluent and fluent aphasics. There are things the measurements do not pick up, and I am sure many of them are very important.

*Osgood:* Did you make any breakdowns in terms of parts of speech?

*Geschwind:* I will discuss that later. Figure 23 shows rates of speech plotted against the parameter $\mu$, which may be roughly taken as a measure

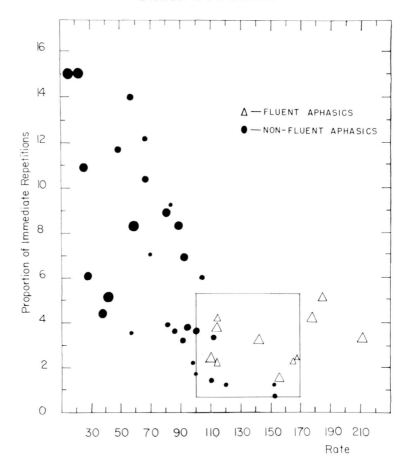

**Figure 24.** Percentage of sample made up of immediate repetitions (i.e., words or short phrases repeated immediately) plotted against rate of speech (words per minute). Normal range is indicated by the inner square. Note that for nonfluent aphasics the percentage of immediate repetitions increases with decreasing rate, while there is no obvious relationship between these variables for the fluent aphasics. (From Howes, 11.)

of vocabulary. Fluent aphasics show little correlation between speech rate and this parameter. One also finds for the nonfluent that in general the greater the functional impairment (measured roughly by clinical criteria), the more the vocabulary parameter is shifted and the slower the rate.

Figure 24 shows repetition rate in relation to rate of speech. By repetition rate we mean the percentage of the sample made up by immediate repetitions of a word or a short phrase. In fluent aphasics, the repetition rate has no relation to the rate of speech. In nonfluent aphasics, repetition rate rises as rate of speech falls.

*Wepman:* Do you count repetitions in the word groups?

*Geschwind:* We have made some counts of our patients in which we include repetitions as separate words, and other counts in which we omitted

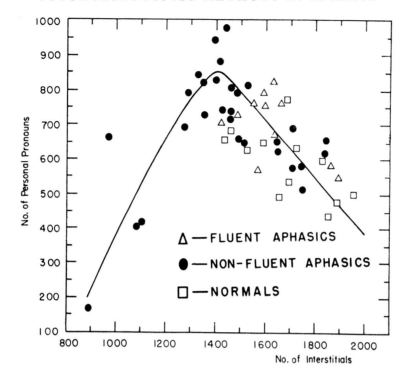

**Figure 25.** Number of personal pronouns (contained in 5000-word samples of speech) *versus* number of interstitial words (i.e., the first fifty words of the Thorndike-Lorge count, consisting mostly of small "connective" words except the personal pronouns). Note that as the number of interstitials drops, the number of personal pronouns increases in normals and in both types of aphasics. However, when the number of interstitials drops below 1400 (which occurs only in nonfluent aphasics) the number of personal pronouns declines.

them. The symbol $\overline{R}$ in Figure 21 indicates a word count without inclusion of repetitions.

We studied grammatical words, but not in the same way as Dr. Wepman. We took the first 50 words in the Thorndike-Lorge count (19), nearly all of which are grammatical words. This list, with personal pronouns excluded, we called "interstitial" words. Figure 25 shows the curves of interstitial words *versus* personal pronouns. Interestingly enough, the curve is the same for normals and aphasics. As the number of interstitial words goes up, the number of personal pronouns falls. Nonfluent aphasics show a decline in the number of interstitials which is more marked the more severe the aphasia, up to a point. However, as the patient becomes more agrammatic in the sense of decline in number of interstitials, his personal pronoun usage increases. The personal pronoun appears to behave more like a noun than do the other connective words. When the severity of the nonfluent aphasic's disorder increases beyond a certain point, an interesting thing happens: the number of personal pronouns also starts to de-

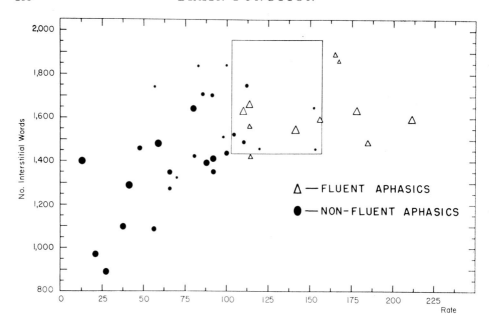

**Figure 26.** Number of interstitial words in a 5000-word sample plotted against rate. The inner rectangle indicates the normal range of values. Note that for nonfluent aphasics the number of interstitials diminishes with decrease in rate, while these variables show no relationship in fluent aphasics.

cline. One might say that the personal pronouns stop behaving like nouns when the severity of the aphasia increases beyond a certain limit.

Figure 26 shows interstitial words *versus* rate. Notice that for fluent aphasics the number of interstitial words is not much affected despite wide variation in speech rates and severity of aphasia. In nonfluent aphasics, however, the number of interstitials declines along with rate of speech, i.e., as the patient becomes slower, he becomes more agrammatical.

Another study is the measurement of latency of word association. This was first done with aphasics by Louis Gerstman and Katherine Harris[*] at the Haskins Laboratory in New York City. In normals, the more frequent a word is as an association, the lower its latency. The same is true in aphasics. The curve, however, changes markedly in slope in aphasics, so that latencies are much longer for low-frequency associations in aphasics than they are in normals. We have made studies of this type and confirmed and extended these results.

*Osgood:* Are there data on the types of word associations of aphasics? It would be interesting to discover whether word associations varied as a function of type of aphasia.

*Geschwind:* Our material might be usable for that purpose. Another type of experiment we have attempted is the measurement of word-thresholds.

---

[*] Personal communication.

Dr. Howes showed that in normals there is a relationship between the frequency of a word in the Thorndike-Lorge count and its threshold as measured by the median duration of the tachistoscopic flash necessary for recognition. If a large body of data taken from normals is pooled, there is a very elegant linear relationship between this flash duration and the logarithm of the frequency. The great difficulty is that these data were obtained from the normals; it would be meaningless to pool the data from aphasics. We therefore must devise a technique for obtaining stable data from a single patient. In fact, we have not yet been able to get nice smooth curves from a single normal. If we can solve this problem, we can apply the technique to audition as well as to vision.

I mentioned earlier that we had data on the number of hemiplegias. Of 26 nonfluent patients, 20 had hemiplegias, of which ten were severe. Only six had no hemiplegia. In a group of 12 fluent aphasic patients, none had a severe hemiplegia and only three had mild hemiplegias. *

In summary then, there is a type of aphasic who usually has no hemiplegia, whose speech is fluent and paraphasic, and whose speech rate is high. This group shows little change in the vocabulary parameter, little loss of grammatical words, and few repetitions of words. None of these changes in this group, except perhaps those in rate, correlate with severity of aphasia. By contrast, there is another type of aphasic who is nonfluent, speaks slowly, and usually has a hemiplegia. In this group there is an increased number of repetitions, a noticeable tendency to omit small grammatical words, and a shift in the vocabulary parameter. The changes in the different measures are definitely intercorrelated and tend to be more marked the more functionally severe the aphasic impairment.

Our techniques and those of Dr. Wepman's group meet at several points. There is no significant divergence in our results, although our points of view are different and are adapted to different purposes. I believe that both kinds of approach are highly useful.

*Hirsh:* I should like to return to two of Dr. Wepman's classifications. He illustrated the utility of analysis of an aphasic patient's speech output classified according to parts of speech. I should like to ask him whether there are specific disturbances that one can follow over time on the reception side that are related to parts of speech. A second question is whether there are other aspects of psycholinguistics, for example the kind of phrases and sentences the patients use, or vocabulary counts, etc., that he would find useful in describing this expressive function.

*Wepman:* We have not yet devised means for studying comprehension by parts of speech. I believe it probably could be done; a new technique

---

* *Editor's note:* A contingency table on these data using the three categories of hemiplegia yields a Chi-squared value (2 degrees of freedom) of 9.8, which is significant at the 0.01 level of confidence. Apparently, nonfluent aphasics tend to be hemiplegic, in contrast to fluent aphasics.

might be required, though matching techniques could be useful. Still, one does not really talk to aphasics much about parts of speech; they do not understand metalinguistics very well.

To answer your second question, we thought originally that we could explain anomia on a frequency basis. We later came to believe frequency did not explain the total process, that probably something like recency of exposure accounted for the rest of the variance, that is, the rest of the words retained by the patients, although we have no evidence for it. For each individual there seems to be a different recency function.

After we had explored the data from the first twelve normals, we built into the computer program all words they used which were unambiguous as parts of speech; these made up a list of 402 words which embraced some 83 per cent of all spoken language. Thus, vocabulary became very meaningful to us. Education did not matter for this percentage: the same 402 words represented 83 per cent of the language whether the subject had no education or was a college graduate. This is not unlike Ogden and Richards' Basic English vocabulary of 550 words plus technical terms as a complete communicative language.

Vocabulary needs to be studied in many different ways; we suspect that the digital computer, for example, can be used to run through the same protocols and discover, by tagging meanings, the semantic uses of words. We have not yet found a way to do it, although a Chomsky-trained linguist spent two years with us attempting to do an analysis of the spoken language of aphasics. Phrase-structure and transformational analysis has not yet developed to the point where we can make use of it in aphasic language structure.

We also do not know enough about the thema involved in the TAT stories of the aphasic patients. These are now under evaluation. They do fall generally into the category of rather concrete stories, which are not very revealing of personality, unless all aphasics have concrete personalities, which may be true. Unlike the Boston group, which I take as a geographical peculiarity, we did not find many patients who could give us 5000 words. Our range, in fact, did not quite reach 5000, even though we explored some 184 aphasics at different times. One technique we are now using, which is surprisingly disturbing to those who have done any form of therapy with aphasic patients, is based on the finding that after an aphasic has become used to responding to pictures, he does better when alone. Therefore, we now include in our therapy program an exposure to film strips and have the patient talk to himself. We find he talks more and, in this way, we may be able to get the 5000 words.

*Geschwind:* So far we have had 60 patients from whom we have been able to obtain 5000 words.

*de Hirsch:* Could I ask you, Dr. Wepman, about the material used? If the patient is shown pictures like those on the TAT, he has to put himself in an "as if" situation and produce a story representing what happens in the picture.

*Wepman:* That is quite true. If one tries to obtain 5000 words from a person, rather structured situations are produced, too. Aphasics do not just freely sit down and say 5000 words. Very few Norman Geschwinds have aphasia.

*de Hirsch:* Responding to the TAT card involves assuming an "abstract attitude."

*Wepman:* To a great degree, it is an abstract task, and yet one of the reasons we used it was that we hoped to make comparisons with patients using other languages; TAT seems to be one stimulus set used in psychological clinics throughout the world. While this is perhaps not so behind the Iron Curtain or in Asia, it certainly is true in every country we have visited so far. Thus in TAT we have a likely constant stimulus of potential use in other languages as well as in English. It also gives us a chance to look at certain words and rule them out as being related to the picture. For example, the word "picture" itself will appear high in a frequency count; we can eliminate it because the patient is asked to respond to the picture, and he may then repeat the word "picture". There are certain words that can be treated as constants in the same way. In our analysis, we did consider contractions; our linguist would not let us operate otherwise. We also eliminated repetitions from the word-frequency counts, although this became a matter of judgment. As Dr. Geschwind pointed out, sometimes it does not matter in a large corpus. We did not limit ourselves to 5000-word patients; our productivity range went all the way down to 465 words, and up to something in the neighborhood of 5600 in the patient group, with a mean of 2872 words. The mean for the normals was, I think, at about the 2500 level, with the range from 1032 to 5300 words.

*Denes:* Despite what you say, the problem of what you call a word is very relevant to the question of how many different words are counted. If you take all the different forms of "will" and "shall" as different words, you will very quickly run up to 5000 words.

*Geschwind:* When I say 5000 words, I do not mean 5000 different words. I mean simply 5000 consecutive words. The number of different words was, of course, much smaller.

*de Hirsch:* When you judge that a patient has quite a large word production, it may be because he has trouble formulating what he says. After all, we conclude that some children use so many more words than others in telling stories just because they cannot get the gist, cannot point it up. Is your judgment made after you have the work-up?

*Wepman:* It might very well be that the word count is high because the patient is struggling to find words. Another factor that must be taken into account is the amount and type of therapy a patient has had, for it will frequently control the kind of words he uses. One of our patients who uses very few grammatical function words did use the phrase "It's a" because he went through a year of therapy with a therapist who began every sentence with "It's a". When the patient was asked what his name was, he would respond, "It's a John"; if asked where he lived, he said, "It's a Racine". He used a number of such words not really in his spontaneous word vocabulary as starting devices.

*Lenneberg:* Much could be said about this provocative study, especially about the different classifications and classification systems. I think one theme emerges, and that is, if we try to make very minute classifications, we run into trouble. The only classification systems that seem to have some clinical and theoretical interest are the very gross ones. They seem to boil down to classifications which have localizing value for both clinical and theoretical purposes. Those are the classes that stand out and seem to yield the greatest interest. I think your scheme, as was pointed out, can be adjusted to one that has value in localizing lesions.

*Wepman:* I would like, however, not to let us become bogged down with a nice convenient system just because it is so. We think the pragmatic patient lies between the jargon and the semantic aphasics and that his constant use of neologisms is very much like the use of jargon, just approaching the use of intelligible language. This seems to be a stage between the use of an incomprehensible free-flowing jargon, a combination of phonemes which are unintelligible, and the patient's starting to use more intelligible words. The stages surely merge one into another.

*Lenneberg:* I would like to take issue with the matter of the aphasic jargon. I would not consider it to be equivalent, phonemically, to babbling. I think jargon has many more phonemic configurations that fall into the phonological system of adult language, which is not really true of babbling, although some people have made that claim.

*Wepman:* I quite agree.

*Lenneberg:* This brings me to the last point. There is one aspect of aphasia we have not stressed sufficiently. It has to do with the problem of activation. Let me cite a case to illustrate it. This was a patient who had global aphasia and could not say a thing. He was in the hospital for two weeks or so, which is a relatively long time. When he was due to be sent home, he became very agitated. It turned out he was going to a mother-in-law or some close relative he could not stand. He was very excited, and in the state of his excitement, he suddenly spoke quite fluently. This is something everybody on the wards has witnessed.

I think one may also see the other side of this matter: some patients can do better when there is nobody around, when they are relaxed. This drives home the fact that there is a physiological level in aphasia. Aphasic symptoms are not purely behavioral derangements; individual elements of language are not simply lost, but some physiological process is involved that cuts across all language aspects. Rather than a loss of phonology or semantics, it is a general level of activation that is lowered or raised, as the case may be.

*Geschwind:* I have heard accounts of patients who spoke when they became excited although they were otherwise mute. I have not personally seen such a case. Most of those I heard about were not, I believe, aphasics in the usual sense but mute patients who, when they do speak, produce normal language. I think they are patients with so-called akinetic mutism who have lesions in the upper brain stem involving the reticular formation, i.e., a quite different localization from what we see in aphasics. Some of them may also have lesions in the frontal lobe anterior to Broca's area. In these patients, spontaneous speech is markedly diminished but "reactive" speech is well preserved, as was pointed out by Goldstein (6) in his monograph on the transcortical aphasias.

*Lenneberg:* Akinetic mutism is a different entity, and I think it can be distinguished from aphasia. There is a *bona fide* aphasia that can be triggered into a heightened state of emotion with an immediate improvement of fluency.

*Wepman:* I think that is true. We have seen many patients who had suffered brain stem lesions and who were or were not aphasics, depending on what is called aphasic. I would prefer discarding the word "aphasia" entirely because we do not all have the same meaning in mind when we use it; I would rather talk about language impairments that people have at different times.

In terms of the developmental process that we have alluded to, we see the importance of it in the handling of children more than in the handling of adults. In working with speechless children whom we have been unable to induce to talk by usual classical methods of conditioning and association, we believe that there is some hope in training them in the use of jargon. One or two children have been able to learn jargon, and then from jargon move into speech. The speech usually is fortuitous and then becomes a semantic type of language very much like the progressive chart we showed.

## REFERENCES

1. Bock, R. D., *Methods and Applications of Optimal Scaling.* Psychometric Lab., Univ. of North Carolina, 1960, Report #25.
2. Eisenson, J., *Examining for Aphasia; a Manual for the Examination of Aphasia and Related Disturbances.* Psychological Corp., New York, 1954.
3. Fillenbaum, S., Jones, L. V., and Wepman, J. M., Some linguistic features of speech from aphasic patients. *Lang. Speech*, 1961, 4: 91-108.
4. Fisher, R. A., *Statistical Methods for Research Workers* (10th ed.). Oliver & Boyd, Edinburgh, 1948.
5. Geschwind, N., Quantitative studies of aphasic language. In: *VII International Congress of Neurology* (Abstracts of Papers). Exc. Med. Found., Amsterdam, 1961: 31-32.

6. GOLDSTEIN, K., Die Transcorticalen Aphasien. *Erg. Neurol. Psychiat.*, 1917, **2**: 352-629.

7. GOODGLASS, H., and BERKO, J., Agrammatism and inflectional morphology in English. *J. Speech Hear. Res.*, 1960, **3**: 257-267.

8. GOODGLASS, H., and MAYER, J., Agrammatism in aphasia. *J. Speech Hear. Dis.*, 1958, **23**: 99-111.

9. HALSTEAD, W. C., and WEPMAN, J. M., The Halstead-Wepman aphasia screening test. *J. Speech Hear. Dis.*, 1949, **14**: 9-15.

10. HEAD, H., *Aphasia and Kindred Disorders of Speech.* Macmillan, New York, 1926.

11. HOWES, D. H., Application of word-frequency concept to aphasia. In: *Disorders of Language* (A. V. S. de Reuck and M. O'Connor, Eds.). Churchill, London, 1964: 47-78.

12. JACKSON, J. H., Affections of speech. In: *Selected Writings of John Hughlings Jackson*, Vol. II (J. Taylor, Ed.). Hodder & Stoughton, London, 1932: 119-212.

13. JAKOBSON, R., and HALLE, M., *Fundamentals of Language*, Mouton, The Hague, 1956.

14. JONES, L. V., GOODMAN, M. F., and WEPMAN, J. M., The classification of parts of speech for the characterization of aphasia. *Lang. Speech*, 1963, **6**: 94-107.

15. JONES, L. V., and WEPMAN, J. M., Dimensions of language performance in aphasia. *J. Speech Hear. Res.*, 1961, **4**: 220-232.

16. LURIA, A. R., Brain disorders and language analysis. *Lang. Speech*, 1958, **1**: 14-34.

17. MORRIS, C. W., Foundations of the theory of signs. In: *International Encyclopedia of Unified Science*, Vol. I (O. Neurath, R. Carnap and C. Morris, Eds.). Univ. of Chicago Press, Chicago, 1938: 77-137.

18. SCHUELL, H. M., *Minnesota Test for Differential Diagnosis of Aphasia.* Univ. of Minnesota Print. Dept., Minneapolis, 1955.

19. THORNDIKE, E., and LORGE, I., *The Teacher's Word Book of 30,000 Words.* Columbia Univ. Press, New York, 1944.

20. WEISENBURG, T., and McBRIDE, K. E., *Aphasia; a Clinical and Psychological Study.* Commonwealth Fund, New York, 1935.

21. WEPMAN, J. M., BOCK, R. D., JONES, L. V., and VAN PELT, D., Psycholinguistic study of aphasia: a revision of the concept of anomia. *J. Speech Hear. Dis.*, 1956, **21**: 468-477.

22. WEPMAN, J. M., and JONES, L. V., *The Language Modalities Test for Aphasia.* Univ. of Chicago Industrial Relations Center, Chicago, 1961.

23. ———, *Studies in Aphasia: An Approach to Testing.* Univ. of Chicago Education-Industry Service, Chicago, 1961.

24. ———, Five aphasias: a commentary on aphasia as a regressive linguistic phenomenon. *Ass. Res. Nerv. Ment. Dis.*, 1964, **42**: 190-203.

25. WERNICKE, C., *Der aphasische Symptomencomplex. Eine psychologische Studie auf anatomischer Basis.* Cohn & Weigert, Breslau, 1874.

26. ZIPF, G. K., *Human Behavior and the Principle of Least Effort; an Introduction to Human Ecology.* Addison-Wesley, Cambridge, 1949.

# LINGUISTIC STRUCTURE AND THE
# PRODUCTION AND DECODING OF DISCOURSE[*]

SYDNEY M. LAMB
University of California
Berkeley

The object of this study is to try to infer from examination of linguistic data the kind of mechanism that would be required to produce and decode such data. We cannot observe the production mechanism, of course, but we can observe the output; we can also observe some of the input, that is, the situations in which people say things.

This investigation may be divided into two parts: first, by examining discourse, by analyzing verbal data, we may try to deduce the simplest structural system that can account for the data; second, we can try to determine the simplest mechanism that would be able to operate with such a system to produce and decode such data. The term "simplest" is important because it is possible to arrive at any number of systems which would account for the data observed. Similarly, if we are trying to find a mechanism able to produce such information, it is important to try to figure out what its simplest form might be. Such a mechanism, of course, may or may not resemble the brain, but we might expect some kind of correspondence.

This is a rather broad topic; just one component of linguistic structure would be a broad topic. Therefore, it will be necessary to oversimplify with regard to certain areas and to leave some things unsaid. In fact, I will practically ignore decoding in order to give proper attention to production, but it appears that the system which most simply and adequately accounts for the production process is also suitable for decoding.

We may look at language as a system which relates meanings to sound and think of it as a code, as something which will encode messages into speech sounds. But that is a little too simple because it is more revealing to think of language in terms of a series of codes rather than just one. The important point is that we do not find a simple relationship between meaning and sound; instead, we find discrepancies from a simple relationship. These can best be described with illustrations, as shown in the following figures. (I should say that I am not presenting here the general point of view of all

[*] This work was supported in part by the National Science Foundation.

173

linguists; there is no general view that can be used for the purpose of making inferences about the production and decoding processes.)

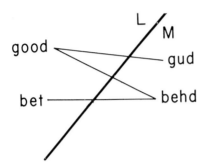

Figure 27. Discrepancy between the lexemic (L) and the morphemic (M) strata. "Good" and "bet" as examples of the diversification and neutralization relationships. See text.

Figure 27 shows the element "good", which we know has a comparative. But the comparative is not "gooder", it is "better". The element "good" is thus represented by "bet" ("behd") when it is followed by the comparative suffix "er". In other words, "good" has alternate representations (or realizations). What we want to recognize is that somewhere in the structure of the language there are obviously two different units, "good" and "bet", which at that level have absolutely no resemblance, yet which, somewhere else in the structure of the language, are also obviously one and the same unit. We want to recognize both situations. This relationship may be called diversification; it is present when an element on a stratum is represented by different units on the next lower stratum. Moreover, the unit "bet" exists not just as a representation of the adjective "good" but also, in exactly the same form, as the representation of a particular verb meaning "to wager". This relationship may be called neutralization; it is present when a unit on the lower stratum represents two or more different units of the upper stratum.

Another type of discrepancy from a simple one-to-one relationship is illustrated in Figure 28. Again, we do not say "badder" for the comparative of "bad", we say "worse" (M/wərhz/). This situation is somewhat different from that of "good" because M/wərhz/ is not segmentable into two parts representing L/bad/ and L/er/; rather, as one unit it represents the combination L/bad er/. This is another type of discrepancy, which we may call portmanteau representation (or portmanteau realization), in which two

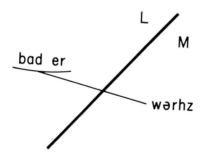

Figure 28. Discrepancy between the lexemic (L) and the morphemic (M) strata. The comparative of "bad" as an example of portmanteau representation. Note also that one-to-one correspondence between alphabetic characters and structural elements exists only at the morphemic stratum.

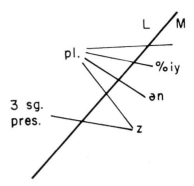

**Figure 29.** Discrepancies between the lexemic (L) and the morphemic (M) strata, illustrated by the plural lexeme of English (pl.) and the third person singular present (3 sg. pres.). The common form ᴹ/z/ also represents both lexemes. Other forms illustrated are the plural as in "oxen", ᴹ/ən/; as in "geese", ᴹ/%iy/; and as in "sheep", where there is no morpheme (open end).

elements have to be taken together as a single unit in order to be related to the next lower stratum.

The opposite situation can occur and is also illustrated in Figure 28: ᴹ/wərhz/ itself is not a single element but a string of five elements. Here the notation of linguistics is confusing; in writing ᴸ/bad/, three letters are used, but ᴸ/bad/ is structurally a single indivisible element. The notation is also alphabetic for ᴹ/wərhz/ at the morphemic stratum, but structurally each letter represents a separate element. We like to use alphabetical notation but it is appropriate only on the morphemic stratum, where a one-to-one correspondence exists between alphabetic characters and structural elements.

Figure 29 illustrates another example of lexemic-morphemic discrepancy, that of the plural lexeme of English and the third person singular present. Four plural representations are shown (actually, there are more): the common form (z), which also represents ᴸ/3sg./; the plural as it occurs in "oxen" and "children" (ᴹ/ən/); the plural of "goose", i.e., "geese" (%iy): and the form of ᴸ/plural/ that entails no change (as in "sheep", for example), represented by the line leading to nothing on the morphemic stratum in the figure. The latter illustrates the type of discrepancy in which there is an element represented by nothing (zero realization).

The opposite is also possible: an element can represent nothing (empty realization). For example, ᴸ/do/ on the lexemic stratum represents nothing on the sememic stratum in such expressions as "I do not see", which is not simply the negative of "I do see" but is rather the negative of "I see"; the grammatical system does not allow the form "I not see".

The same kinds of discrepancies found between the lexemic and morphemic strata are also found between the sememic and the lexemic. For example, two well-known meanings (no doubt there are more) of the lexeme ᴸ/man/ are shown in Figure 30: ᴸ/man/ is used for "human being" in general, and specifically for "adult male human being". We can account for this situation by recognizing two different sememic units which can be represented by ᴸ/man/ in the kind of relationship I call neutralization. The elements at the upper stratum ("S") may be called semons; each is an indivisible unit even though it is represented notationally by a combination of letters.

*Osgood:* In the theory, are these semantic components?

*Lamb:* Call them semantic components, if you wish.

Four types of discrepancy can be seen in Figure 30. First, a combination of elements on the upper stratum must be taken together to be represented: there are S/thing/, S/animate/, S/adult/, S/human/, and S/male/, five elements in the sememic stratum represented by a single lexeme L/man/; this is portmanteau representation. Second, neutralization is found, in that L/man/ is also a representation of a different combination of semons, namely S/thing/, S/animate/, and S/human/. Third, diversification, since this latter combination of semons—we may call it a sememe—has as alternate realizations not just L/man/ but also L/person/ and L/human being/. And fourth, an instance of composite realization in that one of these realizations, L/human being/, is not elementary but a combination of three lexons, L/human/, L/be/, and L/-ing/.

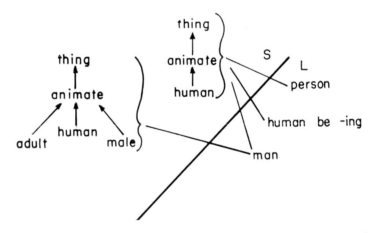

**Figure 30.** Four types of discrepancies between the sememic (S) and the lexemic (L) strata: portmanteau representation, neutralization, diversification, and composite realization, as associated with the lexeme L/man/. See text.

To generalize, what we have observed is that a unit can have alternate realizations (diversification), that a unit can be a realization of two or more different units of the upper stratum (neutralization), that some units are realizations of combinations of upper-stratum elements (portmanteau realization), or of nothing at all on the upper stratum (empty realization), and that some realizations are combinations of lower-stratum elements (composite realization), or consist of nothing at all (zero realization). Representing elementary units by Greek letters (as Roman letters were used for strata), our findings may be diagrammed as in Figure 31 (left), which covers all the possibilities between two strata except differences in ordering (which also occur), with the understanding that, although only two alternate realizations for one of the lexemic units are shown, the number could be three or

four or more. A circled letter designates a combination of one or more elements, or zero.

Since the same relationship existing between the two strata is also present
at a higher and at a lower level, the diagram (simplified as on the right in
Figure 31) can be extended to include the next lower stratum (phonemic),
again with multiple possibilities of both kinds. It can also be extended upwards into the sememic stratum, again with lines to indicate neutralization
and diversification. Figure 32 illustrates these relationships and shows all
the possibilities that exist, except discrepancies in ordering.

We quite commonly find that an element of an upper stratum is represented by a combination of elements on the lower stratum. For example, a
unit such as $^L$/good/ is commonly represented not by a single element but
by a combination, e.g., $^M$/g/, $^M$/u/, $^M$/d/. In other words, composite realiza-

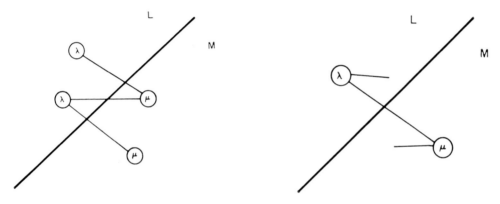

Figure 31. *Left:* Relationship possibilities between two strata, lexemic (L) and morphemic
(M). Elementary units in the strata are represented by λ and μ respectively; circles around
symbols mean that they stand for a single element, or a combination of two or more, or
nothing. *Right:* Simplification of the diagram shown on left; multiple possibilities indicated
by interrupted alternate lines.

tion is usual. The two most important units that will have to be identified
on any stratum are therefore (*a*) the unit which represents something on the
upper stratum and (*b*) the elementary unit on a stratum.

The traditional terminology that has been built up in linguistics over the
last thirty years is not quite adequate to deal with this situation; there are
many awkward features in the traditional terminology of linguistics, as for
example the fact that different linguists use the same terms in different
meanings. Indeed, some terms, morpheme being the most notorious, are
used in different ways by the same linguist, even within the same publication. The terms with the suffix "-eme" that have become popular have for
the most part not been used for the elementary structural units but for the
combinations which relate to the upper stratum. Thus, for example, the
term "phoneme", as it has generally been used, is the term not for one of
the elementary units on the phonemic stratum but for a combination which

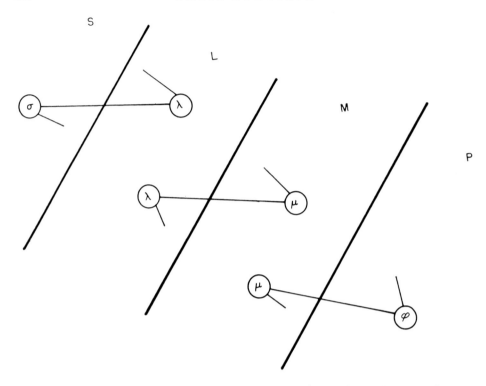

**Figure 32.** Relationships between sememic (S), lexemic (L), morphemic (M), and phonemic (P) strata. As in Figure 31, elementary units are represented by the corresponding Greek letters (σ, λ, μ, and φ). Circles indicate that in any case the unit may be any combination of zero or more elements.

relates to the morphemic stratum. Similarly, the term "lexeme" is not a term for an elementary unit on any stratum, but rather for a combination of elements which relates to the sememic stratum. Such terms with the suffix "-eme" can then be preserved for those units which relate in the simplest way to the upper stratum, and new terms be coined for the elementary units. After experimenting with many different devices and meeting objections from one linguist or another on every possibility, in trying to find something which will be consistent, simple, and unobjectionable, I have come up with a device that strikes me as less awkward than any other I have tried: simply to adopt the suffix "-on" from physics, where it is used for elementary particles.

As shown in Figure 33, the elementary particles of linguistic structure would then be semon, lexon, morphon, and phonon. The terms with the suffix "-eme" are retained pretty much in the same meanings that many of us are now accustomed to. Lexeme and phoneme correspond to fairly normal usage. "Morpheme" has a different meaning to different linguists—to many it means what I have called "lexon", to others it means a combination of phonemes, to others, including me, it means a combination of morpho-

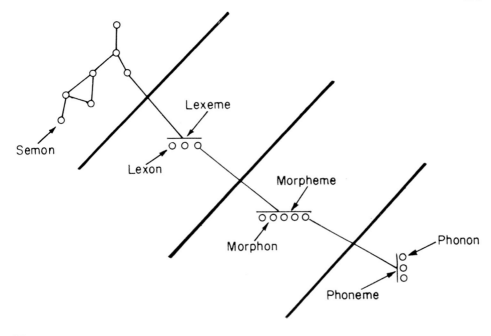

**Figure 33.** Diagram of a small portion of some hypothetical typical situation, showing in an abstract form the relationships between and within strata. Elements are represented by circles. The terms *semon, lexon, morphon,* and *phonon* are proposed for the elementary units in each stratum, while *lexeme, morpheme,* and *phoneme* indicate combinations of elements relating to the upper stratum. Linear combinations (strings) illustrated by lexons and morphons; three simultaneous phonons form a phoneme (bottom); semons occur in networks (top).

phonemes. For those who are familiar with the term morphophoneme, morphon is the same thing. Morpheme, then, is a term for a combination of elements.

One may take what is shown in Figure 33 as a typical example. I show a lexeme with a line going up to the sememic stratum indicating that this lexeme, which is a combination of three lexons, is the representation of an element of the upper stratum. For example, in $^L$/human being/, there are three lexons. Other examples of lexemes which consist of more than one lexon are: "red-headed woodpecker", "North American pit viper", and—there are many of this type—"white oak", which is a species of oak (just as "North American pit viper" is a particular species of viper). This may be compared to "tall oak" or "white flower". "White oak" is a lexeme that has to be taken as a unit in order to be related to the upper stratum, but "tall oak" is two separate lexemes, consisting of one lexon each. The same is true of "white flower"; these are two independent lexemes.

As further examples, consider "undergo", one word in written English; we can consider this a lexeme consisting of two lexons, because the past tense of "undergo" is "underwent". Or, similarly, consider "stand", "understand", and "withstand". "Understand" has no connection at all with "stand" from a semantic point of view. But the past tense of "understand" is "understood", and the past tense of "withstand" is "withstood"; if these are treated as combinations of two lexons, the code has to account for the past tense of "stand" only once, and the rule that does so will automatically take care of "understand", "withstand", etc. Similarly, only one rule is needed to take care of the past tense of "go"; it will also take care of "undergo" if this is recognized as two lexons. While considering "go", let us look at some more examples: the lexon $^L$/go/ is present not only in "undergo" but also in "go crazy", "go to pieces", etc.; here again the past tense is the same regardless of the various combinations with their wide variety of different meanings. This is further evidence of the separability of these different codes from each other.

*Hirsh:* Would "go crazy" be two lexemes?

*Lamb:* I think I would be inclined to call it one lexeme. The principle is that if one can predict the meaning of the form from its components, then it is more than one lexeme. If one cannot, it is a single lexeme.

*Osgood:* The same form can be differently analyzed, like "look up the word in the dictionary" *versus* "look up the chimney".

*Lamb:* Yes, "look up" is a very good example. It can occur both as a single lexeme and as a combination of two lexemes.

I want to mention two other things shown in Figure 33. The combinations of lexons and of morphons are shown horizontally, which is to say that they are strings; they are linear; they occur one after the other sequentially. That is not the case on the top and the bottom. On the bottom, the phoneme depicted consists of three simultaneous phonons; on the top, the elements occur in networks, and lines are drawn between them to show the connections. (It would be redundant to draw lines within strings; one thing follows after the other.) The diagram does not show that, although the lexons of a lexeme occur in a string, the lexemes occur with one another in trees.

Although I am indebted to Chomsky for several very acute, interesting observations about English and other languages, I differ from him regarding the interpretation of some of the phenomena. In particular, certain properties such as the networks at the highest level and trees at the lexemic stratum make it unnecessary to have transformations in a grammar. Chomsky needs transformations because his original generation is done by constituent-structure rules which generate strings (1). It is then necessary to transform these strings into other strings by the use of transformational rules. In the system I propose, the initial generation is not done by constituent-structure rules but by rules of a different kind which generate not strings but networks.

We may now go on to consider the structure of a linguistic description, diagrammed in Figure 34. The boxes labeled Lexology, Morphology, and Phonology are the codes which relate the four strata; each one is a set of

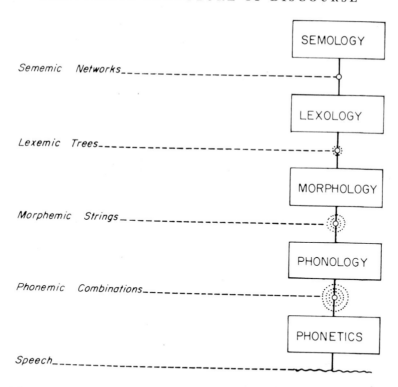

**Figure 34.** Diagram showing the structure of a linguistic description. See text.

rules which specifies how units of the stratum above are to be encoded into units of the one below. Phonetics is the code relating the phonons to articulations. Each of the "boxes" consists of rules of two types: realization rules, which specify the lower stratum realizations, and tactic rules or construction rules, which specify what combinations of units are well formed on the stratum in question.

The generative process consists of the following stages: we start with the semology; it has rules which specify what combinations of sememes are allowable. So, it generates networks of sememes, each of which is composed of one or more semons; the output is represented by the small upper circle in the figure. This is an infinite set of networks, and if the rules are correct it consists only of the well-formed sememic networks. This stage of semology we might call message creation. It is one of the two parts into which the production process may be divided, i.e., message creation and encoding of the message: message creation is generation by the semological rules, then there are four stages of encoding.

Sememic networks may be encoded into lexemic trees by the lexological rules. The lexons may be converted to strings of morphemes by the morphological rules. The following is an example of a morphological realization rule:

$$\text{good} \parallel \text{---- er / behd}$$
$$\parallel \text{---- est / be}$$
$$\parallel \text{----} \quad \text{/ gud}$$

It may be read as follows: $^L$/good/, when followed by $^L$/er/ has the representation $^M$/behd/; $^L$/good/ is the lexon, $^M$/behd/ is a morpheme consisting of four morphons. When followed by the superlative $^L$/est/, it is realized as $^M$/be/; elsewhere it is realized as $^M$/gud/. These three subrules will be applied in order. On the "input" side is the element of upper stratum to be encoded. On the output side we have three "outputs" for three different situations. The "inside" of each subrule specifies the conditions under which one gets the corresponding output, and the latter belongs on the lower stratum; that is, each of the morphemes is made up of one or more morphons. The conditioning factor is always the environment and invariably the immediate environment, which is important for reasons which I will not discuss at this time. The dash indicates the position in the environment. No environment need be given in the third subrule because, as I stated, a property of these rules is that the different subrules are to be executed in order; one first checks for the initial environment listed. (If one is to write a grammar efficiently, one will write the most restricted environment in the first subrule.) If it is not in the first environment, one goes on to the next one; the last one means "anywhere else". After the morphological rules, we proceed to the phonology, which will give phonemes, each of which is a combination of phonons. These go on to the phonetics. This last converter is connected to the speech-producing mechanisms.

In addition to the realization rules, like that illustrated above for $^L$/good/, each of the boxes in Figure 34 has tactical or constructional rules. The sets of combinations they will generate are indicated by the larger circles drawn with dotted lines. Just below the lexology, the smaller circle encloses those lexeme trees which are representations of the sememic networks in the circle above. The larger circle encloses those lexeme trees which are generated by the lexology if it is not controlled by the semology. Both are infinite sets, but the larger one includes the smaller one, and the difference, i.e., what the larger has that the smaller has not, is made up of all those sentences which are grammatical but nonsensical. For example, Joos', "I have never heard a green horse smoke a dozen oranges" (3) would be in the larger circle because it is grammatical, but not in the smaller one because it does not make sense. Similarly, the morphology would generate the infinite set containing all those combinations of morphemes which are morphologically acceptable if not controlled by the lexology. It would be a still larger set. Likewise, the phonology is a device which, by itself, would allow all combinations of well-formed syllables, many of which would not be allowed if the phonology were controlled by the morphology.

One could start the generative process with one of the lower boxes for

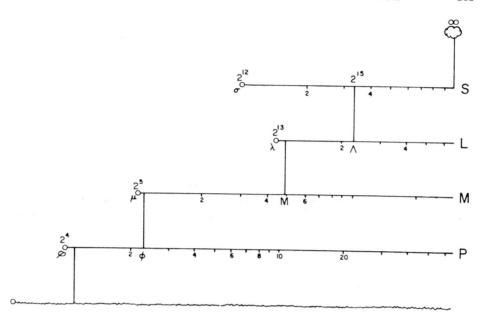

**Figure 35.** Quantitative estimates for a typical language. Strata represented by horizontal lines: sememic (S), lexemic (L), morphemic (M), and phonemic (P); wavy line at bottom represents the phonetic stratum, considered to be outside the structure. The logarithmic scale on each stratum indicates larger number of units from left to right, starting with the representation of a single element as a small circle: semon ($\sigma$), lexon ($\lambda$), morphon ($\mu$), and phonon ($\varphi$). Vertical lines indicate connections between strata; phoneme ($\Phi$), morpheme (M), lexeme ($\Lambda$). See text.

experimental purposes, but this is not what human beings do unless they are playing with their language. Each of the lower sets of tactic rules is simpler and will generate a larger set of combinations, including combinations that would be unacceptable from the point of view of a more complete system.

Figure 35 shows certain rough quantitative estimates for a typical language, based on my experience with various languages. Strata are represented by horizontal lines, with logarithmic scales to indicate increasing numbers of elementary units. The points at which it is possible to make connections from one stratum to another are joined by vertical lines; we make the rules for the smallest elements possible. For example, we do not set up a lexical rule for "tall oak", since it will be automatically handled by the rule for "tall" and the rule for "oak"—but we do have to set up a rule for "white oak". Note that the vertical lines are placed so that they have their connections slightly to the right of the upper-stratum elementary units; this means that on the average the number of elementary units that serves as the input for one of the conversions is slightly larger than 1. Thus, while the rules for conversion from lexons to morphemes can usually be stated in terms of single lexons, occasionally a rule has to be stated in terms

of a combination of lexons: for example, $^L$/bad er/ has to be treated as a
unit in order to be related to the lower stratum. In the same way, most mor-
phophonemic rules can also be stated in terms of single morphons, though
sometimes two or more morphons have to be taken together, as in Korean,
where the combination $^M$/w/ followed by a back unrounded $^M$/ï/ comes
out as $^P$/u/, in which two morphons are treated as a unit. The same applies
for the connection from the phonemic to the phonetic stratum. We have a
rather different situation at the top of the diagram, in the conversion from
the sememic stratum to the lexemic. I estimate that on the average slightly
more than three semons must be taken in combination as a unit in order to
be related to the lower stratum; the line showing that connection is therefore placed just to the right of 3. As an example, $^L$/man/ in one of its meanings is the representation of a combination of five semons: $^S$/thing/, $^S$/ani-
mate/, $^S$/adult/, $^S$/human/, $^S$/male/.

The diagram also shows the units named by linguists with the time-honored
suffix "-eme", i.e., those which are representations of the upper stratum
units. They are found at the bottom of the vertical lines, where these inter-
sect the next lower stratum. Capital Greek letters are used to denote the
lexemes ($\Lambda$), morphemes (M), and phonemes ($\Phi$).

The number 2 with an exponent found at the left of each stratum represents an attempt to make quantitative estimates with regard to a typical
linguistic structure as held in the mind of a single speaker (rather than
about the total available lexicon as found for example in the Oxford English dictionary). I have made estimates for each of the fundamental units,
rounded upwards to the nearest power of 2; the powers of 2 were chosen
because they can be used to estimate the number of bits in a linguistic
structure as held in the mind of a single speaker: to find the number of bits
one has to estimate the number of different things in any category to the
nearest higher power of 2 (for example, it takes five bits to represent each
item in a category of up to $2^5$). The number of phonons in the typical language illustrated in Figure 35 is between 8 and 16 ($2^4$ for ç)—it is not exactly 16, but the number is always rounded upwards to the nearest power
of 2; four bits are required. The number of morphons is shown to be between 16 and 32; according to traditional analyses there are many languages with more than 32 morphophonemes, but these are usually analyses
that have been unduly influenced by the alphabet—if a proper criterion for
determining the morphophonemes is used, a smaller number will be found
than is usually accepted. The number of lexons is given as $2^{13}$, and the
number of semons as $2^{12}$; on the sememic stratum the figure $2^{15}$, or about
32,000, is shown for those combinations of semons which relate to lexemes
(i.e., semolexemes).

*Osgood:* Do you mean the number of lexemes estimated?

*Lamb:* This is the number of semolexemes, which means the sememic
combinations for which there are lexemes; it is not necessarily the same as
the number of lexemes.

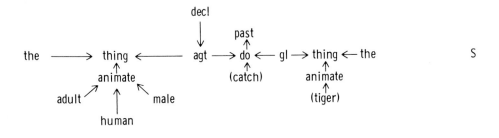

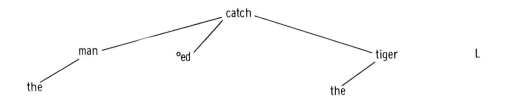

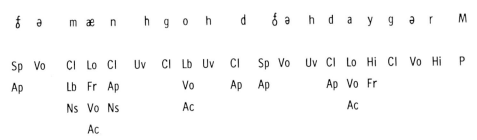

$$\text{ð ə m æ n \quad ɦ g o h \quad d \; óə h d a y g ə r \quad M}$$

| Sp | Vo | Cl | Lo | Cl | Uv | Cl | Lb | Uv | Cl | Sp | Vo | Uv | Cl | Lo | Hi | Cl | Vo | Hi | P |
| Ap |    | Lb | Fr | Ap |    |    | Vo |    |    | Ap | Ap |    | Ap | Vo | Fr |    |    |    |   |
|    |    | Ns | Vo | Ns |    |    | Ac |    |    |    |    |    |    | Ac |    |    |    |    |   |
|    |    | Ac |    |    |    |    |    |    |    |    |    |    |    |    |    |    |    |    |   |

**Figure 36.** Sentence ("the man caught the tiger") analyzed on all four of the structural strata depicted in Figure 35. From top to bottom: sememic network (S), lexemic tree (L), morphemic strings (M), and phonemes (P). See text.

At the upper right-hand corner of the diagram in Figure 35 is a line going up from the language to the outside world, with a cloud-like figure to represent an infinite number of semantic phenomena. With this type of structure, that is, linguistic structure, one can talk about an infinite number of things with only 16 or fewer fundamental elements (i.e., the phonons) emitted as speech.

Figure 36 provides an example of a whole sentence on all four of the structural strata. The clause chosen is "The man caught the tiger", an extremely simple example, brought to mind by my current concern with machine translation research: a couple of years ago I gave a paper at a machine translation meeting, in which I castigated other machine translation workers for trying to build machine translation programs before they had analyzed the structures of the languages they were dealing with; I said that the machine translation problem reminded me of the old Chinese recipe for tiger stew which begins, "First, you must catch the tiger."

We have "the man caught the tiger" as a sememic network at the top of

Figure 36, with the lexemic tree underneath. Although on these two strata combinations of letters are used for "the", "man", and so forth, they must be taken as single elements: it happens that each of the lexemes consists of only a single lexon in this example. Then, at the morphemic stratum there is a string of morphemes, each of which is composed of morphons (more commonly known as morphophonemes). There are certain problems about the way I have analyzed the phonemes; I am not an expert on English, but I do know something about it, and what I have done, I have done advisedly. Each phoneme is a bundle, if you will, of phonons, and the phonons are written one under another. The first phoneme consists of the phonons "Spirant" and "Apical". For the second I have specified nothing but "Vocalic"; it is the neutral vowel, as indicated by varied evidence: for example, the hesitation vowel "uh" $^P$/ə/ is neutral vocalizing. Every other vowel I take to be "Vocalic" with some further specification.

*Osgood:* Can you try that rule on Dr. Jakobson's presentation? There is no single, simple rule for his hesitation vowels!

*Lamb:* Dr. Jakobson's phonology is Russian, not English. The output of his English morphology goes directly into Russian phonology.

Figure 37 illustrates a sentence with a relative clause, a type which, according to the transformational school, requires a transformational rule. It is intended to illustrate my contention that transformations are not necessary when starting with networks instead of strings. Some string structure is perfectly appropriate to language because speech is a sequential process which takes place in time, but since the structure is separated into different strata, there is no reason to preserve the strings at the top.

The second part of the study attempts to construct models of mechanisms that would be able to deal with the kind of structure described. We might ask ourselves, what are the structural elements, what are the phonons, morphons, lexons, and so on? Ordinarily, one tends to think of them as objects of some sort; I want to propose the idea that they are best not regarded as objects or items of any kind, but rather as names: we can say

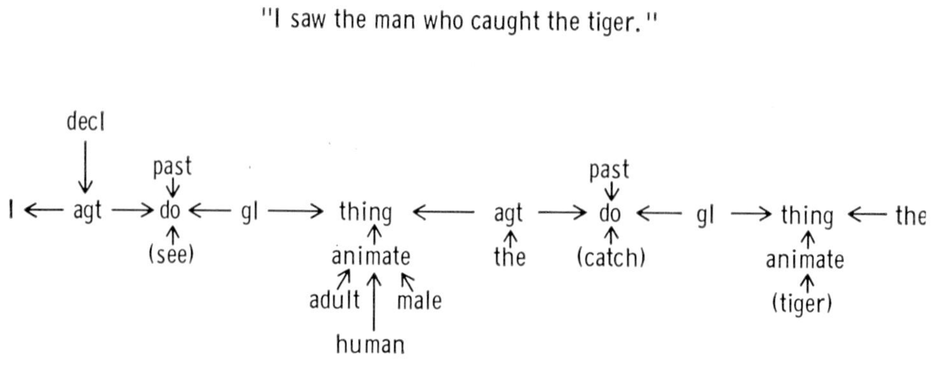

"I saw the man who caught the tiger."

**Figure 37.** Sentence with a relative clause, as analyzed at the sememic stratum.

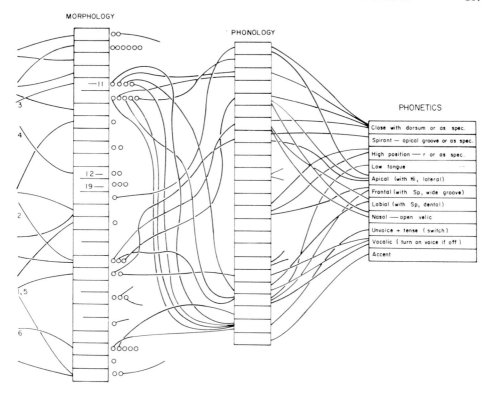

**Figure 38.** Illustration of a production device which offers an alternative view of the system shown in Figure 34, with connections (wires) from one set of rules to another. From the left, the wires that are the outputs of the lexology (not shown) act as inputs for the morphology; the outputs of the morphology (circles) lead into the simple phonology shown in the center; from there, the wires lead to the phonetics, considered as instructions to the muscles that control the speech mechanism. See text.

that a lexon is nothing but the name of a morphological realization rule; the occurrence of a lexon is then nothing but an indication that a specific morphological rule is to be executed. Or we can consider the lexon to be the address where a particular morphological rule is stored in the memory of the system.

Another way to consider the problem is in keeping with the diagram shown in Figure 34, taken as a representation of a production device. It shows that the semology produces an output consisting of actual objects suitably arranged; these objects go into the lexology, and so forth. In this model, the lexology, morphology and phonology can be characterized as transducers; each has an input and provides an output. Each of the units, e.g., the lexons, is a sort of object or symbol. An alternative view is illustrated in Figure 38, which shows the rules as boxes in ladder-like arrangements: at left, a portion of the morphology, with only a few simple realization rules; in the middle, the simplified phonology; at the right, a very sketchy indication of the phonetic rules, considered as instructions to the

muscles that control the speech mechanism. The details of the latter are outside the province of the linguist and better left to the physiologist. Each
box (rule) has, instead of objects as inputs and outputs, wires or lines indicating connections. For instance, starting from the top phonological rule,
we see its output as two wires going down to two boxes in the phonetics
which together say "close with the apex"; that is, $^P$/d/. The output of this
rule is not an object; it is just an impulse going along the wires to the corresponding phonetic rules. The only rules of this entire system that produce
actual objects as output are the last ones at the right, the ones that produce
the actual speech sounds; everything else in the system is just connections,
indicating that certain rules are to be executed.

*Osgood:* You used the word "objects" for the physical output of this entire nervous system operation. You apparently also used it to refer to something which is well within the nervous system, that is, the global intention,
or the pattern of an intended utterance.

*Lamb:* It is becoming a little involved. I am offering as a mechanism an
alternative to the model that may be suggested by what is shown in Figure
34, where the output of each subsystem comes out as little units, or elements, or objects—I do not want to be too specific about this—or symbols,
let us say, which are retained somewhere in memory. For example, Hockett[*]
has devised as a model a machine with a moving tape between each two
transducers; the elements are written on the tape. As the tape moves, those
elements just written out onto it go into the next lower converter, and then
(after the tape moves slightly farther) they may be erased; so the tape can
be considered as a loop. An important feature is that for the conversion one
needs only the immediate environment. Figure 38 shows an alternative
view, highly simplified. Instead of being written down somewhere to serve
as input to other rules, in this system there are no material elements as outputs of rules.

*Osgood:* Is this nervous output different from what one says? Or is it intended to represent what one actually says?

*Lamb:* At the bottom of Figure 34 there is a box for the phonetic trans-
ducer, about which I consider myself ignorant for I am not a physiologist.
There I might talk in terms of nerves and muscles, but here I want to
speak in more abstract terms; I prefer to leave it to other people to relate
this to human beings. For me, Figure 38 is just a model.

*Lenneberg:* From your diagram, it looks as if you already start with a
formed string. Then you have leading wires, and at the end you say,
"These are muscles, and I do not know anything about them." I am not
sure why this is a synthetic generating device.

*Lamb:* The point is that the four transducers are not ordinarily genera-
tors, but the semology is a generator.

---

[*] C. F. Hockett, unpublished lecture at the Rand Corporation, 1963.

*Lenneberg:* You are saying you start with the string.

*Lamb:* There is no string to start with. The semology, which is not shown in Figure 38, does not start with a string; it starts at the initial or start rule. This rule offers a choice of three or four ways to begin the construction of a network and leads to other rules which continue the process. I have not shown any of these rules. The mechanism starts only with the start position; it has no input, and it generates networks as output.

This is, of course, greatly oversimplified, but what is given inside each box corresponds to the part of the rule which gives the conditions under which a particular representation is obtained. Those conditions are to be stated in terms of immediate environment. There are many cases of morphons which always have the same representation, so each has only one subrule and no environment has to be specified. Actually, I have oversimplified by giving each of the morphons only one subrule, but in the converter on the left I have shown rules with more than one subrule: a number within a morphology box identifies another rule, whose associated lexon acts as a conditioning environment.

I have not shown all the wires, but the ones shown are not drawn at random. In fact, anyone with a fondness for puzzles can figure out each one of the morphons given. Actually, there is one for each box; the top one is the rule for the morphon $^M$/d/, and so on; one rule is shown for each of the ordinary morphons. Although there are many rules in a real morphology, only very few are shown here. Farther left, outside the diagram, would be the lexology, the largest area of the grammar; the figure shows some of the wires coming in from it. Only half the wires between the phonology and the phonetics are shown, to avoid clutter. There are a couple of places where wires are shown just starting out; this only means that the machine has not been drawn in its entirety. For other boxes no wires have been drawn, but actually wires go both in and out.

Along with this machine, there must be some sort of temporary memory, which serves as a kind of control to keep track of the sequence that must be followed. At the extreme left of the figure there are some numbers; if each of the numbered wires is followed in the order specified, from 1 through 5, if from each rule encountered its output wires are followed, and if when the phonetic instructions are reached one does what they indicate, one will say, "The man caught the tiger." Thus, the numbers at the extreme left of the figure may be considered occurrences of lexons in the proper order for the sentence, "The man caught the tiger."

A slightly different machine is shown in Figure 39, which can be considered as either a simpler representation of the device in Figure 38 (by saying that the difference is merely in the diagram) or, by emphasizing the differences, as a separate machine. The wires shown in the previous machine have been substituted for by addresses as in a computer. Each of the rules is numbered sequentially and the rules to be followed are indicated

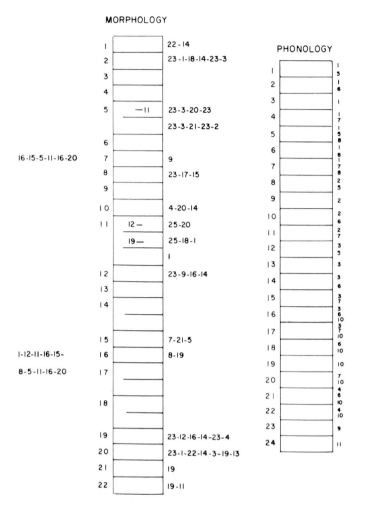
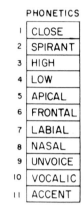

**Figure 39.** Model of a production device on the same principles as that of Figure 38, with rules and connections indicated by numbers instead of wires. For each conversion column, the rules (boxes) are numbered sequentially at the left, and their outputs are indicated at the right by numbers which refer to the next stage. Linear arrangement for the output of the morphology indicates that the corresponding rules are to be followed sequentially; vertical arrangement for the phonology output means simultaneity in execution. Series of numbers at the extreme left are lexological outputs, serving as inputs for the morphology: upper set, when followed through to the phonetics, results in the phrase, "the man caught the tiger"; lower set, in "I saw the man who caught the tiger."

by numbers on the output side of each column; their arrangement indicates whether they are to be executed simultaneously (phonology) or sequentially (morphology); these latter are, of course, addresses to phonological rules. According to this diagram, the structural elements of language are the addresses of conversion rules.

Although the result is similar, there is actually somewhat less information in this machine than in the one of Figure 38: in the earlier model one can go in both directions, whereas in this one it is possible to proceed directly only in the encoding direction. For decoding it would be necessary to search through the outputs of higher rules instead of following the wires directly to the right ones.

In Figure 39 the numbers 16-15-5-11-16-20 (extreme left) specify the phrase "The man caught the tiger." So, following those rules in the order given—that is, morphological rule No. 16, leading to phonological rules 8 and 19, of which 8 in turn leads to phonetic rules 2 and 5, and so forth—one ends up again saying, "The man caught the tiger." Execution of the rules indicated at the lower left (1, 12, 11, 16, etc.), will result in saying, "I saw the man who caught the tiger."

By executing the morphological rules in various other orders, one can say, "I caught the man who saw the tiger", "the boy saw the tiger", and many variations. But since the lexological rules have not been provided, nonsense phrases like "Catch tiger the man" can also be generated.

It is interesting to speculate about a number of features that go along with this model. For example, what kind of temporary memory is required to keep track of the sequence of operations? Without it one would run into conflict: if we start as directed at the left with morphological rules 16 and then 15, 5, etc., when we execute 16, it tells us to execute phonological rules 8 and 19. Do we execute them first, or retain in a temporary memory the fact that we have to do it, and go on to morphological rule 15? These are problems that still have to be worked out. We have some evidence about this process but more work is needed.

A more general version of this general scheme might account for certain phenomena we observe in language use which have not really been very well explained in the past. For one thing, the pauses that occur when people are talking spontaneously, often in the middle of what we would think of as grammatical constructions from the point of view of lexology, are probably related to the fact that only a partial network of sememes is generated before they start the encoding process. I have not worked with this enough to know the details, but apparently one does some encoding and then goes back and generates a little more of the sememic network.

The tactical construction rules of the lexology are apparently oriented toward the production of sentence-length units, but pause can occur in the middle of a sentence while more of a network is being formed or while suitable lexemes are being searched for. As the sentence relates to the lexology, there are other kinds of units which apparently relate to the morphology and phonology, namely words and syllables, respectively. Junctures are apparently put in as boundaries by the morphology. A great deal of work is needed to show how the functioning of the various types of construction rules is integrated with the interstratal conversion.

*Osgood:* What is the evidence that the two levels you have shown are both going on simultaneously? Is it changes which occur in the actual motor output, anticipatory effects at the sound level, at the motor level? Is one already anticipating a phonemic bundle while executing the one in progress?

*Lamb:* There is a great opportunity for research in that question. It is an alternative to my proposition, certainly a worthwhile one. It is very easy to conduct such research, on ordinary slips of the tongue, for example.

*Osgood:* We should build a machine to produce human slips of speech.

*Lamb:* Slips of the tongue can be induced, for instance, by giving alcoholic drinks to a subject and letting him talk to a girl. A tape recorder could collect extremely valuable data for working out the mechanism.

I would like now to return to the diagram in Figure 35 and work through the calculation of the storage requirement for a grammar. Since I have worked out in some detail what forms the rules have, and since it is possible to make a rough estimate of the required number of rules of each type, it is possible to calculate the information content of a linguistic structure as it would be remembered in the mind of a single speaker. This must of course be distinguished from the total language available to the whole speech community. These are necessarily very rough figures, and I would say that probably they are correct only to within a factor of 2 in either direction.

I will be giving these estimates only for a system of the type outlined in Figure 39 (but somewhat more elaborate than the oversimplified version in that diagram), which is efficient for production but not for decoding. For a more efficient decoding capability we must add a certain amount of additional information, but I have not figured out how much. For this calculation I will define grammar to include lexology, morphology and phonology. Each of these systems has construction rules and realization rules.

First we may consider briefly the construction rules of the lexology. For this area I would guess only very roughly that the number of rules might be several hundred and that the average number of bits per rule is probably less than forty. Since the total number of bits is probably less than 50,000, and since the figures are being rounded to the nearest hundred thousand, we need not be too concerned here about this figure.

The greatest requirement is for the realization rules of the lexology. This section corresponds to what we usually think of as the lexicon. I am assuming here about 20,000 lexemes, many of which, however, are ambiguous in that they can represent multiple sememic units; on the other hand, many are not ambiguous, especially the strings like "red-headed woodpecker". What we have to count is the subrules because each subrule will link a specific semolexeme to a specific lexeme. I am estimating 40,000 subrules for a person with a vocabulary, as vocabularies are usually counted, of something like 10,000 to 15,000 words. The trouble is that the way vocabulary is counted is vague; the unit counted has not been properly defined. But let us say there are 40,000 subrules. In these rules, the specification of the conditioning environment requires, I shall say, an average of 3 semons at 12 bits each, giving 36 bits. The output of the subrule is a combination of one or more lexons, an average of, let us say, 2⅓, which would require 30 bits at 13 bits per lexon. We thus find 66 bits as the average information in a single subrule; I will round that value up to 70. Seventy times 40,000, the number of subrules, gives a total of 2,800,000 bits.

In the morphology, the construction rules contain even less information than those of the lexology; the total is probably well under 20,000 bits, a negligible amount in the present context. For the morphological realization rules, which convert lexons to morphemes, I am assuming 8000 subrules, a somewhat higher number than the number of lexons. Since many lexons do not have alternate representations, it is often not necessary to specify a conditioning environment, so the average conditioning environment for a subrule I will take to be slightly less than one lexon, say ten bits, at 13 bits per lexon. The average morpheme, the output of one of these rules, consists of about five morphons, as shown in Figure 35, at five bits each for a total of 25 bits. So we get 35 bits per rule times 8000 rules. If we round upwards to the nearest 100,000, we have 300,000 bits for the morphological rules.

The phonology, which takes us from the morphons to the phonons, requires a very small amount of storage space. We are dealing here with only about 25 to 30 elements, several of which do not have alternate representations. So, if we assume 40 subrules with conditioning environment of, on the average, six bits, (i.e., slightly more than one element) and output averaging 11 bits, the total is 40 times 17, or 680—not 680,000, but 680—which is very small in comparison to the other figures. Consequently, we do not have to include it in the calculation.

Thus for this very rough calculation of the storage requirement for a grammar efficient for production for a single typical speaker, we add 2,800,000 and 300,000 for a total of 3,100,000. This is all very rough, and we ought to allow a possible error factor of 2. But even though it is rough, when I first made the estimate I was very surprised that it turned out to be so small. The immediate access memory of the 7090 computer is about one million bits. Our figure is only three times that much.

### Discussion

*Osgood:* Dr. Lamb, it seems to me that much of your particular quantitative estimation depends upon how you go about estimating the number of semantic components. The reason I am particularly interested is that in solving this problem rigorously, you would also come close to a way of measuring denotative meaning. However, the kinds of dimensions worry me: those that work for "kinship" simply do not transfer to any other semantic area. How did you arrive at a finite number without doing, as it were, a kind of encyclopedic analysis of the whole world?

*Lamb:* I gave an estimate of about 4000 semons and, as I said, it is obviously subject to error. What you mention about kinship systems is true, and the same would be true of a number of systems which are in themselves unified. This is not necessarily bad. I do not know how many kinship terms there are in a typical system, perhaps 100, and they may be reduced to 20, 10, or 15 components. I have not done much work with kinship.

People may think that this kind of analysis cannot really be carried very far, an impression they may gain after discovering the large number of semons which are unique constituents, i.e., those which occur in only one combination. An example is the word "tiger" in Figure 36: it appears in parentheses to indicate what is left of "tiger" after the components $^s$/thing/ and $^s$/animate/ are extracted. It thus distinguishes "tiger" from other animals. Linguistically, all we have is a single structural element which it is not our responsibility to relate to the real world. One of the factors here is that there is a great deal of individual difference: different people have varying amounts of information on what it is that differentiates tigers from other animals. But linguistically all we have is a single structural element that can be symbolized $^s$/(tiger)/. There are many such elements that have the property of occurring in a single combination only. Consequently, their identification as components will not reduce the inventory of individual units that one has to deal with. However, the question has to be raised of how many these are. Remember that I am speaking in terms of what one individual speaker happens to know. Offhand, at first look one is inclined to think that the average person knows a great many things of this type—all of the animal names would come under this category, for instance—but if they are actually counted, their number turns out to be rather manageable. Of course, accurate counts have not really been made in this area. But I, for example, worked on an American Indian language for some time and was amazed that my informant was able to give me 13 different words for different kinds of mushrooms, many local place names, and so forth; yet, when I tried to accumulate all the material, there were only about one or two thousand morphemes in the whole corpus. Therefore I estimate that perhaps there are as many as one or two thousand of these unique constituents, and perhaps another one or two thousand semons which occur in numerous combinations. If they number somewhere in the neighborhood of three or four thousand altogether, their many combinations can result in further thousands of actual units represented by lexical items.

I am not analyzing this stratum to the extent that some might desire; I think one must resist the temptation to go too far in trying to say what something is—like introducing components such as "stripes" to differentiate tigers.

It is also the case that much of this thinking comes from Hjelmslev (2) of the glossematic school, who was of the opinion that there was a great deal of correspondence between the plane of content and the plane of expression. We must realize that there are severe limitations in that regard; on the plane of the expression, i.e., the phonemic stratum, we can analyze down to less than 16 fundamental elements, but nothing like that is possible at the sememic level. Still, something is accomplished if one can analyze down to three or four thousand elements. It seems to me reasonable to expect that this can be done.

*Osgood:* I am not quite clear about your reasons for making distinctions of the bundles in the sense of simultaneous features at the phonemic level, or what you call networks at the sememic level. It seems to me you have a simultaneous bundle of components as contrasted with the sequential pattern. I do not see why one is called network and treated differently, in a sense, than the other one.

*Lamb:* They are structurally different; all that has to be specified about things occurring simultaneously is that they occur simultaneously; they could be put in any order; specific order can be chosen only by a convention. If there are three of them, say Cl, Ap, Ns (Figure 36), there is no closer connection between, say, "Nasal" and "Apical" than between "Apical" and "Close". This is not true at the sememic stratum, where there are various ways in which units can be connected to one another, even though we may think of them as being simultaneous. Figure 40 illustrates some of the

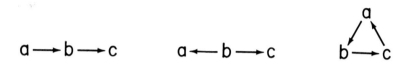

**Figure 40.** Three possible ways in which elements could be connected.

ways in which three elements could be connected. In general, then, the difference between one type of connection and another would be distinctive at the sememic level, whereas no such difference is found at the phonemic stratum.

*Osgood:* Is this because of hierarchy?

*Lamb:* It is because the properties of arrangement are different.

*Stockwell:* Could you give us an example of the three terms in Figure 36 arranged so that they would result in a different lexeme?

*Lamb:* Arrangement (a) is allowable, but (b) is not:

We should say in case (a) that ˢ/human/ presupposes ˢ/animate/, while case (b) would not be a well-formed combination.

*Stockwell:* What you are saying is that the semological rules would generate the first arrangement but not the second.

*Lamb:* Yes, whereas in the case of the phonological rules, they will generate only one combination, i.e., the bundles without respect to order. But in the case of networks there are connections indicated by the lines drawn between units.

*Osgood:* Why select "human", "male", and "adult" rather than "short", or "tall", or "light", or "wealthy," or "poor", or what have you?

*Lamb:* As any speaker of English knows, although he may not be able to say so in these terms, a man is an adult human being by contrast to a woman, boy, or girl. Woman has the same components except for "female" instead of "male". It is specifically this way because of the properties of the English language, not because of anything in the real world.

*Geschwind:* You said that man was "human", "male", and "adult" by contrast with certain other groups, e.g., "female" and "child". It seems to me that this does not exhaust the possibilities. One might as easily contrast "man" with "God"; then "mortal" and "immortal" become important contrasts. Other contrasts could probably also be set up.

*Lamb:* In any of these cases, I am not saying that wherever it is possible to identify a negative one has to do so, as with binary distinctive features. Something is there or it is not; when it is not, one does not say anything about it. I would think that not being God is more neutral than being divine. Whatever God is to a speaker of a particular language ordinarily would be an additional attribute.

*Carterette:* Since you have characterized a structural system which has fundamental differences from the Chomsky system, I wonder if you would contrast the measure of information in your system to his. For example, it seems to me you could substitute a transformational rule for rule of choice. You start out with strings in the one case and perform certain transformations. However, you are still dealing, presumably, with the same basic corpus of language, or one would hope you were. I wonder if, in some sense, this is a more economical system in terms of an information measure. Is there no reason to expect the two measures to be identical since they must describe the same corpus?

*Lamb:* We have to distinguish two things: the sentences which will be generated by the two systems and the information content of the grammar. Actually, there are differences in both of these respects, because something that I intend for the semology to do is to specify not only what combinations are grammatical but what combinations make sense. To the extent that transformational grammar does not go as far as the structural system I propose, the latter is a more complete system; it will (if implemented) exclude certain grammatical but nonsensical utterances. With regard to the surface informational content of the grammar, I would expect this would turn out to be considerably less than in the transformational system.

*Carterette:* How many bits do you have altogether ?

*Lamb:* Somewhat above three million in terms of bits in the grammar, not including the semology. I would expect the transformational grammar to involve perhaps twice as many or more, since the rules with which Chomsky (1) starts the generative process are constituent structure rules, so that it is necessary to have many transformational rules, which are very complicated.

*Ladefoged:* Dr. Lamb's presentation was certainly stimulating. But for most of us, it was a unique presentation in the sense that it represents simply his own view. I could, of course, go through a number of other views about linguistics and explain how they are all related to each other and to Dr. Lamb's view, but I think enough complex terminology has been introduced very rapidly to make it completely unprofitable to describe other linguistic theories.

The second difficulty I have is that I am a phonetician and I had always thought of myself as being a linguist. But Dr. Lamb relegated me, perhaps I should say promoted me, to being a physiologist because he said that phonetics was outside the bounds normally discussed by linguists. If this were really so, it would mean that linguists were producing many hypotheses, many schema, and then having no possible way of testing them.

*Lamb:* I was referring just to the articulatory mechanism.

*Ladefoged:* I am referring specifically to the articulatory part. If we really had no way of coming out into reality, so to speak, if the whole of linguistics were a description of something that never made contact with sounds in the end, we would have no possible way of verifying our linguistic statements. I feel this is rather important. For this reason, I would like to challenge some of Dr. Lamb's remarks and present some other data that goes contrary to what he has been saying.

First, I think he has confused the process of linguistic description with the mental processes that may go on in the production of speech. His scheme of linguistic description was given to us as if it were a possible model of how human beings talk, as if we might encode messages in that way. There is a great deal of evidence to show that this is just not true. Nobody knows much about the production and control of the higher linguistic units. But we do know something about the actual process of making noises; and if you want to talk about how a human being produces noises, it is no good thinking in terms of a set of rules that convert strings of phonemes into utterances, because human beings probably do not have a store of phonemes which they use as the input control signals to the noise-making devices.

We can show quite clearly that when one wants to stress a particular word, when one makes it louder, one has to produce a contraction of the internal intercostal muscles so as to push out more air. Because the chest contains a large volume of air, a quite considerable contraction has to be produced before a stressed sound is emitted. If I am going to say a sentence like "This is the house that Jack built" and I want to stress the word "house", then the stress pulse for this word must be innervated at the same time as the muscles of the tongue are being innervated to produce the sounds of the word "the". One cannot account for these actions simply in terms of strings of phonemes going along one after another.

There are other examples, one of which was mentioned earlier. If one is going to say, for instance, the word "key" or the word "car", the two "k" sounds must be made differently. In a sentence like "That is my key" or "That is my car", the tongue gestures are different throughout the whole of the "k" sound. Before one even makes the closure between the back of the tongue and the roof of the mouth, one, so to speak, anticipates the next vowel. In other words, it looks suspiciously as if the words "key" and "car" are being innervated as a whole; they are being triggered off as whole segments. In fact, as I understand physiological principles, it seems unlikely that one would trigger off segments as small as single phonemes. If we want to think in computer terms as a useful analogy, we can think of human beings as having quick access to a very large amount of storage and simply not having complicated control programs which produce complex sequences of partially simultaneous actions. In other words, I doubt whether we produce ordinary speech as a result of operating on phonemes, as opposed to using bigger stored units such as syllables.

The kind of evidence that some people cite against this claim is that provided by lapses and spoonerisms. If I refer to Syd Lamb as "Lyd Samb", which would be an unusual thing to do, it is also an unusual spoonerism. Most spoonerisms do not turn "Syd Lamb" into "Lyd Samb" but turn him into "Lyd Lamb". What is far more common than a complete transposition is simply an introduction from something yet to come. But there is another thing about spoonerisms: sounds cannot be introduced in any of the possible ways but only in so far as they form parts of whole words. "Syd Lamb" is not a good example; if I take a phrase like "short stop", I will never change it into "stort shtop" simply because, being an English speaker, "shtop" is not in my ordinary possibilities, and I can transpose only things that make possible combinations of phonemes. In other words, I do not have access to phonemes in isolation. I can trigger off only large bundles of phonemes, perhaps of the order of half a syllable, perhaps even of the order of whole syllables, or longer.

These are my kind of arguments on the lowest level for saying that Dr. Lamb's scheme is incorrect when it comes to how one produces sounds. I suspect that we have equally good evidence for saying it is wrong at the higher end. We cannot really show that the separate strata exist, and that one goes from one to the other in the way suggested. This is the model that is produced by a linguist trying to describe a language and bears no necessary relation to the mental processes required in producing speech.

*Lamb:* Let me state again what I was trying to do: first, figure out the simplest system or structure which will account for the linguistic data which linguists have observed, and second, find the simplest possible mechanism which would be able to use such a system to produce such data. I separate from this the problem of what correlations might or might not exist between such a system and the human brain because this is something I am not competent to discuss.

On the other matter, I think the information on stress and intercostal muscles is very interesting. However, in that case, as well as in the case of "key" and "car", and so on, what Dr. Ladefoged says does not invalidate the system I presented because in all of the converters one has environmental conditioning; in fact, environmental conditions constitute the main content inside the system. Other things in the chain are taken into consideration: before one can close with the dorsum, one has to know what the following vowel is going to be. In my system it is understood that one does take this into consideration.

## REFERENCES

1. CHOMSKY, N., *Syntactic Structures*. Mouton, The Hague, 1957.
2. HJELMSLEV, L., *Prolegomena to a Theory of Language*. Univ. of Wisconsin Press, Madison, 1961.
3. JOOS, M., Semology: a linguistic theory of meaning. *Stud. Ling.*, 1958, 13: 53-70.

# CONTEXTUAL CONTROL IN SENTENCE
# UNDERSTANDING AND CREATING

**CHARLES E. OSGOOD**
University of Illinois
Urbana

Although the interest of psychologists in language behavior is of long standing—witness Wundt's 1921 work *Die Sprache* (48) and Kantor's 1936 book, *An Objective Psychology of Grammar* (22)—psycholinguistics as a field of specialization is very new. Only within the past decade have psychologists and linguists been interacting at close range and at high intensity. The impact of this exchange upon linguists has been, among other things, to make them more statistical in their thinking and more concerned with language universals; upon psychologists, it has been also to loosen their fixation upon words-in-isolation and convince them that there is more to language than association and meaning.

This meeting of minds and ideas has already led psycholinguistics into a kind of crisis—at least as far as psychologists are concerned—which is the problem presented in this paper: can psychological theories incorporate and render comprehensible the way human beings understand and create sentences? If not, our theories are at best insufficient and at worst erroneous. Some psychologists seem to have concluded that our theoretical house is in complete disorder and would prefer to live in a tent while a new one is being constructed. I am a conservative in this respect. I have grown fond of the old mansion, built at such effort and expense, and hope that some relatively minor alterations and extensions will make it livable again.

### Nature of the Problem

To understand what the issue is, we may start with a simple unanalyzed string of words and trace through a series of increasingly powerful models designed to analyze them and define their validity as a sentence. Figure 41 displays one possible string of words: THE MAN HITS THE COLORFUL BALL, which is certainly a simple enough sentence. Or is it? The linguist's problem (cf., 4) is to design a grammar for a language, English in this case, which will generate all possible sentences that are grammatical and none that are not.* Since any sample of sentences is finite, whereas potential sentences are not, a grammar must include a set of rules which project onto any potential sentence and determine its grammaticalness. As Chomsky points out, a grammar is thus a kind of theory of a language.

A possible model for generating sentences—and one appealing to psychologists because of their familiarity with the complementary approaches to behavior of learning theory and information theory—is the finite state grammar. Since sentences have a way of proceeding sequentially in time (or from left to right on a printed page), it seems intuitively reasonable that each subsequent word should be probabilistically dependent upon the antecedent words. Hence a Markov process should be sufficient for generating them. Chomsky (4) has demonstrated on logical grounds that such a finite state generator could not produce the indefinite set of sentences that characterizes a natural language—including novel utterances that are sentences, but not utterances that are not sentences. Miller, Galanter & Pribram (32) have computed that it would take a childhood lasting 100 years to be exposed just once to each of the possible sentences that could be generated by an ordinary vocabulary, given a 20-word sentence length limit. In particular, a finite state generator could not handle the potentially infinite imbedding that characterizes natural languages (e.g., "The man who said that I know that John is the one who likes the cars that . . . is here").

A model that seems to resolve these logical difficulties, and the one commonly employed by linguists, is the phrase structure grammar. As diagrammed in Figure 41, our sentence (S) is first resolved into its immediate constituents, a noun phrase (NP) plus a verb phrase (VP); these in turn are resolved into their immediate constituents, and so on, generating a hierarchically organized "tree". Whereas the Markov model is a sequential hierarchy of choice-points and alternatives, the phrase structure model is a simultaneous hierarchy of units-within-units at various levels. Note that the shifts from level to level are accomplished by a series of rewrite rules which must be applied in a particular order; these are like principles in a psychological theory, relating construct to construct. Note also that what I have called the dictionary rules—which transform the terminal symbols, T + N + V + T + A + N, into a string of words such as, "the man hits the colorful ball"—are of a very different kind; these are analogous to the rules of identification or correlation by which constructs in a psycho-

---

* *Dr. Carterette's note after the Conference:* This goal is too strong and would cause any grammar to fail. A very recent modification apparently retains the goal in the strong form yet at the same time recognizes that men produce and understand sentences that do not meet a strict criterion of grammaticalness. Thus, according to Miller & Chomsky (31), "It would then be correct to say that a grammar not only generates sentences with structural descriptions but also assigns to each string, whether generated or not, a degree of grammaticalness that measures its deviation from the set of perfectly well-formed sentences as well as a partial structural description that indicates how this string deviates from well-formedness."

REWRITE RULES                    TREE DIAGRAM

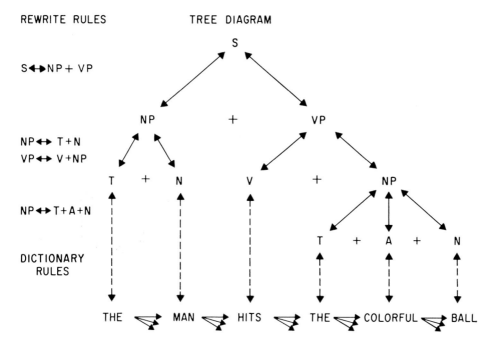

$S \leftrightarrow NP + VP$

$NP \leftrightarrow T + N$
$VP \leftrightarrow V + NP$

$NP \leftrightarrow T + A + N$

DICTIONARY
RULES

**Figure 41.** Model showing phrase structure grammar. The sentence "The man hits the colorful ball" is resolved into a hierarchically organized tree. See text.

logical theory are related to events in the real world. Note finally that any application of the dictionary rules to this terminal string of symbols must yield a grammatical sentence in English, e.g., "the cow plays a drastic mountain". The question of meaning or sense (vs. meaninglessness or nonsense) is of no concern at this point.

Contrary to usual linguistic practice, I have deliberately made all my rewrite rules bi-directional. This is to express the fact that while in encoding (creating) sentences each element is expanded into its immediate constituents, in decoding (understanding) sentences immediate constituents are fused or amalgamated into the supraordinate elements they constitute. To use an analogy, in creating sentences we begin at the trunk (a global intention, if you will) and end up at the leaves (a sentence), while in understanding sentences we begin in the leaves and hopefully end up at the trunk.

*Stockwell:* Some of us would want to contend that the decoding process is rather a simultaneous encoding and matching process, and not a reversal of the arrows: that one, as it were, starts generating (and it is not at all likely that we generate from the top down) and seeks to find successively closer matches—correspondences—between his internal output and what he hears. Both the hearer and the speaker are in some sense encoding simultaneously.

*Osgood:* I am familiar with that notion, though I disagree with it. According to that view, the sentence interpreter receives a certain pattern of input and stores it briefly while running through (generating) a number of syntactic alternatives, ending up in most cases with a "tree" that matches the one followed by the sentence creator. I think there are difficulties there.

*Stockwell:* There may be, but I would point out that there is serious trouble with the notion that you can reverse these rules.

*Osgood:* As I understand the Katz & Fodor (23) argument on the interpretation of sentences—to which I will return later—you have, in effect, to reverse the arrows in order to account for semantic amalgamation of the material under each node. Furthermore, the picture of a listener's sentence generator running wildly, trying to match a long and complicated sentence structure, is not a satisfactory one. I think the decoding and encoding operations are quite different. There are a number of relevant experiments on the matter, but it is by no means resolved.

Let me return now to the question of types of grammars. One of Chomsky's major contributions has been his elaboration of the rationale for a transformational grammar (4). Such a grammar contains two types of rewrite rules: first, rules of the type already discussed for generating so-called "kernel" sentences; second, rules which operate on whole "trees" to transform kernels and combine them into complex sentences. Thus any active sentence like "the man hits the colorful ball" can be transformed into its passive, "the colorful ball is hit by the man", or even into its negative-passive-question, "is the colorful ball not hit by the man?" And several kernels may be combined, e.g., given "the man is running" prior to our sample sentence, we can generate "the running man hits the colorful ball." Many transformation rules are quite complicated—at least, as seen by the poor psychologist!—but this is a price paid for overall economy and elegance of the grammar. A relatively small number of such rules serve to generate a very large number of potential sentences from a relatively small number of kernel types.

What is the problem for the psycholinguist here? To answer this question we must contrast the goals of linguistics and psycholinguistics. We may start by invoking a distinction made by one of the grandfathers of modern descriptive linguistics, Ferdinand de Saussure (10), between *la langue* and *la parole*. *La langue* refers to language as an abstract system or theory; *la parole* refers to language as actualized speech events. The linguist is characteristically concerned with the former; the psycholinguist is characteristically concerned with the latter—although to account for actualized language behavior he also requires his own kind of theory. In other words, in this paper I am concerned with a theoretical model of the speaker, not of the language *per se*. The fact that users of a language do generally (although not always) follow the rules of its grammar in creating sentences, and can use the rules intuitively (if not explicitly) in interpreting sentences, points to a kind of "knowledge" and a lawfulness of behavior that must be incorporated within any psycholinguistic theory that pretends to be sufficient. However, this does not mean that the grammar of a language describes how its users operate with it. As George Miller (30) puts it, "These rules of formation, and the trees that represent the structures of grammatical sentences, are purely formal devices for representing word groupings. How a sentence is actually manufactured or understood by users of the language—what particular cognitive processes he performs—is not a linguistic problem, but a psychological one."

Let me illustrate this last point with the matter of syntactically ambiguous sentences. One of the arguments for a transformational grammar is that without knowing the derivational history of such a sentence it cannot be disambiguated. Without knowing whether "the shooting of the hunters" in the sentence "the shooting of the hunters was terrible", was derived from "the hunters shot" or from "they shot the hunters", we do not know whether to say "they should practice more" or "they should have been wearing red jackets"! But in *la parole*, the speaker is seldom ambiguating (unless he is punning) and the listener is seldom ambiguated, by virtue of the contexts within which such utterances ordinarily occur.

*Geschwind*: An adequate theory of human behavior must account for grammar but not necessarily for individual items. The problem is much like the old one in anthropology of the reasons for a particular item in a culture. That item may simply reflect the history of the group being studied; on the other hand, new items may appear which reflect the pattern of the forces in the culture. In the same manner certain grammatical items may simply reflect the history of the language and the fact that every child is taught these items. By contrast, grammatical change in particular will reflect forces at work in the structure of the language. A theory of language has thus two separate problems: How does the child learn to use the established forms in the proper way? How does the structure of the language influence the behavior so that particular items in the grammar change?

*Osgood:* I am not sure that I see your point. If it is that grammars are tautological because they merely reflect historical regularities in behavior, then I would have to disagree completely. The generation of novel utterances is a case in point—whatever may be the psychology of it. If you mean that grammatical behavior, despite its complexity, is learned behavior, then I would have to agree equally completely. And this brings up another goal of the psycholinguist—at least, this psycholinguist. It is that, in agreement with Skinner (44), I would insist that language behavior is essentially learned behavior—granting that there are innate propensities and maturational factors as well, as Dr. Lenneberg has pointed out—and that therefore we cannot have a special theory of language. Language behavior must be understood within the same set of principles that govern behavior in general. This makes things a little rough, but I think it is necessary.

There are at least two other points where the goals of linguists and psycholinguists differ. For one thing, psycholinguists must concern themselves with semantics, the meaningful aspects of language, whereas linguists have been able to avoid this area. However, this situation seems to be changing, as evidenced by a recent paper by Katz & Fodor (23) and by presentations made here by Drs. Lamb, Lounsbury, and others. The second point concerns the relation in general between language as a system and events in the real world—the entire area of pragmatics, if you will. Psychologists are particularly concerned with this dimension but linguists not so much.

Two of my colleagues, Howard Maclay and Mary Sleator (29) made an empirical test of the ability of normally fluent English speakers to judge the grammaticalness of utterances ranging from items which were grammatical, meaningful and familiar at one extreme (e.g., "they finished it yesterday"), through items which were grammatical but neither meaningful in the usual sense nor familiar (e.g., Chomsky's favorite, "colorless green ideas sleep furiously") to items that were not grammatical sentences but were meaningful and familiar (e.g., "sometime early in the morning") or nothing at all (e.g., "label break to calmed about and"). Although people agreed 100 per cent that utterances which were simultaneously grammatical, meaningful and familiar were sentences, less than 50 per cent judged items like "colorless green ideas sleep furiously" to be sentences in English. Yet utterances which were meaningful and familiar, but not grammatical, like "sometime early in the morning", were judged to be sentences by nearly 35 per cent. Grammaticalness would not appear to be a self-evident property of utterances. Of course, when one observes spontaneous speech as Maclay and I have done (28), one finds that ungrammatical sentences tend to be the rule rather than the exception.

*Wepman:* Will your system, the system you now present, generate such ungrammatical sentences as some of those you have been quoting?

*Osgood:* In theory, and in the general case, yes. Chomsky (5) took Skinner to task for claiming to predict unique and specific bits of verbal behavior. I believe this was a misconception created by Skinner's anecdotes in his *Verbal Behavior* (44). No psychologist, functioning as a scientist rather than a clinician, is concerned with predicting unique events but classes of subsequent events from classes of antecedent events. Thus, as Dr. Lounsbury predicted a long time ago (40), we can expect hesitation phenomena to occur more often before items of low frequency-of-occurrence than the reverse. So in that sense my theory—although I hesitate to dignify it this way—would predict ungrammatical utterances under certain conditions.

*Stockwell:* False starts are in no way a contradiction of Chomsky's point of view (6). He has clearly pointed out that the grammar is not expected to generate the utterances that actually occur in a large percentage of instances. What you are dealing with here is a blueprint which must be available to the speaker of the language, in order to account for the false starts, corrections, and so on that he comes out with. The grammar does not generate it. The strategy for the utilization of the grammar, the way in which the speaker handles this kind of blueprint, must be more explicitly described than it has been so far, in order to account for his way of dealing with the blueprint he has.

*Osgood:* Chomsky (5) speaks of the entire area of non-obligatory aspects of language, where he thinks the psycholinguist should find a purchase. I have no argument with that.

*Ferguson:* There is an important assumption here which is not defended. Chomsky is really saying that the best way to understand all these fragments and false starts is first to have the kind of grammar which accounts for all and only the grammatical sentences. I think this is one of the basic assumptions made.

*Stockwell:* This basic assumption has not only been made: it is the only explicit assumption that has been offered as to how such behavior might be interpreted. If you have alternatives, let us, by all means, compare them.

*Ferguson:* I was only suggesting that perhaps one should look for alternatives.

*Osgood:* By way of illustrating the fundamental difference between linguistic and psycholinguistic goals, I would like to summarize Katz & Fodor's article, "The Structure of a Semantic Theory" (23). Their basic proposition is that linguistic description minus grammar equals semantics. An optimal grammar specifies the immediate constituents of sentences, the rules by which they are combined at each level, the rules by which kernels can be transformed, and the ways in which sentences can be syntactically ambiguous. What is left for semantics? In the first place, we note that this grammar will provide identical structural descriptions for sentences that obviously differ in meaning, as well as vice versa. The familiar newspaper headlines, "Man Bites Dog" *versus* "Dog Bites Man", illustrates the former (identical structure, but obviously different meaning) while "the dog bit the man" *versus* "the man was bitten by the dog" illustrates the latter (different structure but same meaning, at least in the sense that linguistics uses the term "meaning"). But now take: (*a*) a sentence that is structurally unambiguous but semantically ambiguous, like "he will get the case" (of beer? at law? in the railroad station?); (*b*) a sentence that is structurally unambiguous but semantically anomalous, like "he was aware of the subliminal stimulus" (I realize that a number of psychologists have failed to recognize the anomaly here!); or (*c*) a sentence that is a paraphrase of another and yet structurally different, as the sentence "she is my mother-in-law", when spoken by a male, is to "she is my wife's mother".

Katz & Fodor (23) define the lower bound of the domain of semantic theory to be an explanation of the abilities of native speakers to recognize semantic ambiguities, anomalies and paraphrases, which together they refer to as the ability to interpret sentences. Their definition of the upper bound of semantic theory may satisfy linguists and philosophers, but it certainly would not satisfy psychologists. They rule out any interest in the way situational, motivational, or even linguistic settings, beyond the limits of the single sentence, may influence its interpretation. They admit that a semantic theory that included the influence of context would be more powerful, but justify the more limited goal on the grounds that "a sentence cannot have readings in a setting which it does not have in isolation", and therefore semantic theory is logically prior to context theory.

Now let us look at the sentence in Figure 41 again and subject it to semantic analysis *à la* Katz & Fodor. Structural analysis determines the grammatical alternatives we select from the dictionary—thus "man" (N) rather than "man" (V) and "hits" (V) rather than "hits" (Npl)—but it does not select semantic alternatives within the same form class. Combining the two dictionary alternatives for "colorful" ("abounding in contrasting bright colors" *versus* "having distinctive character") with the three dictionary meanings of "ball" ("large assembly for the purpose of dancing" *versus* "having globular shape" *versus* "solid missile for projection by engine of war") and applying a semantic rule which eliminates anomalous compounds (here "globular object" or "solid missile" plus "having distinctive character"), Katz & Fodor retain four viable amalgamations of "the" + "colorful" + "ball". Applying a similar operation to "the man" we come up with a single viable amalgamation—"specific human adult male". We are now faced with the problem of amalgamating "hits" (V) with "the colorful ball" (NP). Looking up "hits" in our dictionary and following only the grammatical path marked V (verb), we find two alternatives: "collides with an impact", as in "the rock hits the ground with a thud", and "strikes with a blow or a missile", as in "the man hits the ground with a rock". Combining these alternatives with the four viable alternatives for "the colorful ball" and again using a rule of anomaly, "ball" in the sense of "large assembly for the purpose of dancing" is completely eliminated. The final combination of "the man" with "hits the colorful ball" does nothing further to disambiguate this sentence, and Katz & Fodor conclude (*a*) that this sentence is not semantically anomalous and (*b*) that it is four ways semantically ambiguous.

I have gone through this laborious analysis to make two critical points. First, semantic analysis of this type takes no account of the varying probabilities of alternative interpretations. I take it to be intuitively obvious that the four alternatives here differ markedly in the probability of what was intended by the speaker or writer, and this can be shown by paraphrasing the alternative readings: (*a*) the man strikes the colorful round object with a blow (very high probability); (*b*) the man collides with the colorful round object (conceivable, but it would have to be a rather large ball!); (*c*) the man strikes the colorful solid missile with a blow (conceivable, but even less probable in this day and age, and they are not usually very colorful); (*d*) the man collides with the colorful solid missile (all one could say to this would be, "What, is Tom Thumb drunk again?")—as a matter of fact, one of the alternatives Katz & Fodor dismiss as anomalous seems much more probable than all but the first they keep, and this is "the man hits the distinctive assembly for dancing" (that is, the professional gate-crasher "hits", in the colloquial sense of "goes to", the affair being given by the governor). Second, semantic analysis of this type is unable to select among ambiguities and resolve them. If such an innocuous sentence as "the man hits the colorful ball" is open to no less than four unresolvable interpretations, I suspect that the vast majority of sentences we encounter in everyday life would remain ambiguous under analysis.

The reason for this state of affairs, of course, is that precisely what Katz & Fodor must leave out in order to make their analysis rigorous linguistically is what is required for disambiguation—knowledge on the part of users of a language about the nature of the world and about the momentary situational, motivational and linguistic context in which a particular sentence occurs. This is in no sense a criticism of what Katz & Fodor have done; it is rather an indication of what they have not done—which makes what they have done inadequate from the viewpoint of a psycholinguist.

## An Approach to Behavior Theory

Time will not permit me to go into much detail here. I have written about contemporary behavior theory elsewhere (c.f., 36, 37, 38) and, in any case, want to get on with The Sentence. Figure 42 might help us touch the main points sufficiently for our present purposes. The heavy line stands for the boundary between the nervous system and its non-neural environment, and we shall be concerned with several ways in which the nervous system represents for itself, or "mirrors", properties of its environment. I am not going to present a neurological model, however, but a behavioral one—even though I believe that principles of behavior are nothing more than hunches about how the nervous system operates.

Figure 42A represents, most schematically, a single-stage model—which, as I have indicated, is really not a completely "empty organism" view. I am sure Skinner (44), with whom we identify such a theory, would admit to the existence of sensory and motor projection systems. However, for purposes of behavior theory the grossly one-to-one nature of the relation between sensory (or motor) surfaces and what I call the sensory and motor signals ($\dot{s}$ and $\dot{r}$) at the termini of the projection systems makes it possible to treat this as a single-stage model. So, Skinner's theory could be called a sensory-signal-to-motor-signal theory, with no intervening processes assumed. Reflexes are innate, wired-in connections between S and R, respondents are acquired dependencies of R upon S where the S is specifiable; operants are acquired dependencies of R upon antecedent conditions where the S is not specifiable (e.g., emitted *versus* elicited behavior). According

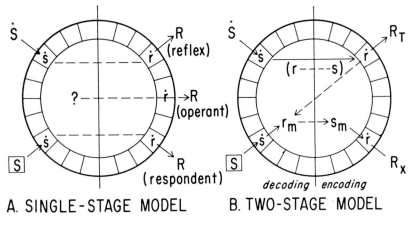

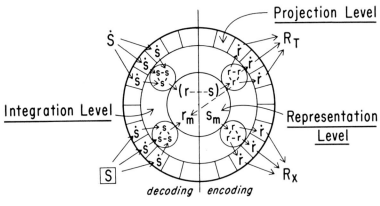

**Figure 42.** Behavioral models based on ways in which the nervous system reflects properties of its environment. A: Single-stage model of a sensory signal-to-motor signal theory. B: Two-stage model demonstrating Hull's "pure stimulus-act" and dividing the S-R sequence into decoding and encoding processes. C: Illustration of behaviorist closure principle by adding to the two-stage model an integrative system modifiable on the basis of experience.

to Skinner, language behavior is largely made up of various kinds of operants—"mands" (under control of motivational variables), "tacts" (under control of external stimuli, e.g., labeling), "echoic" (under control of the verbal behavior of others), and so on—whose dependencies upon antecedent conditions are developed by the rather ubiquitous operation called reinforcement.

A major insufficiency of this model, as I have seen it, is that it yields no satisfactory account of symbolic processes. Indeed, such processes as meaning, attitude, intention, and the like are deliberately eschewed as myths.

*Hirsh:* When you say that the model is incapable of handling symbolic behavior, are you making a distinction between symbol and sign, as Charles Morris (35) would?

*Osgood:* No, I mean symbolic processes in the sense of mediating representational mechanisms, as I will try to show in a moment. This insufficiency of the Skinnerian model appears most clearly when he is reduced to claiming that to "comprehend" a lecture or a book one must mimic the speaker (echoic operants) or subvocally form the printed words (texting operants). There are no other observable and relevant R's. Similarly, to handle spontaneous speech, where there is no obvious S, Skinner must assume that the determinants are intraverbal operants formed during original exposure to events. Yet when a speaker is given a random list of words, he will come out with a list clustered according to meaningful categories, not in the original order. The well-documented phenomenon of semantic generalization provides further evidence: train an adult subject to lift his finger (to avoid shock) when he hears "joy" among a list of words, and he will regularly transfer this reaction to other words of similar meaning (e.g., "glee") but not to words of similar form (e.g., "boy"). But where is similarity of meaning in the single-stage model? Nowhere—because there is no provision for meaning.

*Stockwell:* In your example, what would be the case for the word "join"?

*Osgood:* I do not know, but I would confidently predict there would be no response. With young children there often is transfer on a phonetic basis, but with adults it is usually semantic .

Figure 42B diagrams the essence of the two-stage model. Here we postulate an implicit, mediating reaction ($r_m$) which is assumed to produce a distinctive, mediating stimulus ($s_m$). This is the "pure stimulus-act" of Hull's behavior theory (19). (Incidentally, I am aware that many people are uneasy about diagrams with S's and R's—particularly $s$'s and $r$'s used to represent hypothetical events in the nervous system. I sympathize with this feeling and hasten to point out that these are simply constructs which enable one to bring principles of learning theory to bear within a two-stage model. They have much in common with the linguist's phoneme.) The basic notion here is that whenever a sign ($\boxed{s}$) is repeatedly associated with a significate ($\dot{s}$), which regularly and reliably elicits some total pattern of behavior ($R_T$), the sign will come to elicit some distinction portion of this behavior pattern as a representational mediation process ($r_m$), the self-stimulation from which ($s_m$) can come to mediate certain instrumental behaviors ($R_x$) which "take account of" the thing signified. Such processes are representational because they are literally part of the behavior made to the thing signified (hence their distinctive semantic quality); they are mediational because they elicit behaviors appropriate to things other than the signs which initiate them. Note that this provides one possible basis for a behavioral theory of meaning; note also that it divides the S-R sequence into two separably modifiable parts, one that can legitimately be called a decoding process ($\boxed{s}-r_m$) and another that can legitimately be called an encoding process ($s_m-R_x$).

The advantage, in a sense, of using *s* and *r* merely as theoretical constructs is the fact that responses produce self-stimulation. Whenever I hold
up my hand, I get a certain feedback, the sensory effect of making a response; it is mediational because it produces self-stimulation, which can
become connected with responses which take account of, or are appropriate
to, the thing signified, and can be learned on an ordinary learning basis.

*Geschwind:* This then would be a theory of representation as being, so to
speak, the process of playing out the drama in the outside world on a small
inner stage?

*Osgood:* Precisely. I have said that the nervous system appears to have
ways of representing several aspects of its environment. What I have
termed sensory and motor signals, at the most central termini of the projection systems, provide a faithful mirror of "what is", in terms of both input
and output. Fortunately, this mirror is unmodifiable by experience. Representational mediators provide a mirror of the outcomes of past behaviors
in relation to stimuli which produced them—hence the significance of signs
of the not-here and not-now. Finally, I should like to suggest a third kind
of mirror—one that reflects for the organism redundancies within its own
past experiences and past behaviors.

The two-stage representational model encounters no difficulties with the
symbolic processes (in principle, that is!), with phenomena like comprehending, spontaneous speaking, and semantic generalization—which is not
exactly surprising, since it was designed to handle such processes. But is it
sufficient for language behavior (or behavior in general, for that matter)? I
am convinced it is not, and for two fundamental reasons: first, this model
has nothing whatsoever to say about perceptual organization—the important phenomena of closure and perceptual grouping, for example, with
which our gestalt colleagues have done so much but behaviorists practically nothing; second, it has equally little to say about motor skill—the kind of
mechanism that will provide for central programming of response elements
into smoothly executed sequences. Karl Lashley (24) clearly identified this
problem many years ago. The underlying reason for failure here is that perceptual organization involves S-S learning and motor skill organization involves R-R learning, and no theory limited to S-R connections is going to
handle them.

Figure 42C shows a further differentiation of function within the nervous
system, adding an integrative system on both sensory (decoding) and motor
(encoding) sides. Unlike the projection systems, these sensory and motor
integrative systems are assumed to be modifiable on the basis of experience
—but modifiable according to sheer frequency and independent of motivation and reinforcement (in contrast to S-R type associations). The basic notion can be stated this way: the greater the frequency with which stimulus
events (S-S) or response events (R-R) have been paired in the input or output experience of the organism, the greater will be the tendency for their

correlates in the integrative systems to activate each other. High frequencies of input or output pairing will yield evocative integrations—the "cell assemblies" (17) which, once activated, complete themselves centrally and fire as wholes. This is a behavioristic closure principle, and it is assumed to underlie the formation of tightly bound perceptual and motor units in language. Lower frequencies of input or output pairing will yield what I call predictive integrations—activation of one central event serves to lower the threshold for another, but is not sufficient to fire it. This latter mechanism is assumed to reduce the "noise" in both decoding and encoding, thereby facilitating complex sequential activities (24).

I introduced these notions in papers written in 1955, 1956, and 1957 (37, 38, 39) but for the most part my behaviorist colleagues have remained oblivious to them—perhaps the mere idea of S-S and R-R type learning is so repugnant to S-R theorists that it produces emotional shock, distortion, and denial! Gestalt psychologists to whom I have talked see sensory integration as a crude, unsophisticated, mechanistic invasion of their private domain—which, of course, it is. Nevertheless, there is a great deal of evidence, particularly in psycholinguistics, which is consistent with this notion and not easily amenable to either S-R or gestalt interpretations.

All of the extensive literature demonstrating a lawful reduction in the tachistoscopic threshold for words as a function of frequency of usage is a case in point. Gestalt principles have little to say about frequency as a variable in perceptual closure and grouping in any case, and the S-R theorist has to search about to find the R's and the reinforcement in this situation. Particularly apropos is a recent experiment by Tyler (47) demonstrating that deliberate manipulation of reinforcement had no effect upon changes in visual thresholds for nonsense materials, whereas manipulation of frequency of exposure had the expected effect. I do not know of any equivalent evidence for response integration, but casual observations on the speed of pronouncing familiar *versus* unfamiliar words suggest that integration as a function of frequency holds here as well.

These integrative mechanisms provide the organism with an effective means for unitizing or "chunking" its decoding and encoding operations. They provide a mirror of "what ought to be" or what is predictable on the basis of frequent redundancies in past experiencing and past behaving. Of course, being merely predictive mechanisms, they will occasionally make errors—they will produce an illusory perception of familiar "sure" when the visually flashed stimulus was actually the unfamiliar "sere", and they will make for repeated typing of "ration" when "ratio" is intended, for example —but this is a small price to pay for predicting the future from the (related) past with overall efficiency.

This three-stage, or three-level, model may strike you as quite complicated conceptually—and it certainly is in comparison with most behavior theories—but I am sure it is going to turn out to be not complicated enough. At this point let me sketch in one additional complication that is necessary for a psycholinguistic theory of the sentence.

This is the notion of decision and control within hierarchies of alternatives. Both within and between each level in this model, and for both decoding and encoding processes, we are dealing with associations between complex patterns of antecedent and subsequent events. On the basis of past experience, each particular antecedent will be associated with a divergent hierarchy of subsequents, but to varying strengths; if the alternatives are incompatible, this is a competitive choice situation. Each particular subsequent will be associated dependently with a convergent hierarchy of antecedents, but also to varying strengths; this is a facilitative recruitment situation. I make what I hope are two simple and clarifying assumptions here: "decisions" in behavior is simply the occurrence of that dependent alternative within a divergent hierarchy which has the highest momentary excitation strength. (Note: this is not a probabilistic system, although probability estimates over subjects or occasions are usually employed to estimate relative strengths of alternatives.) "Control" in behavior is simply modification of the monetary excitation strengths of dependent alternatives as a function of combination and patterning in convergent hierarchies. For hypothetical events transpiring within the sensory integration system when a word is flashed in the tachistoscope, Figure 43 illustrates how given (antecedent) information in the display can convergently facilitate the filling in of missing (subsequent) information, here $\dot{S}_d$. Convergence of this sort is the basis of contextual control over sentence understanding and creating.

### SOME EVIDENCE ON CONTEXTUAL CONTROLS

Verbal behavior is learned, and transpires for the most part, within the tripartite context provided by a speaker, a hearer, and a situation. The characteristics of each put constraints upon what messages will be produced and how they will be interpreted (26). I have already ascribed the insufficiency of the Katz & Fodor (23) approach to sentence interpretation, for psycholinguistic purposes at least, to the failure to take context fully into account. The problem, of course, is to deal rigorously with context. At present the best we can do is point to ample evidence for its importance.

The relevant situational context may be either linguistic or non-linguistic (perceptual). The role of the latter is perhaps so obvious that few experimental studies have been made. One's interpretation of "duck" is likely to be quite different in a barnyard than in a baseball park. As noted earlier, "the shooting of the hunters was terrible" is hardly ambiguous to a mourner when he is standing bareheaded at their funeral. And the thousands of homonyms in a language, such as "light", "case", "reserve", and "class", could hardly be tolerated without the disambiguating effects of convergent con-

GIVEN                                    ASSOCIATED

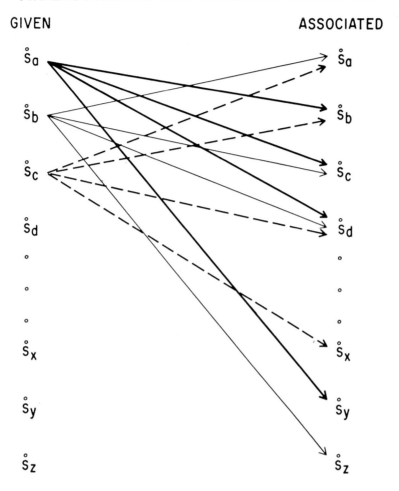

**Figure 43.** Effects of redundancy upon selection of alternative sensory integrations. See text.

text. On the encoding side, we have naturalistic studies by Carroll (3) and Maclay & Newman (27), in which a speaker must influence the behavior of a listener when they are separated by a screen on the middle of the table. Carroll found that the types of sentences produced by the speaker were highly dependent upon the instructional situation, e.g., binary yes-no questions predominated when instructed "if his left-hand peg is green . . .", whereas predominantly imperative forms ("give me . . .", "put your . . .", etc.) occurred when instructed "proceed so that your . . .", and so on. Maclay & Newman found that when the speaker had to identify selectively one of a set of geometric designs for the hearer, both the homogeneity of the designs to be differentiated and the type of feedback from the hearer (stooge) significantly influenced both the amount and lexical diversity of the speaker's output.

Sequential dependencies in the linguistic context have been much more

fully investigated. Miller & Selfridge (34) found ease of recall of word-pas-
sages to increase as the order of approximation to English increased, i.e., as
the contextual constraints increased. Miller, Heise & Lichten (33) demonstrated that words in sentences could be perceived more accurately under
conditions of noise than the same words in isolation. On the encoding side,
both Goldman-Eisler (15) and Maclay & Osgood (28) report that pauses are
more probable just before points of high uncertainty in spontaneous
speech, i.e., at points where sequential constraints are low. Many studies
using "cloze procedure" (46), in which every nth word in a passage (usually
every fifth) is deleted and subjects must try to replace them correctly, provide further evidence. For example, Aborn, Rubenstein & Sterling (1)
found that probability of correct replacement varies inversely with the
number of alternatives in the form-class deleted. Shepard (43) finds that as
the amount of newspaper context increases from zero to forty words, the
number of different words subjects can list for the blank in five minutes
drops from about 100 to about ten; in other words, the larger the context
the greater the convergence upon a limited number of alternatives.

It is evident that sequencing of form-classes is far more constrained than
lexical content. In the cloze frame, "the old man——along the road", nearly
every subject will insert some verb form, and of course semantic determinants refine the lexical selection. In a study in which every second, third,
fourth, fifth, or sixth word was deleted from the same passages. Fillenbaum, Jones & Rapoport (11) report that correct form-class replacement
was nearly perfect with a deletion rate of every third word, whereas correct lexical choice continued to improve with increasing context. It is interesting to note in this connection that Tannenbaum & Stolz (45) have been
able to program a computer to assign form-class membership to sequences
of words in newspaper English about as well as college students can do this
task. Although linguists typically restrict their analysis of language to the
sentence as a maximum unit, it is clear that sequential dependencies span
larger segments of a text. The uses of "she" and "also" in the sentence "she
also dyes her hair" are just as dependent upon some preceding sentence,
such as "Mary uses a lot of mascara", as the use of "her" is dependent upon
"she" in the same sentence. The psycholinguist must go beyond the
boundaries of the single sentence in many directions.

*Garvin:* This is not necessarily a dependence, because you could just
have two people looking at a picture of a woman who obviously has a lot
of mascara and one says, "She also dyes her hair". The connection here is
not as necessary as within the sentence.

*Osgood:* Notice that you are also going outside the sentence to the situational context.

*Stockwell:* You are familiar, of course, with Zellig Harris's work on discourse analysis (16) which clearly is an attempt to analyze features that extend far beyond single sentences. There is at least one fairly extensive

grammar, not yet published, by T. R. Anderson, a former student of mine now in the Philippines, who is working on one of the Philippine languages and English. He starts his first rule not with "S" but with "Discourse", by which he means everything up to where there is a break, as it were, in the continuity; he generates all sorts of relationships, such as the "also" one, the pronominal relation, the definite determiner, etc. He generates by starting from "D", coming down to a sequence of sentence types, and having a number of grammatical relationships appearing between the sentences in the discourse. So there is an effort to do something about this problem. It is extraordinarily complex, though the sentence itself is complex enough.

*Osgood:* The motivational and emotional states of speaker and hearer also exercise contextual constraints upon what is said and how it is understood. In a paper titled "Motivational Dynamics of Language Behavior" (39) I detailed all the evidence I could find at that time. A few examples will have to suffice here. Postman & Brown (42) have shown that induced states of felt success or failure sensitized tachistoscopic thresholds selectively for perceiving words of congruent meaning. We are all familiar with analogous phenomena at the sentence level—the listener misinterpreting sentences in keeping with his emotional state. The extreme case of this, I suppose, would be the hallucinatory "voices" heard by the psychotic. The entire concept of language is based upon the interpattern relationship of other speakers and the producers of the message. Some of the psychologists here will remember Kantor's book of the 30's on the psychology of grammar (22). I reread it in connection with this meeting. At this point, with new emphasis on the context of problems, it makes rather interesting reading, though it seemed to be old hat a while ago.

It is obvious, but by no means trivial, that the momentary motives of speakers determine what they talk about and how. Questions and imperatives become more probable when speakers have needs to satisfy—thus "Where is Route 66?" to the policeman when I am lost and "Give me the hammer" when the nail is in position but the hammer is not. A little more subtle is the way a speaker's ego-involvement with the agent or the object of an observed interpersonal action may influence selection of an active or passive construction (3). On the assumption that suicidal people encode their notes under higher motivation than non-suicidal people writing ordinary letters to relatives, or pseudo-suicide notes, Evelyn Walker and I (41) made certain predictions about what comparative content analyses should reveal. As predicted, Skinner's "mands" as sentence types (commanding, demanding, pleading, etc.), qualification of verb phrases (e.g., "I might have loved you" *versus* "I loved you"), and several measures of stereotopy (use of shorter words in terms of syllables per word, lower lexical diversity in terms of type/token ratio, and more "allness" terms like "always", "never", "everything") were significantly more frequent in genuine suicide notes. I must also mention the significant paper by Brown & Gilman (2) titled "The

Pronouns of Power and Solidarity", in which they show how the selective use of *tous* and *vous* (and their analogous in other languages) varies with the relative power-status of speaker vis-a-vis hearer and the degree of solidarity or closeness speaker feels with hearer.

## IMPLICATIONS FOR A PSYCHOLINGUISTIC THEORY OF THE SENTENCE

On the face of things, we have what appears to be a paradoxical state of affairs. On the one hand, there is ample evidence for sequential, Markov-type dependencies at many levels of language units and for both decoding and encoding processes. On the other hand, we have the compelling arguments of Chomsky (4), Miller (30), and others against the adequacy of a Markov-type sentence generator. In searching for some resolution we should note, first, that there is no necessary reason a theory of the speaker should be isomorphic with a theory of the language; it may well be that the users of a grammar display the limitations of finite-state devices. Second, there is a fallacious implication often drawn from Chomsky's arguments—namely that Markov-type dependencies can operate on only one level of units in the vertical hierarchy at a time, i.e., the word level; there is nothing about the model that sets such a restriction. Finally, it should be noted that there is nothing in a generative grammar *per se* that accounts for selection among alternatives ("decisions") at each level. Having rewritten S as NP + VP, what determines whether the NP will be expanded as $T + N$, or $T + A + N$, or $T + N + $ Rel. Phr.?

Figure 44 suggests how left-to-right (Markovian) and up-to-down (generative) hierarchies may be integrated in the process of sentence understanding and creating. For each "+" representing a rewrite rule in the original tree diagram of the sentence, "the man hits the colorful ball", I have substituted a divergent "decision" hierarchy. This is to incorporate the fact that what-follows-what within the verb phrase, for example, is transitionally dependent upon antecedent context. By adding both an antecedent sentence, $S_0$, and a subsequent sentence, $S_2$, I suggest that sentences as wholes are transitionally dependent upon antecedent sentences and hence context bound. This diagram does not attempt to represent the nth order, multiunit dependencies that presumably operate on each level (e.g., the way the singularity of "the man" influences the selection of "hits" *versus* "hit"); nor does it attempt to represent convergent mechanisms within each level. And finally, this diagram deals only with grammatical dependencies, omitting the effects of simultaneous semantic and motivational contexts. It is clear from it that vertical and horizontal determinants converge in the selection of form classes; the noun class of "man" (but not its lexical nature) is jointly dependent upon its vertical relation to NP and its horizontal relation to T.

There is some experimental evidence: Forster (12) tested the ability of speakers of English (a predominantly right-branching language) and of

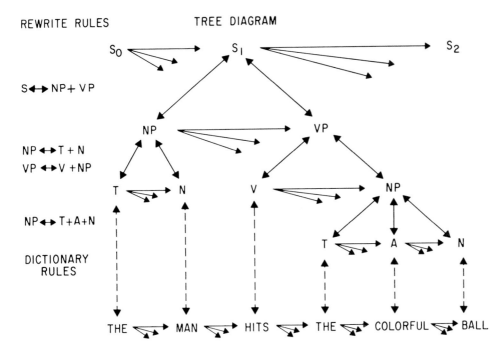

REWRITE RULES                    TREE DIAGRAM

S⟷NP+VP

NP⟷T+N
VP⟷V+NP

NP⟷T+A+N

DICTIONARY
RULES

**Figure 44.** Integration of Markovian and generative hierarchies in sentence understanding and creating. Use of "decision" hierarchies shows that phrase pattern is transitionally dependent upon antecedent context.

Turkish (a predominantly left-branching language) to generate complete grammatical sentences when given either the left half only or the right half only, e.g., given "–– –– –– –– –– thought about his dog" (left-deleted) or given "Slowly he sat down and –– –– –– –– ––" (right-deleted). If speakers normally generate whole "trees" in an up-to-down direction before uttering a sentence, there should be no difference between types of deletion or between languages. Quite to the contrary, for English speakers left-deleted sentences were much more difficult than right-deleted sentences, whereas for Turkish speakers this difference was much less marked (although in the same direction). For English speakers, the number of transverse nodes in sentences correlated highly with completion difficulty for left-deleted but not for right-deleted sentences. (Transverse nodes in a sentence's tree structure control terminal elements in both presented and deleted halves, thus providing an index of grammatical constraint.) In other words, for right-deleted sentences the normal left-to-right construction habits of speakers automatically take into account transitional constraints and thereby are unaffected by their complexity.

A recent experiment by Johnson (21) is also apropos. He had subjects learn sentences of two types: (a) "The tall boy // saved the dying woman," where linguistic analysis would locate a major break between "boy" and "saved", and (b) "The house / across the street // is burning", where analy-

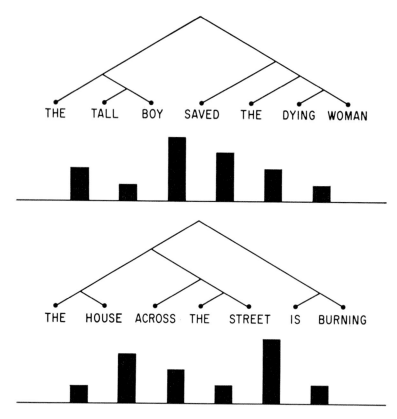

**Figure 45.** Frequency of transitional errors in two types of sentences: an illustration of the probability that transitional recall errors are greater across phrase boundaries than within them (after Johnson, 21). A near-linear decrease in these errors occurs from left to right in each phrase.

sis would locate a minor juncture between "house" and "across" and the major juncture between "street" and "is". Johnson predicted that the probability of transitional errors in recall would be greater across phrase boundaries than within them. This prediction was confirmed, as can be seen in Figure 45. What was not predicted, but is clearly evident in the figure, was that within each phrase there would be a near-linear decrease in transitional errors running from left to right. We thus have evidence here both for "chunking" attributable to the phrase structure inherent in vertical hierarchies and for transitional dependencies attributable to Markov-type processes inherent in horizontal hierarchies.

Contextual determination presumably operates simultaneously on several levels of behavioral organization through such convergent mechanisms. One example must suffice. Dr. Jakobson (20) has made a componential analysis of the verb "to kill". In a particular encoding situation, what determines which of the 28 forms he lists will be selected? Suppose the speaker is observing the on-going strangling of an old man and has already pro-

duced "the old man . . ." The fact that an on-going action is being perceived facilitates such forms as "is killing" and "is being killed" as against
such forms as "killed" or "would kill". The motivational state of the speaker
(here perhaps fear or anxiety) facilitates occurrence of such forms as
"afraid", "murder", "help", and the like, as well as forms of the verb "to
kill". The fact that the speaker has already encoded "the old man" (this selection itself presumably reflecting motivation effects), in conjunction with
perceptual signs from the real world indicating that "the old man" is the
object and not the agent of the action, dictates some passive construction—
but this $T + A + N$ antecedent, without the simultaneous context of perceptual signs, could eventuate in any of the forms of the verb phrase. The
entire context of semantic (here, perceptual), grammatical, and motivational determinants converges upon "is being killed", which is uttered. Note
that this may well be a novel utterance, in the sense that the speaker may
have never produced this particular sentence before—but then, neither has
he ever been in this particular total context before.

The three-stage (or -level) behavioral model sketched earlier (Figure 42C)
has some things to say about other aspects of sentence understanding and
creating. Consideration of the sensory and motor integration processes, for
example, leads to some principles governing the nature and formation of
perceptual and motor skill units in language behavior—word units as meaningless forms in sentence decoding, I suspect, and syllables in sentence encoding. Consideration of representational mediation (symbolic) processes,
as a complex kind of componential coding, leads to some suggestions about
the nature and development of semantic and grammatical coding of these
word forms at the meaningful level. Consideration of the dynamics of cognitive interaction among simultaneously activated "bundles" of such cod-
ings or representations leads to a conception of how phrases may be amalgamated in the process of understanding and how global intentions may be
expanded in the process of creating. But time does not permit further elaboration of these aspects here. And, in any case, I am still far, far away from
anything that could be called a "theory" of this complicated business of understanding and creating sentences.

### Discussion

*Denes:* One thing that caught my attention was the statement that "no
special theory of language behavior is required" to explain speech perception. I think that certain experimental evidence we now have does in fact
indicate that the listener deals with speech differently from the way he
processes other auditory information. For example, there is the experiment
on learning to identify acoustic patterns which was carried out by Stevens
and House (18) at MIT. Stevens and House generated a variety of synthetic sounds, starting with simple tones and in later tests making them more
and more complex. The most complex of these was not synthesized: it was
naturally produced speech. They tested how easily people could learn to

identify these signals and found that the more complex a signal became, the less well did the subject learn to identify.

*Osgood:* Not the more complex but the more like natural language.

*Denes:* That is just the point. For the moment let us say the signals just became more and more complex. As the test sounds became more complex they also became less learnable until they reached the most complex of all sounds, natural speech. All of a sudden, learnability shot up and the naturally produced speech sounds were easier to learn than any of the other sounds. To my mind, what this shows is that there is something special about signals from natural speech, and that the reason why the more complex acoustic signals were less learnable was because, in fact, they never reached the stage where the subject reacted to them as he would react to speech signals.

This leads us to an interesting question. If I am right in my assumption, what is it that makes speech signals more learnable, what is their special feature? Some think it is that we can make reference to articulatory patterns in interpreting these vocal tract generated acoustic patterns; that in recognizing speech we do not primarily carry out the process of auditory classification, but first search our articulatory memory associated with those auditory patterns, and then carry on at the articulatory level. This is what is sometimes called the motor theory of speech perception. I think it would be very interesting to carry out more experiments on this particular effect.

Dr. Osgood has on occasion referred to the identification of distinctive features on either acoustic or motor grounds, and to the possibility of identifying the syllable on the basis of chest muscle action.* This strikes at the root of what I consider the nature of the speech process to be, a multilevel organization. There are the acoustic level, the articulatory level, the physiological level (which includes muscle activity and neurological activity in the end organs and the brain), and a psycholinguistic level including grammar, semantics, etc. Events on these levels are necessarily separate and different in essence from events on other levels, although, obviously, there are correlations, and sometimes very strong correlations, between events on two levels. But I do not think we can ever say that an event on one level can be defined or even described by events on another level. We can come to very misleading conclusions in our investigations of speech unless we remember that corresponding events on different levels of speech activity are only related events and definitely not identities.

As an illustration, there is the difference between voiced and voiceless phonemes. To me, "voice" and "voiceless" is a linguistic discrimination. It separates one class of phonemes from another class of phonemes; it distinguishes the word "ice" from the word "eyes", for example, and the difference is not necessarily determined by the presence of vocal cord vi-

---

* Personal communication.

bration. In fact, the last phoneme in the word "eyes" is quite often pronounced without vocal cord vibration, yet armies of phoneticians have been investigating the voice-voiceless distinction by trying to determine whether the vocal cords were vibrating or not. The same applies just as strongly to intonation. Intonation is an element of linguistic organization but, again because of the articulatory connotation of its name, "intone" and "vocal cord vibration", phoneticians often equate it with vocal cord frequency. They ask electrical engineers to build instruments that measure vocal cord frequency and use them as intonation meters; they then arrive at some mistaken conclusions about intonation which would not have arisen had they realized that patterns of vocal cord frequency are not the same as intonation patterns. A good illustration of the nonidentity of intonation and vocal cord frequency patterns is provided by whispered speech, which by definition is produced without vocal cord vibration. I have carried out a number of experiments (7, 8, 9) in which I have asked people to speak in a whisper while trying to transmit the kind of information that we conventionally associate with intonation, such as differentiating between a question, a statement, doubt, hesitation, etc. I then asked a panel of listeners to judge the information transmitted by these whispers. This type of experiment was also repeated with speech pronounced normally, not whispered, but where the speech wave was subsequently processed by an electronic device which removed the effect of vocal cord vibration, thus producing whispered speech artificially. In both experiments the listeners could distinguish between statement, question, doubt, hesitation, etc. without undue difficulty.

People listening to whispered speech have no difficulty in distinguishing between words like "his" and "hiss" or "eyes" and "ice". When these word pairs are whispered in isolation, as they were in the tests I am referring to, they are distinguished only by the voiced-unvoiced opposition of the final phonemes. The distinction can be perceived even though the vocal cords do not vibrate when whispering. In fact, listeners are more successful in making these voiced-unvoiced distinctions in whispered speech than in making other distinctions, such as between "thin" and "thing".

*Marschak:* Are you saying there is no physical counterpart?

*Denes:* All I am saying is there is no one-to-one relationship between these linguistic units of classification and acoustic events. I am not saying that vocal cord vibration is never produced in the formation of "voiced" sounds; of course it is. But vocal cord vibration is not the only cue for the voiced-unvoiced or for intonational distinctions; these distinctions can be made without reference to vocal cord frequency, the articulatory feature implied in the name given to these elements of linguistic organization.

I thought that this might be particularly interesting to those concerned with the pathology of speech. In the case of some speech errors, which have names derived from the articulatory or from the acoustic levels of the

speech event, but which in effect are errors in the linguistic code, some pathologists may search for explanations which are in fact not valid.

So far I have stressed mostly the multilevel structure of speech and the
importance of not confusing corresponding events on these different levels.
There is only one more point that I would like to make. It concerns our
search for the kind of relationships that exist between events on different
levels of speech activity: how intonation is related to vocal cord frequency,
phonemic distinction to formant frequency, etc. There is a strong tendency
among investigators to make two assumptions: one is that only the strong
correlations between events can be significant, and the other one that once
a significant correlation between a linguistic unit and an acoustic event has
been found, no other acoustic feature is likely to have a significant relationship with the same linguistic unit. In other words, if intonation and vocal
cord frequency are related, then intonation cannot have a strong correlation with other acoustic features such as duration, formant frequency, or
overall intensity. Both these mistaken notions are the result of the now
rather outdated idea of an "invariant" relationship between the linguistic
and acoustic elements of speech. We now have plenty of evidence for be-
lieving that linguistic units are related to changes along a variety of acoustic dimensions (13). For example, as I have indicated previously, intonation
is related to changes in the fundamental frequency, the duration, the intensity, and even the formant frequencies of the speech wave. Any one or all
of these changes may be present on a particular occasion, and we know
that the listener can use them, on their own or in combination, in recognizing the spoken message. Also, the correlation between linguistic and
acoustic events is sometimes strong, sometimes weak, and quite often there
is just no acoustic correlate present even though the listener has no
difficulty in distinguishing the appropriate linguistic unit. This is so because
speech perception is influenced not only by acoustic and articulatory cues
but depends to a much larger extent than is usually believed on various
contextual cues. These cues are the result of constraints on phoneme and
word sequences, etc. arising partly out of the nature of language structure
and partly from meaning.

It is reasonable, after all, that speech should have developed in this multiconditioned manner. Only in this way could it have evolved into this
amazing system of communication that can operate successfully under such
extremely unfavorable conditions. Communication by speech is maintained
despite severe distortion by background noise and by room echoes; it
works regardless of the great variety of dialects and the large range over
which the size of speakers' vocal tracts vary; it works for men's, women's,
and children's voices even though there inevitably must be large differences
between the characteristics of the acoustic output of their respective vocal
tracts.

What I found particularly attractive in Dr. Osgood's paper as a whole is that he is so obviously aware of the multilevel structure of speech and of the fact that the varied needs of human communication have necessarily imposed a multiconditioned structure on the speech process.

*Osgood:* I do not think I will say much in response to Dr. Denes' presentation because it was in a specific area in which he is obviously the expert and I am not. I have one point, however: the voiced *versus* voiceless distinction in the case of whispering. Is it not true there are many redundant features, for example, the length of the preceding vowel? I think perhaps redundant features help to substitute for voicing.

Now, pertaining to transitionals, let me make the matter more extreme by proposing S1, S2, S3, and their transitional relations. The fact that sentence S2 may have a question form can be, I think, shown to be in part a function of the antecedent sentence form. Much of communication, of course, involves not sentences but fragments: "Where'd he go?"—"Into the house." "Into the house" clearly is a fractional sentence but is dependent upon antecedent, transitional events.

*Stockwell:* I have a question about the Johnson experiment on transitional probabilities you mentioned (21), which I have not read personally. *A priori*, and from my own experience with this kind of testing, I have some doubts about it. For instance, in very many cases, in carrying out tests of the same sort (doubtless more informally), I find the big breaks tend to be not necessarily between the large syntactic classes (between noun phrase and verb phrase in this case) but rather at the point where one has an open class item, that is to say, the choice of noun after determiner. These two are syntactically very closely linked. Time and again, the point at which enormous breaks occur is right in the middle of a closed phrase of this sort, where the first item is a closed class item and the next an open class item, and where the number of choices possible in the second instance is very large.

Leaving this aside until I have seen the results of the experiment in detail, I think there must be some way other than the one Dr. Osgood proposed to account for them. I do not believe that one will consistently get large temporal breaks, hesitation pauses, at the points of maximum syntactic disjuncture.

*Osgood:* I was not talking about hesitation. Rather, there is an entire series of sentences having different structural forms. What these results indicate would be the transitional ease; if the subject gets this item, he will get the next one. The point is that, in recall, he tends to get "the man" as a whole or "the colorful ball" as a whole, but there are breaks between the two main classes.

*Stockwell:* That is, of course, different from what I was talking about. The kind of thing I spoke about is where one says to a class of students, "I have in mind a sentence. Start guessing." You can see how many guesses it takes to obtain each item in sequence. The big breaks, under those conditions, are not at the syntactic disjunctures. You are talking about the uncertainty problem, which does not correspond with syntactic breaks. These are two very different things.

*Osgood:* Recall does seem to show this. Enclosed in or superimposed on the chunking are the transitional effects.

*Stockwell:* Another question I want to raise is whether, in fact, your suggestion that the grammar might incorporate not only the hierarchical kinds of rules but also the linear relationship implies that the latter ought to be at all points down through the tree. That is, what is the motivation for assuming transitional probabilities at all levels of the hierarchy in the tree?

*Hirsh:* I want to raise two theoretical points, one having to do with the choice between the chaining model and Chomsky's structural model of syntax. At the end of his exposition, Dr. Osgood put them together in the sense that both may operate. In his earlier review, however, it seemed to me that the choice between the two models is a choice between grammar as it is intended to be, i.e., an abstract description of what happens in a language community, as opposed to grammar as, for example, a system to be taught to someone else.

It is quite clear that there are many people who speak as if they were chaining and as if there were no structure available to them, particularly children in developmental stages and also some of the patients about whom we have heard. And there are other people who talk as if there were structure-imposing rules upon their subsequent output. Thus, I think there are at least two kinds of language behavior, perhaps, to be accounted for by these two kinds of model.

My second point has to do with the level of discourse contained within the second circle from the outside of Figure 42. Dr. Osgood, having been brought up properly as a twentieth century psychologist, has successfully repressed the words "mind" and "consciousness". Although he chooses not to make physiological referents for such terms as the organism or the central nervous system, I believe that these are, as some would have put it, Skinnerian mythological substitutes for mind and consciousness. If he would accept that criticism then I fail to see the great difference between his formulation and that offered by Bishop Berkeley and John Stuart Mill in the eighteenth century.

*Melkanoff:* I do not understand the situation with regard to meaning. In particular, I am not quite sure whether meaning is assigned to the individual sign and words, or to the total sentence structure, because in some cases it changes the situation entirely.

*Geschwind:* I believe that Dr. Denes was making a point with which I should like to agree and to extend. We constantly speak of "a theory of language". I think it may be quite possible that what we really want are theories of many different mechanisms which have come together almost by accident and are used in similar ways. The underlying heterogeneity of mechanism may be masked by the apparent external unity. Let me cite an example. The act of carrying out verbal commands might easily be treated as a unitary phenomenon. There is, however, good evidence that we may carry out different types of commands by quite different anatomical routes. Thus a patient who does not carry out individual limb movements may yet do complex whole-body movements to command, as Liepmann (25) first noted casually, and which I have studied in greater detail (14). I suspect that this type of heterogeneity may be present in many aspects of language and that we may end up with many theories rather than an overall master theory.

## REFERENCES

1. ABORN, M., RUBENSTEIN, H., and STERLING, T. D., Sources of contextual constraint upon words in sentences. *J. Exp. Psychol.*, 1959, **57**: 171-180.

2. BROWN, R., and GILMAN, A., The pronouns of power and solidarity. In: *Style in Language* (T. A. Sebeok, Ed.). Technology Press, M.I.T., Cambridge, 1960: 253-276.

3. CARROLL, J. B., Process and content in psycholinguistics. In: *Current Trends in the Description and Analysis of Behavior.* Univ. of Pittsburgh Press, Pittsburgh, 1958: 175-200.

4. CHOMSKY, N., *Syntactic Structures.* Mouton, The Hague, 1957.

5. –––, Review of: B. F. Skinner, *Verbal Behavior. Language*, 1959, **35**: 26-58.

6. CHOMSKY, N., and MILLER, G. A., Introduction to the formal analysis of natural languages. In: *Handbook of Mathematical Psychology*, Vol. II (R. D. Luce, R. B. Bush and E. Galanter, Eds.). Wiley, New York, 1963: 269-321.

7. DENES, P., Effect of duration on the perception of voicing. *J. Acoust. Soc. Am.*, 1955, **27**: 761-764.

8. –––, A preliminary investigation of certain aspects of intonation. *Lang. Speech*, 1959, **2**: 106-122.

9. DENES, P., and MILTON-WILLIAMS, J., Further studies in intonation. *Lang. Speech*, 1962, **5**: 1-14.

10. DE SAUSSURE, F., *Course in General Linguistics* (W. Baskin, Transl.). Philosophical Library, New York, 1959.

11. FILLENBAUM, S., JONES, L. V., and RAPOPORT, A., The predictability of words and their grammatical classes as a function of rate of deletion from a speech transcript. *J. Verb. Learn. Verb. Beh.*, 1963, **2**: 186-194.

12. FORSTER, K. I., *Left to Right Processes in the Construction of Sentences.* Thesis, Univ. of Illinois, Urbana, 1964.

13. FRY, D. B., and DENES, P., An analogue of the speech recognition process. In: *Mechanisation of Thought Processes*, Vol. I. Her Majesty's Stationery Office, London, 1959: 375-384.

14. GESCHWIND, N., Disconnection syndromes in animals and man. *Brain*, 1965, **88**: 237-294.

15. GOLDMAN-EISLER, F., Speech analysis and the mental processes. *Lang. Speech*, 1958, **1**: 59-75.

16. HARRIS, Z. S., Discourse analysis. *Language*, 1952, **28**: 1-30.

17. HEBB, D. O., *The Organization of Behavior; a Neurophysiological Theory.* Wiley, New York, 1949.

18. HOUSE, A. S., STEVENS, K. N., SANDEL, T. T., and ARNOLD, J. B., On the learning of speech-like vocabularies. *J. Verb. Learn. Verb. Beh.*, 1962, **1**: 133-143.

19. HULL, C. L., Knowledge and purpose as habit mechanisms. *Psychol. Rev.*, 1930, **37**: 511-525.

20. JAKOBSON, R., Boas' view of grammatical meaning. *Am. Anthropologist*, 1959, **61**, Mem. 89: 139-145.

21. JOHNSON, N. F., Linguistic models and functional units of language behavior. In: *Directions in Psycholinguistics* (S. Rosenberg, Ed.). Macmillan, New York, 1965: 29-65.

22. KANTOR, J. R., *An Objective Psychology of Grammar.* Indiana Univ. Publ., Science Series, Bloomington, 1936.

23. KATZ, J. J., and FODOR, J. A., The structure of a semantic theory. *Language*, 1963, **39**: 170-210.

24. LASHLEY, K. S., The problem of serial order in behavior. In: *Cerebral Mechanisms in Behavior* (L. A. Jeffress, Ed.). Wiley, New York, 1951: 112-146.

25. LIEPMANN, H., Das Krankheitsbild der Apraxie ("motorischen Asymbolie") auf Grund eines Falles von einseitiger Apraxie. *Mschr. Psychiat. Neurol.*, 1900, **8**: 15-44; 102-132; 182-197.

26. MACLAY, H., A descriptive approach to communications. In: *Decisions, Values and Groups,* Vol. II (N. F. Washburn, Ed.). Pergamon, New York, 1962: 201-226.

27. MACLAY, H., and NEWMAN, S., Two variables affecting the message in communications. In: *Decisions, Values and Groups,* Vol. I (D. Willner, Ed.). Pergamon, New York, 1960: 218-228.

28. MACLAY, H., and OSGOOD, C. E., Hesitation phenomena in spontaneous English speech. *Word*, 1959, **15**: 19-44.

29. MACLAY, H., and SLEATOR, M. D., Responses to language: judgments of grammaticalness. *Internat. J. Am. Ling.*, 1960, **26**: 275-282.

30. MILLER, G. A., Some psychological studies of grammar. *Am. Psychologist*, 1962, **17**: 748-762.

31. MILLER, G. A., and CHOMSKY, N., Finitary models of language users. In: *Handbook of Mathematical Psychology*, Vol. II (R. D. Luce, R. R. Bush and E. H. Galanter, Eds.). Wiley, New York, 1963: 419-491.

32. MILLER, G. A., GALANTER, E. H., and PRIBRAM, K. H., *Plans and the Structure of Behavior.* Holt, New York, 1960.

33. MILLER, G. A., HEISE, G. A., and LICHTEN, W., The intelligibility of speech as a function of the context of the test materials. *J. Exp. Psychol.*, 1951, **41**: 329-335.

34. MILLER, G. A., and SELFRIDGE, J. A., Verbal context and the recall of meaningful material. *Am. J. Psychol.*, 1950, **63**: 176-185.

35. MORRIS, C. W., *Signs, Language and Behavior.* Prentice-Hall, New York, 1946.

36. OSGOOD, C. E., *Method and Theory in Experimental Psychology.* Oxford Univ. Press, New York, 1953.

37. ———, Behavior theory and the social sciences. *Behav. Sci.*, 1956, **1**: 167-185.

38. ———, A behavioristic analysis of preception and language as cognitive phenomena. In: *Contemporary Approaches to Cognition.* Harvard Univ. Press, Cambridge, 1957: 75-118.

39. Osgood, C. E., Motivational dynamics of language behavior. In: *Nebraska Symposium on Motivation* (M. Jones, Ed.). Univ. of Nebraska Press, Lincoln, 1957: 348-424.

40. Osgood, C. E., and Sebeok, T. A. (Eds.), Psycholinguistics; a survey of theory and research problems. *J. Abnorm. Soc. Psychol.*, 1954, **49**: Suppl.

41. Osgood, C. E., and Walker, E. G., Motivation and language behavior: a content analysis of suicide notes. *J. Abnorm. Soc. Psychol.*, 1959, **59**: 58-67.

42. Postman, L., and Brown, D. R., The perceptual consequences of success and failure. *J. Abnorm. Soc. Psychol.*, 1952, **47**: 213-221.

43. Shepard, R. N., Production of constrained associates and the informational uncertainty of the constraint. *Am. J. Psychol.*, 1963, **76**: 218-228.

44. Skinner, B. F., *Verbal Behavior*. Methuen, London, 1957.

45. Tannenbaum, P. H., and Stolz, W. S., *Markov Chains in the Grammatical Structure of English*. Private distribution, Univ. of Wisconsin, Madison, 1963.

46. Taylor, W. L., "Cloze procedure": a new tool for measuring readability. *Journ. Quart.*, 1953, **30**: 415-433.

47. Tyler, V. O., Jr., Sensory integration with and without reinforcement. *J. Exp. Psychol.*, 1962, **63**: 381-386.

48. Wundt, W., Die Sprache. Vol. I in: *Völkerpsychologie; eine Untersuchung der Entwicklungsgesetze von Sprache, Mythus und Sitte*. Engelman, Leipzig, 1900.

# THE PROBLEM OF PRIMITIVE LANGUAGES

HARRY HOIJER
University of California
Los Angeles

"Primitive language" is sometimes used by teachers of English composition to describe the speech and writing they find in their freshman composition classes. And I have heard it used at least once in these sessions to characterize the impaired speech of certain varieties of aphasics. On this particular subject I must say that my knowledge of aphasia has increased 100 per cent.

The word "primitive", as frequently used in the phrases "primitive language", "primitive culture", and "primitive man" is often ambiguous: the paleontologist uses it to describe animals such as the Eocene horse, which are ancestral to modern animals; the physical anthropologist follows a similar reasoning when he describes such early hominids as *Pithecanthropus* and *Sinanthropus* as primitive and as more or less directly ancestral to modern man.

A second common use of the term occurs when certain contemporary animals and men preserve bodily features similar to those found in animals and men of earlier geological periods. Thus we find a contemporary fish species, called *Latimeria*, which is almost exactly like one that lived about 300 million years ago. No such impressive example of a modern primitive is found for man, but there are modern populations, like the Australian aborigines, who display a number of bodily traits more common among Paleolithic populations than among those of today. Australian aborigines can therefore be called primitive in the same sense, though certainly not to the same degree, that we refer to *Latimeria* as a primitive fish.

The archeologist generally uses "primitive" in reference to cultures which existed during the Paleolithic, Neolithic, or earlier periods. These cultures were, for the most part, characterized by a stone-tool technology and by social, economic, and political systems underdeveloped in comparison to cultures of the present day. Many may be viewed as ancestral to present-day cultures and, therefore, as attesting to earlier stages in the development of man's civilizations.

Cultures of the modern period are also called primitive if they appear to preserve certain cultural traits more common in the Paleolithic, Neolithic, or earlier periods. Thus, the Australian aborigines and many Indian tribes of the Americas made all or most of their tools from chipped or ground stone; they lived in small, extended familial groups and possessed other traits presumably characteristic of the late Paleolithic or the early Neolithic. Peoples such as these, many of whom were found when European adventurers made their first explorations in the Americas, Oceania, Australia and Africa, might be called contemporary primitives, at least so far as their cultures are concerned.

In speaking of the cultures of contemporary primitives, the point must be emphasized that these are not to be equated loosely with the primitive cultures evidenced by archeological deposits of the Neolithic or Paleolithic. This does not mean, however, that the cultures of contemporary primitives offer no guides to the study of the evolution of culture, or even that they fail to offer useful clues for the reconstruction of the cultures of prehistoric times. All modern cultures, primitive or otherwise, have a long and largely unknown history, but the cultures of contemporary primitives have developed, or evolved, at a slower rate than those which characterize the great civilizations of today. The difference in the rate of evolution is seen most clearly in technology; the stone-using peoples of aboriginal Australia and many areas of aboriginal North America quite clearly stand in sharp contrast to the vastly more advanced technologies of modern civilizations. Similar contrasts might be cited between the socioeconomic and political systems of contemporary primitives and the world civilizations, though here the contrasts are neither so marked nor so easily determined. It might not be thought, however, that all cultures of contemporary primitives are at the same evolutionary level; there is no simple dichotomy between primitive cultures and those which have gone beyond the primitive level of cultural development. Among contemporary primitives anthropologists find widely varying degrees of evolutionary development. The contrast in aboriginal America between the cultures of such primitives as the Fuegians and those of the Mayan Indians of Guatemala and Yucatan is as great as that which separates the primitive cultures of Tierra del Fuego from those of early Egypt.

Languages, however, are not preserved in archeological deposits, except in the case of the few found in written form on stone or clay tablets, and these are too few and too recent in geological time to be significant in any evolutionary sense. There is, therefore, no evidence in the form of archeological remains of early stages of language evolution, though we must assume that language, like other aspects of culture, underwent a period of evolutionary development. Clearly "primitive", in the sense "primitive in time", while it is justified in the case of cultures and man's bodily development, is not so justified in reference to language since there is no trace of languages "primitive in time".

The term "primitive languages", it should now be clear, cannot refer to

languages spoken in the Neolithic, Paleolithic, or earlier ages, since we possess no data whatsoever on these idioms which long ago passed out of existence. If the term is used at all—and there are many anthropologists who
prefer not to use it—it must refer to the languages spoken by contemporary
primitives, whatever their level of evolutionary development, short of the
modern industrialized and urbanized civilizations. There are many such
languages; they are, indeed, far more numerous than the languages of civilized folk. Some of these languages are extinct; many others, like those of
the Indians of North America, are on the verge of extinction. The last one I
worked with was a language of Oregon, and my sole resource was a man
80 years old. He was the last speaker of this particular dialect, one of a
group of Oregon and North California Athapaskan languages. But there are
a considerable number of languages commonly classed as primitive, found
in Latin America, Southeast Asia, Oceania and North Africa, that are spoken by populations ranging in size from a half million to several millions. In
modern Africa and parts of Oceania and Southeast Asia, languages once
restricted to more or less primitive cultures are becoming increasingly important as the peoples who speak them assume a larger role in world affairs.

What can now be said of the languages spoken by contemporary primitives? Do these languages, like the cultures of some contemporary primitives, have any evolutionary significance? If it is possible, as many anthropologists maintain, to learn something of cultural evolution from a careful
comparative analysis of all modern cultures, is it equally possible to learn
something of the evolution of human language from a comparative study of
all modern languages?

Scholars of the latter half of the 18th century and the earlier portions of
the 19th hoped to find somewhere on earth truly primitive societies whose
languages and cultures would attest to earlier stages in linguistic and cultural evolution. The search, insofar as the discovery of crude or primitive
languages is concerned, was a failure. Despite current popular belief to the
contrary, no language has yet been found which is primitive either in the
same sense that anthropologists designate a Paleolithic culture as primitive
or apply the term to a contemporary culture.

This means that all languages, whether spoken by peoples like the Australian aborigines or by cultivated Frenchmen, Englishmen, or Germans,
possess a fully developed system of distinctive sounds or phonemes and
equally well developed grammatical systems. Earlier scholars not infre-
quently described the language of contemporary primitives as imperfectly
developed grammatically and, therefore, possibly illustrative of an earlier
stage in the evolution of language. When, however, these languages were
examined more carefully, it became clear that they had been described by
persons untrained in linguistic field methods but thoroughly exposed to the
traditional grammars of Latin and Greek, or to similar traditional grammars of English, French, or German written on Graeco-Roman models.

Such scholars interpreted any absence of traditional European grammatical traits as evidence of primitiveness and failed to understand that a language must be described not in terms of its differences from classical or other models, but in its own terms, and that the linguist's task is to discover and describe the grammatical systems peculiar to the language under investigation. A language like that of the Navaho Indians, for example, lacks most of the grammatical features of ancient and modern European languages. The nouns of Navaho are not classed by gender, nor are they declined for case and number; Navaho verbs are regularly conjugated in seven paradigms, but none of these has reference to the tenses and moods of many European tongues. The classical eight parts of speech of many European languages find no precise parallel in Navaho. Navaho, for example, lacks the adjective class found in English and other European languages; in Navaho, words functioning roughly like the English adjectives are identical in grammatical form and treatment to Navaho verbs.

It might be of interest to illustrate this point by examining two words borrowed by the Apache (whose language is very similar to Navaho) from Spanish. The two words are "loco" (crazy) and "rico" (rich), both of which are Spanish adjectives. In Apache the two words assume a slightly different pronunciation which we can symbolize by "lóògò" and "žìígò," respectively. But this is not the most significant difference. More important is the fact that "lóògò" and "žìígò" are interpreted as verbs, not adjectives, and have the meanings "he is crazy" and "he is rich", respectively. Since in both Navaho and Apache verbs may be conjugated for both person and number, these two forms are similarly conjugated. Thus we find, in the case of "lóògò", the following created forms: "lóòšgò" (I am crazy), "lóngò" (you are crazy), "lóhìígò" (we are crazy), etc. Obviously, these are not derived from Spanish (as "lóògò" is) but are created by the Apache as a result of their classifying "lóògò" as a verb rather than an adjective.

It should now be obvious from these illustrations that Navaho and Apache grammars, which are very close to each other, are wholly unlike the grammars of the better known languages of modern Europe and America. But this fact does not make Navaho grammar inferior or underdeveloped. When we describe Navaho grammar in its own terms rather than in terms of a European model, we find it in no sense primitive.

It is often pointed out, however, that the languages of contemporary primitives frequently differ from modern European languages in respect to the size of their vocabularies, insofar as vocabulary size can adequately be measured. The languages of primitive societies have smaller vocabularies than are found in the languages of modern world civilizations, though this difference is frequently exaggerated. One writer on linguistics, in a book published as late as 1962 (9), makes the extraordinary and completely erroneous statement that most American Indian languages do not even have words, since all of their words are or can be sentences.

Vocabularies of widely divergent languages frequently reveal other differences. Words that are commonplace among speakers of English, whatever their social class or education, often have no precise analogs in an American Indian language and must therefore be translated by descriptive phrases or other modes of circumlocution. Most such terms, however, are closely linked to the culture of English speakers and foreign to the cultures of their Indian neighbors. In the last analysis, it turns out that the bulk of any vocabulary is closely linked to the culture of the people who use it, and translatable, if at all, only with difficulty into the vocabulary of peoples with a widely different culture. If we encounter difficulty in finding Navaho translations for English culture words, we also find the same difficulty in finding adequate translations in English for Navaho culture words. To illustrate, such ordinary terms in English as our kin terms "brother" and "sister" find no counterpart among the Navaho, where one's siblings are designated in terms of two systems, one containing four terms, divided by age and sex: older brother, younger brother, older sister, younger sister; while the other system has only two forms: the first used reciprocally between siblings of the same sex, and the second reciprocally between siblings of the opposite sex.

The intimate relationship of vocabulary to culture has recently been demonstrated in the attempt to construct a list of meanings which can be easily translated into any language by simple one-word constructions. Obviously such meanings must be free not only from cultural influences but from any influence that the geographic or biological environment may exert on a vocabulary. We should not expect to find a one-word equivalent in English for a concept peculiar to Eskimo or Hottentot cosmology or religion, nor would Eskimo possess simple forms for animals or plants of temperate zones or for climatic phenomena peculiar to a tropical environment. But it is, *a priori*, reasonable to assume that body parts, features of the environment common to all men, and other meanings necessarily expressible in all societies would translate easily and by one-word equivalents in all the vocabularies used in the world today.

The results are surprising. The first list of meanings so developed contained 218 items, and it was confidently expected that this list might be extended to several hundred items. As it turned out, the list of 218 had to be pruned drastically, first to 200 items and later to only 100 items. Still later, when attempts to translate the 100-item list had increased in number, there occurred numerous instances in which as many as 25 of the 100 items offered difficulties in translation. An item might (rarely) not be translatable at all or, more often, be translated by two, three, or more words in certain languages, but precisely translated by none of them.

We can illustrate this point by referring again to Navaho. Here, it turns out, the simple item expressed in English by the verb "go" has no simple Navaho equivalent. There are in Navaho four verb stems which might be used in constructing a verb "go", but none of them expresses this meaning solely or precisely. Instead, each of the stems has a broader meaning, conveying also a reference to number; thus, one refers (or can refer) to one person's going, a second to two persons' going, a third to several persons' going, and a fourth to the going of a group moving *en masse* (as, for example, a crowd or an army unit). These four stems, it should be noted, are wholly unrelated, as unrelated as the English forms "go", "walk", "move", and "run". There is obviously no way of representing the English meaning "go" by one Navaho word.

The attempts to translate the 100-item list of meanings into a number of highly divergent languages clearly demonstrates, in my opinion, that the cultural influence on vocabulary is far stronger and more pervasive than was originally expected. It is almost certainly true that there exists a body of meanings that is common to all peoples, regardless of their culture and environment. But it does not follow that this body of meanings is divided in all languages into one hundred similar segments each expressed by a simple linguistic form; it is far more likely that the experience common to all men is, in different societies, differently organized into components designated by simple linguistic forms, and that these different organizations of experience become greater as the culture of the societies vary more widely.

Differences in vocabulary between two or more languages have little or no linguistic significance. The size and resources of a vocabulary are dependent, not on the adequacy of the linguistic structure that produces it, but on the culture of which the language is a part. Smaller and more isolated societies, since these have cultures of the type we have called primitive, will also have vocabularies that are smaller and less rich in resources than those of societies which possess highly developed civilizations. Furthermore, it may be noted that the vocabularies of contemporary primitives who in recent times have had numerous and long continued contacts with modern civilizations become considerably larger and more diverse in response to the newly imposed cultural milieu. Examples of such vocabulary growth abound among American Indian societies, many of which have lived in intimate contact with their European conquerors for centuries.

If it is conceded, as it must be, that languages all over the world reveal an essential equality in structural development, it is obvious that language is of considerable antiquity; that it is, in fact, as old as any other aspect of culture. Anthropologists have demonstrated that language is prerequisite to culture and that culture could not have begun before at least a rudimentary language had come into being. The reasoning behind this conclusion rests on the fact that culture is, among other things, cumulative; it is, in effect, an accumulation of patterns of behavior which is the work of countless generations. Without a means for the sharing of experience within a generation, a means of abstracting from this body of knowledge ways of behaving necessary to the continuance of human physical existence and, finally, a means of transmitting a society's cumulated ways of behaving to successive generations, culture could neither have come into being nor developed from its crude beginnings more than a million years ago to its present sophistication and complexity. Language provided the means to achieve these ends and, for this reason, its beginnings must have taken place as early in time as we find the first development of the crudest stone tools. The last statement might lead to some misconception: I emphasize the words "development of the crudest stone tools"; conceivably crude tools might be found that show no development, in which case one might have a tool-using animal but still a cultureless animal.

A final word may be in order in respect to the evolution of language. As we have said, there is no evidence yet of significant differences among present-day languages that support an evolutionary hypothesis. The differences which do exist, in that the languages of modern civilizations possess greater resources of expression, do not point to the inherent superiority of one language over another. Placed in the same cultural framework as English, French or German, the languages of such people as the Eskimo, the Bushman of Africa, or the Navaho have equal potentialities for the development of such linguistic resources.

Language is, however, part of a larger aspect of culture, frequently called "communication", which includes not only language (which certainly has a central and key position) but many other behavioral complexes in terms of which human beings interact. Biologists have shown that forms of communication exist among nearly all animals, even though language, in the sense we are discussing it here, is confined to man. Among the men who lived in the early archeological periods and those of modern times to whom the adjective primitive applies, communication rests in large part on spoken language.

Writing, invented only some 5000 years ago, provided a new mode of communication and made possible the preservation of speech forms over long periods of time. Writing, of course, was originally limited to relatively few societies, and even today there exist many societies which have not acquired or have only recently acquired writing. And writing, as it existed among the early civilizations of Europe, Asia, Africa and America (for example, the Egyptians, the Mayans of Guatemala and the Chinese) was a handicraft limited to a very small proportion of the population. Interestingly enough, there is considerable evidence that the writings of early times served less as media of communication than as art forms or religious symbols.

Mass media of communication did not begin until the invention of movable type, which occurred late in human history, and printing, which occurred even later. Today, of course, the mass media are many and have developed to the point where those with ready access to them can speak directly not only to audiences within the reach of their voices but to millions all over the world.

It is evident, then, that while the earlier steps in the evolution of communication, when communication depended almost solely on spoken language, cannot be demonstrated, we can discern some correlation between communication and the evolution of culture as a whole.

### Discussion

*Garvin:* I should like first to say that the notion of primitiveness in language was linked very closely to the notion of linguistic evolution during the 19th century. An attempt was made at that time to give certain criteria for what is primitive. For instance, it was considered that language evolves by stages from what was then called isolating to agglutinative to inflectional. One source (12) illustrated this with Chinese as an isolating language, Turkish as an agglutinative language, and Latin as an inflectional language.

This notion was abandoned when it was pointed out that English, in many ways, might be considered an isolating language. The notion was subsequently current in the linguistics of the past century, and in some circles to this day, that so-called polysynthetic languages are primitive; that is to say, languages that are like a certain type of American Indian languages. Eskimo is the classical example of a polysynthetic language found in the literature (12). I do not know any Eskimo, but I can give you an example of Kutenai, an American Indian language spoken in Northern Idaho and Southern British Columbia. In Kutenai, "I shall build a house" is said "hu-n-it-itɬaʔ-ne·". The various portions of this word can be translated literally as follows: hu-, "I"; -n-, "this word is a predicate"; -it-, "make"; itɬaʔ-, "house"; ne·, "indicative mood". This is undoubtedly the source of the statement in a popular book (13) that in American Indian languages "the distinction between word and sentence is partly effaced." And whether this is a reasonable criterion for primitiveness, I shall not venture to discuss. There are no modern European languages that can be considered polysynthetic unless one takes a language like French where, from a phonological standpoint, word boundaries tend to be erased: something like "Je le lui donne" might be said to be single word phonologically and has a structure similar to one of the sentence-long Eskimo words. It is easy to see that polysynthetism is not a good criterion for primitiveness by present-day standards.

One might want to speculate about primitiveness from some other standpoint and say that, since we have no historical evidence of primitive language comparable to the archeological equivalent, we might want to call a language primitive if it is in some way inadequate. Two conceivable inadequacies might be that it has less abstraction or that it is in some way less well organized and more difficult.

This raises very important problems. First, how would you define what is more and what is less abstract in regard to a language? My own preference would be to look at it in terms of possible behavioral criteria. It could, for instance, be said that, in the vocabulary of a language, anything that can be named by pointing at is more concrete than something which cannot be named by pointing at. And it could also be said that abstract is more or less that which lacks a definite outline. If these criteria are applied, it might be found that it is extremely difficult to decide whether a language such as Navaho, for instance, really is less abstract than a language such as English.

Another possible criterion for primitiveness might be the degree of organization, difficulty, or similar characterization. Linguists at one time used to deny this by saying that all languages are equally difficult or easy, and that their difficulty just depends upon the learner. I once wrote a paper (3) about the relative difficulty that a language poses to the linguistic analyst, and I found that this was indeed a decidable matter, at least on subjective grounds, of the particular analyst having treated more than one language and having found one harder than the other.

There are certain characteristic criteria that can be pointed out: for instance, the ease with which one can separate utterances into their component parts. In some languages this can be done very simply; in others it is almost entirely impossible. The problem, however, is whether, corresponding to this analytic difficulty, there is also a learning difficulty. This has never really been studied; either it has been assumed that there are languages that are difficult to learn, or the idea has been rejected violently.

This would also have to be considered from two standpoints, namely learning difficulty for the foreign speaker and learning difficulty for the native speaker. The latter, I think, would be a very interesting area because one could, for instance, consider the degree to which children's language differs from adult language as a measure of some type of learning difficulty. I made some extremely casual and totally unreliable observations among the Kutenai Indians in the Pacific Inland Empire, and one conspicuous thing I noted was that, whereas in the adult language there is a great abundance of consonant clusters, with as many as five consonants in a cluster, this is not the case in children's language. This is a significant difference, but there has not actually been a detailed study of the situation.

Thus, the problem of primitiveness, viewed from the standpoint of the intrinsic properties of languages, is totally unresolved for the simple reason that it is not as yet possible to define the notion of primitiveness in an operational way. It may be worth trying, and two avenues for this might be the concrete-abstract distinction, or the relative difficulty of learning. Whether this is, then, really a measure of primitiveness or whether we have simply switched from primitiveness to a less preposterous measure, is another question.

Many anthropologists have replaced the notion of primitiveness with that of the difference between folk and urban; that is, instead of speaking of primitive and civilized societies, they now speak of folk cultures and urban cultures. I have found it extremely useful to draw a parallel to this in regard to language, i.e., it is possible to differentiate between folk speech and a standard language for many speech communities. This is a differentiation which very closely parallels the folk-urban distinction in culture. By "folk speech" I mean such speech patterns as the rural patois in France or, for that matter, the substandard dialects of American English. And by "standard language" I mean a language such as the French prescribed by the Académie Française or the Russian prescribed by its Academy. One can set forth very definite criteria for what constitutes a standard language. The defining criterion would be a formal codification determined by a codifying agency such as an academy or a ministry of education; there are a number of other characteristics that can be stipulated. A good deal of work on this was done by linguists in Czechoslovakia. I will cite one particular feature discussed by the Czech Havránek (8)—intellectualization, the desire and tendency toward an increasingly accurate mode of expression. This is shown, for instance, in the area of the lexicon by the creation of technical terminologies. The phenomenon can be observed even on the folk end of the scale and increases progressively towards the urban end of the scale.

An associate and I did a study of the Guaraní Indians of Paraguay (4), where we observed all the characteristics of a standard language in the making, including the attempt to create a codifying agency in the then existing Academia de la Lengua Guaraní. A typical feature of the emergent standard language was that a defense of the language was written in the language of the higher-prestige population. This is a very interesting parallel to the renascence of the Czech language in the early 19th century, when the first significant grammatical treatise about Czech was written in German (1).

I want to conclude by saying that studying the process of codification, as exemplified by intellectualization, allows one to make very definite judgments about location along the folk-urban scale. It may be a more productive way of looking at the problem then using the notion of primitive *versus* civilized.

*Ferguson:* I want to comment on two points: first, on what we might call the "ratability" of language—is one language better than another language in some way? And, second, on the question of development viewed in terms of standardization or folk-urban.

Dr. Hoijer gave us a very clear presentation of the generally accepted view of linguists on the question of primitive languages, and I will not quarrel with anything he said. But I would be happy to join with Dr. Garvin and others who would, I think, say that if we change our point of view slightly it is perfectly feasible to rate languages in various ways. We would not rate them on a single scale (language A is better than language B in general) or on a single scale of learnability (language A is easier to learn as a first language than language B), but it is possible to rate languages by selecting parts of grammatical structure. Linguists have not done this, but there is no reason why it should not be done. It would be perfectly easy to create a scale of regularity of morphophonemics along which languages could be rated; it could be said that a particular language is more regular, or more symmetrical in its paradigms than another; it would be perfectly possible to point out that the paradigms of two languages would involve the same number or a different number of categories. Languages show striking differences in the ability to form new compounds, and it would be possible to rate languages in this way. I am just repeating what Dr. Garvin suggested, that it is very difficult and perhaps not wise at all to try to rate languages in general terms, but there are many specific points on which we not only can but should try to rate them.

My other point was on the question of evolution, in terms of standardization. Several of us have called attention to the fact that, if we want to talk about natural evolution of language, we cannot do it in terms of grammatical structure but in a more external characterization of how much dialect diversity there is within language, what trends toward standardization there are, and so on. I would call attention in particular to Heinz Kloss' work (10) in trying to develop a scale of standardization in terms of the use of language for written purposes at various levels. In my own concern with standardization, I immediately ran into a difficulty which perhaps is not so obvious in the case of Czech or Guaraní: there are multimodal standardizations. I think of Armenian, or Norwegian, or many languages where the development does not seem to follow the expected classical line of moving from a great variety of dialects to a single norm, but seems to follow other lines. I would certainly think this entire area is one in which linguists, sociologists, and others should work to see if there is such a thing as an evolutionary scale we can talk about in terms of standardization.

*Osgood:* Like Dr. Ferguson, I am intrigued by the possibilities of obtaining actual quantitative measures of languages. I am sure one could characterize the adult norm of a given language and a curve or function which describes the approach relationship of the adult norm to higher or lower levels. This could be done quite rigorously. Along the same lines, one could take errors made by adult speakers; that is, if the rules of the language can be determined and degrees of error in variation from the norm found (e.g., in grammaticalness), one would have another quantitative index for language.

*Garvin:* Or find the areas in which errors occur, say the realms of the structure in which they occur.

*Osgood:* But then there is confusion, in a way, with the problem of language change. This brings me to my second question, about the idea (advanced by Morris Swadesh, I believe) of measuring change in basic vocabulary. I should like to ask linguists who have studied this matter whether rate of change of language is really a constant or whether it depends on the number of interacting speakers, as I should expect. Also, is it not true that the rate of change is very different for different aspects of language? A recent article (5) made the assertion that, although there are continuous changes in lexical items (in English vocabulary), there has not been a single change in function words in a hundred years. There are apparently marked differences in the susceptibility of different aspects of language to change.

Dr. Hoijer mentioned that he thought the differences in sizes of vocabulary had been overrated or overemphasized; I agree with this. Surely, if Navaho and English dictionaries were weighed in a balance, one would say that Navaho is a primitive or undeveloped language compared with English—but if the average English speaker's functioning vocabulary were compared with that of the speakers of Navaho, I think the difference in size would be found to be very small.

Lastly, what are the implicit expectations in this matter? If all those measurements were taken, would one expect to find that the more developed (or less primitive languages) are the more complex, or the more simple, or the more regularized? Is simplification the general trend?

*Marschak:* My question is addressed to linguists as well as to biologists. As an economist, I am used to judging any organization, any system of traits, rules, customs, policies, whether existing or proposed, by the criterion of efficiency with respect to some goals. As a particular case, when comparing systems that exist or existed, one natural criterion is that of fitness for survival in a given environment. It is clear from Dr. Hoijer's talk that many anthropological explanations of observed phenomena are guided by this criterion. In the discussion that followed, several other criteria and comparison scales were proposed: regularity, complexity, learnability, precision, abstractness of a language. They all may be useful for classification purposes. But will they, by themselves, help to explain and predict? That is, will they necessarily coincide in all environments with a high probability of survival of the language itself or of its carrier, a human group? May not complexity, for example, under some conditions, be of no advantage at all? Is it not possible that in a changed economy, or with a dying cult, or a diminished social stratification, an existing language may turn out to be over-precise and hence self-destructive because some shades and distinctions had lost their usefulness and fetter the day's business? In short, my question to linguists is: do you want to explain or merely to classify? Is it impertinent to ask this? I realize that the types of environment, in the relevant sense, are numerous. But their number is presumably smaller than the number of known languages and dialects, living or dead. In any case, a statistical, probabilistic approach to evolution must remain crude; although Mandelbrot's (11) interpretation of "Zipf's law" suggests that such an approach is possible. More encouraging is the success that biology and, I believe, much of anthropology and some of comparative economic and social history, have had in finding qualitative relations between differences or changes in environment on the one hand, and the emergence, survival, or extinction of a trait, biological or cultural, on the other (11).

*Lamb:* With reference to the measurement of the amount of complexity or difficulty in languages, there have been certain very important advances in linguistics during the last ten years which make it possible now to take such measurements with a high degree of accuracy. What has happened is that we have refined our understanding of linguistic structure to the point where it appears to be possible to describe everything that a linguist considers it his job to describe about a language with a list of rules whose form can be specified very precisely; that is, formulaic rules with very definite mathematically describable characteristics. All that is necessary, then, to compare two languages is to calculate the relative complexity of the two lists of rules. This is not easy, since the first step, of course, is to find a complete description, and no one has ever made a complete description of any language. But most of the difficulty in describing languages is in the area of lexical rules; if we would confine ourselves to morphophonemics and grammar, there is a possibility that descriptions could be made. Having put morphophonemics and grammar into formulaic rules, the first approximation would be simply to count the rules of the descriptions to be compared. This is not a very refined approach, since one rule can be more complex than another. Therefore, the next step would be to measure the amount of information in a rule; understanding the structure of such rules, it is actually possible to count the number of bits of information in a rule. The number of bits of information in each set of rules would then give a basis for comparison.

*Osgood:* I would like to suggest another way, a typical psychologist's approach, which could be compared with your suggestion, Dr. Lamb. Imagine a set of culture-free test situations, such as simply describing an object or circumstance, so that one had a range of these situations common to all people everywhere. One then would measure the number of linguistic units per situation used for its description, i.e., for communication in the particular language. Would you expect this to correlate with your complexity of rules or number of rules? I would think it might.

*Lamb:* I see some difficulties in this type of testing because it might be that the people tested, being from different cultures, would find it appropriate to say different amounts about the same subject. One person might be more elaborate in his description than another. It would be hard to control that possible variation.

There are other points about the matter of complexity in languages that are perhaps a little more difficult to handle. What I am thinking of is that some complexity is useless. For example, in English, if one wants to make the comparative of "good", one cannot say "gooder"; one has to say "better". This has no useful function in English; it is an unnecessary complexity. It would be desirable to have measures for distinguishing the useful complexity from that which is useless. Perhaps this would give a measure of the efficiency of the language.

*Stockwell:* You are talking essentially about the degree of regularity.

*Lamb:* Yes. Once a list of the rules had been made, one could say certain of them have no communicative value. By taking the total number of bits of information and determining the number of rules having no communicative value, one could get the measure of efficiency of the language. I think it would be found that different languages differ in efficiency. I would cite Old Irish as an example of an extremely inefficient language, where prepositions are conjugated and other rules exist which apparently serve no useful function.

*Marschak:* Dr. Lamb used the words "useful" and "efficient". That is precisely what I wanted to point out. What presumably is of greatest interest lies not so much in classifying and devising measures of complexity for their own sake, but rather in distinguishing what is useful and efficient. And this means, precisely: more or less adapted to the environment, guaranteeing a greater or a smaller chance for survival. I do not know what else is meant by useful or efficient.

*Garvin:* In regard to the standard language question, if one looks at its implications one can certainly say it has explanatory value. The anthropologists, in talking about folk-urban societies, have a way of describing folk characteristics by saying: "When this is absent, it is urban." In the case of standard language, we are dealing with a complementary case. That is, we can define certain characteristics for a standard language and say that when these are absent, we are dealing with folk speech; thus added explanatory power is given to the folk-urban distinction. This, I think, is a valid distinction in terms of the consistent intuitive judgment of informed observers.

Further, I think the matter of intellectualization is not to be underrated. Rather than an example of precision being found in an increase in the number of terms for the same item, as has been proposed, I think it may be the opposite: in intellectualization—at least as discussed in the Czech literature (8)—the desire is to have as close an equivalency of terms to concepts as possible. This has to be coupled with a second desirable property, called flexible stability: there should be no more standard language rules than necessary and, at the same time, these rules should make easy provisions for new accretions. For instance, the special cases that Dr. Ferguson mentioned violate this requirement of stability, and there the result seems to be a much lesser effectiveness in the use of the standard language than in communities where the situation is more stable.

Whether languages may be rated on a scale of difficulty is simply a matter of having a frame of reference which allows it. Some theoretical frames of reference in linguistics do not seem to permit a comparison of languages in terms of tractability because they do not take into account how these languages are treated by the linguist, and are therefore not the best for making these delicate judgments.

*Geschwind:* It seems to me that in considering the difficulty of a language one should distinguish between its potential difficulty and its actual difficulty in general usage. Thus it is possible in German to construct extremely long words, and in certain highly talented hands full advantage is taken of this. Yet I believe that in general usage the average length of German words is about the same as the average length of English words in ordinary conversation. Similarly, I would think that while German can be far more difficult than Spanish, ordinary German is probably not terribly difficult. A second point relates to the difficulty of phonemes. I have heard from some of my linguistic informants that certain phonemes are very common while others, such as the English "ng" or "r" are rather rare in their occurrence. Could this not give us some measure of phonetic difficulty?

My third question concerns the current evolution of languages. Again I must rely on some of my linguistic informants, who have told me that in many contemporary languages there has been a tendency to simplification. I have been told that Japanese has dropped many highly complex verb forms. The rules current in American English for the use of "shall" and "may" appear to me simpler than those in use one hundred years ago. Similarly, French has abandoned certain verb forms in ordinary speech. Is this a general tendency in most languages?

A final point is that it would be most useful for linguists to study aphasic breakdown in as many other languages as possible. This may give us some measure of difficulty. Thus the possessive "-s" suffers more in aphasics than the plural "-s", as Goodglass showed (6). A similar problem would be to see which features are difficult for children to acquire.

*Lenneberg:* On the problem of rating, I would like to inject a note of skepticism. If one looks at whole languages, one has a tremendously complicated system of patterns on all levels. The patterns are interrelated by even more complex systems of rules, perhaps patterns of rules. Anybody who has ever tried to rank complex configurations, even much simpler ones such as visual patterns, is aware of the tremendous difficulty of arranging them. Any kind of arrangement is possible, but it is invariably based on arbitrary criteria. This goes back to the problem Dr. Marschak raised: who is to decide what is a good criterion?

In my own work I once wanted to rank patterns within English grammar. I wanted to know what we can expect mongoloid children to learn first and later. This raised the question of what is difficult or what is complex in English. We never solved the problem. We consulted with the linguists at MIT, but nobody could answer the question: What is primitive in English?

*Ervin:* I would like to mention the characteristics of child languages as an example of an obvious case where we have, very objectively, more primitive language. I am in the unusual situation of having actually tried to describe grammars of separate two-year-old children as though they were separate languages, taking something of the same approach that linguists take when they describe Navaho or another separate language (2).

Some of the characteristics of the grammars might be of interest as an indication of some properties of primitive languages. I have not looked at the phonological systems. Those who have described phonological systems of children in this fashion uniformly agree that the earlier the age, the smaller the number of phonemes. However, it is also very commonly true that the allophonic complexities can be quite great in children's languages. Thus, from the standpoint of the number of separate phonemes, primitiveness seems to mean a smaller number, but this is not true of the description of allophony in children.

In the grammars that I have been describing, it is a fact that at the beginning stages of grammar all the children have a small number of grammatical classes. Typically, one of these was a nominal class, while others were operators such as "where", "that", "there", "up", and "off". Order was predictable for the operators and was not used contrastively to change meaning. Usually the first grammars seem to involve what one might call optional strings. In English, we have something similiar in the order of adjectives before nouns; that is, I can say "this is a big, black, square box", or I can say "this is a big box", or I can say "this is a black box". The order of the adjectives used, if I have any pair of them, is predetermined, but I do not have to use any particular members of that series. In children, optional strings are often free variants having the same meaning.

The sentences are very short, as is typical of children. In the beginning grammars, none have inflections, and none use function words predictably; what function words there are are part of the optional string rule and can be omitted with no change in meaning. Morphological regularization is greater in children's language; the irregular forms appear much later. So, children's grammars are far more regular the younger the child. The first phrases we found were nominal ones. In a two-year-old, one begins to see such nominal phrases, but the possibility of having a more complex phrase structure does not appear until much later.

Thus we have seen four characteristics of children's very early grammars: they have a small number of classes, including nominals and operators; are morphologically highly regular when inflections appear; have nominal phrases earlier than other phrases; and at first may have optional expansions in free variation rather than hierarchical phrase structure rules. This is one definition of primitiveness.

*Hoijer:* The distinction pointed out by Dr. Garvin between folk culture and urban culture does not quite replace the distinction between primitive and urban culture. Rather, it divides the so-called civilized cultures into folk and urban, at least using the forms of Redfield (14), who devised this scheme to begin with. But that is a trifling point and I think he has an interesting suggestion in making comparisons of this sort.

Similarly, in respect to standardization, we have interesting possibilities to examine. I might add to his examples that of Navaho itself. Since writing was provided for the Navaho by a benevolent government in 1930, there has evolved, according to my late colleague, Gladys Reichard (15), a distinction between classical Navaho and what one might call folk speech. I had difficulty in following her criteria, but perhaps there is such a distinction.

On the matter of rates of change that Professor Osgood raised in respect to the Swadesh list (16), to do Swadesh justice I would like to point out that he confined the constant rate of change to the particular one hundred items that he was examining in all the languages. I agree, as we all must agree, there are certain aspects of vocabulary and other features of language that change at differential rates. It is not a constant rate insofar as linguistic change taken as a whole is concerned. Swadesh's hypothesis was that, if one selected these basic elements, one would find a constant rate of change.

We also might consider the problem of linguistic complexity in relation to the many so-called "jargons" found in the world today. I use the term "jargon" in the sense of such minimum languages as Pidgin English—made up, as some have said, of an English vocabulary coupled with an enormously simplified Chinese grammar. Jargons, insofar as grammar is concerned, tend to be simplified in relation to the grammars of the languages combined to produce the jargon. Perhaps we have a lower limit of grammatical complexity in those minimum languages.

On the point that was raised in connection with word length and complexity, I would like to quote Greenberg's (7) attempt to quantify degree of synthesis by means of an index determined by the ratio of the number of morphemes to the number of words in running text. He found that English, an analytic language, had a low index of synthesis (1.68) as compared to Sanskrit, a synthetic language (index: 2.59), and Eskimo, a polysynthetic language (index: 3.72). These results, taken with other indices developed by Greenberg, suggest that a method for quantifying linguistic complexity may yet be developed.

On the problem of aphasics, of course, we have no information at all for peoples outside of our own civilizations. I suspect there may be aphasics in other societies, perhaps even in the societies we have called primitive. But, as far as I know, no one has ever studied them.

## REFERENCES

1. Dobrovský, J. *Ausführliches Lehrgebäude der böhmischen Sprache.* 1809.
2. Ervin, S. M., Imitation and structural change in children's language. In: *New Directions in the Study of Language* (E. H. Lenneberg, Ed.). M.I.T. Press, Cambridge, 1964: 163-189.
3. Garvin, P. L., On the relative tractability of morphological data. *Word,* 1957, 13: 12-23.
4. Garvin, P. L., and Mathiot, M., The urbanization of the Guaraní language— a problem in language and culture. In: *Men and Cultures* (A. F. C. Wallace, Ed.). Univ. of Pennsylvania Press, Philadelphia 1960: 783-790.

5. GLANZER, M., Grammatical category: a rote learning and word association analysis. *J. Verb. Learn. Verb. Beh.*, 1962, 1: 31-41.

6. GOODGLASS, H., and HUNT, J., Grammatical complexity and aphasic speech. *Word*, 1958, 14: 197-207.

7. GREENBERG, J. H., A quantitative approach to the morphological typology of language. In: *Method and Perspective in Anthropology* (R. E. Spencer, Ed.). Univ. of Minnesota Press, Minneapolis, 1954: 192-220.

8. HAVRÁNEK, B., The functional differentiation of the standard language. In: *A Prague School Reader on Esthetics, Literary Structure, and Style* (P. L. Garvin, Ed. and Transl.). Georgetown Univ. Press, Washington, D.C., 1964: 3-16.

9. HUGHES, J. P., *The Science of Language; an Introduction to Linguistics*. Random House, New York, 1962.

10. KLOSS, H., *Die Entwicklung neuer germanischer Kultursprachen von 1800 bis 1950*. Pohl, Munich, 1952.

11. MANDELBROT, B., An informational theory of the statistical structure of language. In: *Communication Theory* (W. Jackson, Ed.). Butterworths, London, 1953: 486-502.

12. PEDERSEN, H., *The Discovery of Language: Linguistic Science in the Nineteenth Century* (J. W. Spargo, Transl.). Indiana Univ. Press, Bloomington, 1962.

13. PEI, M., *The Story of Language*. Lippincott, New York, 1949.

14. REDFIELD, R., The folk society. *Am. J. Sociol.*, 1947, 52: 293-308.

15. REICHARD, G., *Navaho Grammar*. Augustin, New York, 1951.

16. SWADESH, M., Toward greater accuracy in lexicostatistic dating. *Internat. J. Am. Ling.*, 1955, 21: 121-137.

# LINGUISTIC THEORY AS BEHAVIORAL THEORY

## CHARLES A. FERGUSON
Center for Applied Linguistics
Washington, D.C.

Several people have called my attention to the fact that the title of this paper could cover almost anything. Let me explain that I am not going to try to defend or expound a general statement such as, say, "Language is human behavior, and linguistic theory in some sense, therefore, must be a part of a larger body of theory of human behavior." Instead, I would like to discuss only one point, a rather small one perhaps, but one which I think is relevant to the discussions here: the prediction of human language behavior in terms of linguistic theory. Continuing the approach of a previous paper (7), I want to emphasize the predictive power of linguistic theory and the experimental means that are available to verify linguistic prediction.

Linguists themselves have been very little concerned with prediction. It is true that linguists have often made, rather casually, very detailed predictions about human language behavior, but they seem not to have been aware of the importance of what they were doing, nor do they seem to have the notion that it is a good idea to present theories in such a way that they might be tested. I do not know quite why this is so. Perhaps the reason is that descriptive linguistics comes from a kind of anthropological tradition which is not experimental in its outlook, or perhaps it is that historical linguistics tends to come from a kind of humanistic tradition which does not look for explicit experimentation. But whatever the reason, it seems to be the case that linguists are not much concerned with prediction.

In the last few years I have tended not only to become increasingly in favor of explicit prediction and verification in linguistics but even to take a more extreme position, and perhaps suggest that linguists should make predictions directed toward correlation of linguistic analysis with nonlinguistic phenomena. If the nonlinguistic phenomena should not correlate too well, perhaps the linguists should go back and change their theory. Linguists normally seem to assume they have in linguistics the kind of autonomous discipline which has its own values of internal consistency, simplicity, etc. I have tended, however, to feel more and more that, other things being equal, a linguistic theory that does correlate well with nonlinguistic phenomena is automatically better than some other linguistic theory which does not correlate in that way.

Let me justify for the nonlinguists my statement about linguists from time to time having made very precise predictions in a rather casual way. One example that is quite familiar to linguists, but perhaps not to some of the nonlinguists here, is the old question of the laryngeal hypothesis. In 1879, I believe, the Swiss linguist de Saussure (5) suggested on the basis of his theoretical considerations that there must have existed two additional "sonantic coefficients", as he called them, in the phonological inventory of proto-Indo-European, though he could offer no convincing concrete evidence for their existence. In 1915 the Czech scholar Hrozný (9) pointed out that the newly discovered ancient Hittite language was related to Indo-European, and in 1927 the Polish linguist Kuryłowicz (11) stated that Hittite had a special consonant occurring in some of the positions where de Saussure had predicted his additional elements. Further developments in fact confirmed de Saussure's prediction and added refinements to the hypothetical reconstruction of a proto-language with at least three such so-called laryngeals. Linguists, however, have been concerned with such things as the details of the partially conflicting formulations of this laryngeal hypothesis and, as I suggested, they tend to lose sight of the incredible precision of prediction here.

What de Saussure was saying—although he did not put it in exactly these words—was that some thousands of years before, members of the speech community which was linguistically ancestral to modern Indo-European languages habitually performed certain delicate acts of motor behavior under certain linguistic conditions. Not only did de Saussure say this, but it turned out later through independent evidence that it was possible to confirm that this language, unreported and presumably always to remain unreported, did in fact show this kind of behavior. This is quite a precise and astonishing prediction, although not quite of the same kind as an astronomer's prediction. If we use "predict" in this way for the past, modern astronomers "predict" an eclipse in Anatolia in 585 B.C., and the prediction is verified by the eclipse (associated with the philosopher Thales) which ended the war between Lydia and Media. Of course, when astronomical prediction is involved, we would probably take the modern astronomer's word first and regard it as confirming any account we have from ancient history.

Be that as it may, even if the linguistic prediction is not quite as impressive in detail and scope as the astronomer's, it is quite impressive in the realm of the behavioral sciences. What I mean to say is that linguists have frequent occasions for making predictions of this kind, but usually they do not make them as such and do not formulate their theories that way.

In the first place, in the writings of some linguists there are generalizations which are said to hold for many or even all languages. An outstanding example of this, of course, is Dr. Jakobson, whose writings are full of statements which could be interpreted as very broad generalizations. Some of these statements can be formulated in such a way as to be testable only with considerable difficulty. Others, however, are quite readily phrasable in terms which would allow for prediction and verification. For example, we are all familiar here with Dr. Jakobson's theory of binary distinctive features; he himself believes and states quite explicitly that this is not just a linguistic theory which has some beauty and elegance of its own, but actually is closely connected with such concepts as perception (10).

Given the way this general theory is stated, however, it is very difficult to see how it could be tested, or to understand what kind of evidence would be accepted as refuting it. Dr. Jakobson and his colleagues can find a way of interpreting almost any information as confirmation of the theory. It may be difficult to see how the theory as a whole could be tested, but this is not true of all its parts: there are many which can readily be formulated in such a way that we could think of some kind of experimentation which would tell us, once and for all, whether they make sense or do not make sense. For example, Dr. Jakobson says (10) that there are certain similar phonetic phenomena across languages which, because they are in complementary distribution, should be regarded as analytically the same distinctive feature. I assume he includes the matter of perception, although he does not say this explicitly. He gives a number of examples: one he often uses is that the difference between plain and pharyngealized consonants is the same in some sense as the difference between unrounded and rounded consonants or, in fact, is the same as between dental and retroflex consonants (10). This is quite readily testable.

To give an example of how an experimental situation might be set up, we could think of speakers of South Asian languages—there are many such languages and millions of speakers—for whom dental and retroflex consonants are in contrast, and of speakers of Arabic, where plain and pharyngealized consonants are in contrast. Dr. Jakobson would say the pharyngealization in Arabic is analytically the same as the retroflex in various South Asian languages. It so happens that many of the South Asian languages are written, and Arabic is regularly written. In practically all cases there are distinct symbols for the retroflex as opposed to dental consonants in the South Asian languages and pharyngeal *versus* plain in Arabic. This sets the stage very simply: we can then test how a speaker of a South Asian language hears Arabic material, and how a speaker of Arabic hears South Asian linguistic material. There is the simple means of having an Arab write in Arab script certain sound sequences he listens to in South Asian languages and, vice versa, a Bengali or Marathi speaker write in his own script what he hears in Arabic.

It is reasonable to estimate that there are half a dozen American universities where all the facilities and resources are available for this kind of experimentation, where there is a sufficient body of foreign students, where there are enough linguists around to help in the selection of the material, and where there are enough psychologists or others concerned with organizing experiments so as to make sure the experiment is set up in a reasonable way and carried out to a satisfactory conclusion. If such an experiment would show fairly decisively that pharyngealized *versus* plain and retroflex *versus* dental are the same, perceptually, across languages, then this would be one small building block, one small piece of evidence, for one part of Jakobson's binary distinctive-feature theory. It would be a step toward verification of the theory as a whole, perhaps. On the other hand, if it should show fairly decisively that that is not the case, then it would not destroy the rest of the theory. It would merely mean that this particular part of the theory is not relevant perceptually, even though it may be valid in some other way.

In the work of many authors in linguistics, there are generalizations which could be phrased in testable terms. The fact is they are not so phrased, and linguists on the whole are not concerned with setting up experimental situations. So, perhaps, what I am doing is explaining to the nonlinguists some of the relevance of linguistic theory to the kind of behavioral problems they are concerned with or, perhaps, trying to persuade linguists to become more interested in an experimental approach to linguistics.

My first example was about generalizations of wide applicability; I would like to use one other example of a very different kind: all linguists make statements in their ordinary published work which are susceptible of verification in the sense that they predict very precisely and carefully certain kinds of human behavior in the particular languages studied or analyzed. Anyone engaged in descriptive linguistic analysis should be able to provide nontrivial cases of prediction which call for verification. I would like to offer as an example one set of predictions which grow out of the kind of analysis which I have done on one particular language, to show that any linguist in his ordinary analytic work could come up with this kind of testable prediction. The particular set of predictions which I would like to offer concerns the order in which children learn aspects of their native language, in particular the way Bengali children learn to speak Bengali as regards the order in which semantically parallel constructions of differing grammatical complexity are learned. We start with a very simple, common sense kind of hypothesis: if there are two different constructions having about the same semantic value, children would normally learn the simpler one first (I am using "simpler" in a very common sense, unsophisticated way here: for example, if there are two constructions, one of which has one more element than the other, and there is no reason to think that the shorter one in some way involves a deletion of the element in the larger one, then we assume that the larger one is more complex, and so on). The particular set of constructions which I have analyzed, and on which I would like to base some predictions here, are the ways of making negative clauses in Bengali, more specifically clause negation in Standard Colloquial Bengali. There are five patterns of clause negation in Bengali, each one appropriate for certain kinds of clauses. These five patterns are of differing complexity, and it should be possible to predict the order in which Bengali children tend to acquire them. Elsewhere (8) I have given a rather complicated technical presentation of these patterns, but here I should like to give an ordinary English account of each pattern in such a way that the essential features are clear, using sample sentences with clauses as simple as possible, and using the same words throughout so that the patterns are easy to recognize.

Pattern No. 1 consists simply of the addition of the suffix -na to the main verb of the clause in question. A sentence like "ram baŋla bɔle" (Ram speaks Bengali) is negated by simply adding -na to the verb, so we have "ram baŋla bɔlena" (Ram doesn't speak Bengali).

Pattern No. 2 adds the suffix -ni. This is a rather strange one to us; all but two of the tenses in Bengali verbs add a -na to make the negative, but two particular past tenses simply do not make their negatives this way. Instead, the suffix -ni is added to the present tense, so that this same sentence with -ni in place of -na is not the negative of the present tense but is the negative of two particular past tenses. The sentence "ram baŋla bɔleni" means "Ram did not speak" or "hasn't spoken" or "hadn't spoken". Note that there are two other past tenses which do take a regular -na, but these two form the negative in this special way.

*Hirsh:* Is it similar to the positive conjugation of the past?

*Ferguson:* Not at all; in fact, this makes a very different kind of pattern. In the more technical presentation I use a different kind of formulation altogether. Pattern No. 1 is simply the addition of an element; Pattern No. 2 represents some kind of matching clause in which the negative is not sufficiently explained by knowing the morphemes and the construction.

Pattern No. 3 is the negative of what I call equational clauses; a clause in Bengali, as in many languages, of the type "A is B" has no equivalent for the English verb "to be"; it is simply "A-B". Such clauses in Bengali have as their negative a special verb, "not be", which occurs only in this particular construction. So there is nɔ-, with appropriate ending, for "I am not", "you are not", "he is not", and so on. Thus, "ram chutur"—"Ram is a carpenter", and "ram chutur nɔe"—"Ram is not a carpenter".

Pattern No. 4 refers to another kind of clause which I call existential. There are many clauses in Bengali that contain a form of *ach-*, a special verb, "to be" referring to existence; it may correspond to the English "have". Thus, we might say "ramer boi ache"—"Ram has books", or "of-Ram books there-are", or something like that. It so happens the negative -na simply does not occur with this particular verb. Instead, there is an invariable negative verb, *nei*, which replaces it: we have "ramer boi nei", which means "Ram doesn't have any books". Sableski (12) has now provided a fuller description of equational and existential clauses in Bengali.

Finally, there is a pattern of negation (No. 5) which consists of prefixing *na* to a verb. Like many languages, Bengali has independent clauses and dependent clauses; the first four patterns of negation are used in independent clauses. When dependent clauses are made in Bengali, the negation is somewhat different. None of the first four patterns hold for dependent clauses. In the first type with an ordinary verb form of one of the tenses that take *-na*, instead of adding the *-na* suffix, the dependent clause negation is made by placing *na* before the verb ("ram jodi baŋla na bɔle"—"if Ram does not speak Bengali . . ."). In the other three types there are complications. Pattern No. 3 actually occurs in dependent clauses ("ram jodi chutur nɔe"—"if Ram is not a carpenter"), but the corresponding affirmative dependent clause is ambiguous—a complication we need not discuss here. The dependent negative clauses corresponding to Patterns No. 2 and 4 are formed by placing *na* before a form of the verb *thak-*, which replaces either the tense ending or the verb *ach-*.

Pattern No. 1 is clearly simpler grammatically than any of the others in that it consists of an invariable suffix (*-na*) added always in a certain position, and the correspondence between affirmative and negative is one to one: if an affirmative clause consists of A + B, the negative consists of A + B-*na*, and if a negative consists of A + B-*na*, the corresponding affirmative consists of A + B. Prediction One: *Other things being equal, Pattern No. 1 will be acquired before the other patterns.*

As a matter of fact, other things are not equal, and two additional facts reinforce this prediction: the high frequency of this pattern, which probably occurs in normal adult speech more than any other single pattern and possibly even more than all the others combined; and the fact that *na* is also the common negative particle "no" used in answer to a question.

If Pattern No. 1 is learned first, one would expect also to find "errors" in the child's speech where it is used where the other patterns should be used. In particular, we can predict that at various stages of the linguistic development of a Bengali child occurrences of *-na* will be found: (*a*) attached to the past tenses which do not take *-na* in adult speech (instead of Pattern No. 2); (*b*) at the end of equational clauses in the place the verb usually takes in ordinary predicative clauses (instead of Pattern No. 3); (*c*) attached to forms of *ach-* which do not take *-na* in adult speech (instead of Pattern No. 4); (*d*) as a verb suffix in dependent clauses where it should precede the verb (Pattern No. 5). Of these four kinds of "errors", (*b*) is actually permissible in adult speech, being a less frequent variant of Pattern No. 3; it would be interesting to determine whether this alternative is older in the history of the language or is an innovation spreading by analogy from Pattern No. 1, and whether this use of *na* in an adult's speech continues his childhood use or is reintroduced after mastery of Pattern No. 3.

Pattern No. 5 is clearly more complex grammatically than any of the others, not by virtue of the shape and position of the negative element added (always a preposed *na*), but because of the verb replacements required by dependent clauses. Prediction Two: *Other things being equal, Patterns No. 2, 3, and 4 will be acquired before Pattern No. 5.*

For languages with a clear and pervasive difference between independent and dependent clauses, it is a fair working assumption that the basic structure of independent clauses will be learned before that of dependent clauses. Accordingly, one would predict in any case that the grammar of Bengali dependent clauses would be learned late. But given the complexities of Pattern No. 5, it seems quite likely that control of the negation of dependent clauses will not come smoothly with control of affirmative dependent clauses but will come slowly and with a variety of "errors". In particular we can predict that at various stages of linguistic development of a Bengali child, and even at the same stage, errors of the following kinds will occur in negative dependent clauses: (*a*) instances of Pattern No. 2; (*b*) instances of Pattern No. 2 with *ni* preceding the verb; (*c*) instances of Pattern No. 3; (*d*) instances of Pattern No. 4; and (*e*) instances of *na* preceding *ach-*. Errors of types (*b*) and (*e*) would represent attempts to apply Pattern No. 5 without making the proper intervening replacements.

It might be possible to make still further predictions on the learning of clause negation in Bengali, but the degree of difference of complexity among Patterns No. 2, 3, and 4 is so questionable and the possible influence of other factors is so great that additional predictions would have to be heavily qualified. In fact, however, two precise predictions of order of learning and nine precise predictions of error constitute a substantial amount of anticipation.

I ought to make it clear at this point that I have never observed any Bengali children learning the language and, as far as I know, there have been no published studies of Bengali children doing so. These predictions are being made without previous knowledge of what the results might turn out to be. Accordingly, it would seem that systematic investigation of the language development of the Bengali child to the extent necessary to confirm or refute these predictions would be of value for linguistic theory viewed as behavioral theory.

The particular kind of experimental situation which would have to be set up in Bengal would require careful planning by linguists and psychologists, but it seems clear that it could be carried out within a year or so and obtain quite definite results one way or the other. If the results are positive, this suggests that both the linguistic analysis and the hypothesis of learning order may be valid. If the results are negative, this would prove that either the linguistic analysis or the learning hypothesis is wrong.

Naturally, I would be quite pleased if the investigation were carried out and the results were positive but, whatever the results, further prediction and experimentation could be attempted in order to sharpen or otherwise improve both the analysis and the learning hypothesis. I would be very happy if some particular group would care to undertake this kind of investigation. I think I have gone far enough to make the point I wanted to make: that linguists can perfectly well phrase their theories in terms that are subject to experimental verification and that they should do so much more than they now do. Not only is this true for generalizations on the nature of language but also for the ordinary, everyday analysis in which all linguists are engaged.

### Discussion

*Hirsh:* I would like to ask Dr. Ferguson how general the use of the consonant "n" is for the negation.

*Ferguson:* I cannot say how common this usage is in the languages of the world.

*Osgood:* This brings up an issue that ought to be made clear. And, incidentally, this comment is raised because of my experience of about ten to fifteen years of running contact with linguists. In testing predictions about language universals, one is not concerned with an exception or two, or even three. This is where the problem of sampling languages comes in: one is in a statistical domain and could say for instance that there is a general tendency within "mama" and "papa" words for the male terms to involve bilabial plosives and for the mother words to involve nasals, as Dr. Jakobson has said. Exceptions exist, of course, but the rule is highly significant statistically.

*Stockwell:* I do not think that is true for negatives.

*Osgood:* I meant to say the issue here would be whether it holds for a representative sample of languages, not whether one knows of a language where it is not true.

*Ladefoged:* On the question of negatives, there seems to be a widespread tendency among languages that those which do not otherwise have a contrastive glottal stop nevertheless have a negative interjection, such as English *uh-uh*, which contrasts with the form *huhuh* (conventional orthography is not very satisfactory for representing these forms), in which there is no glottal stop. This is very widespread in several language groups. It happens in many Niger-Congo languages which do not otherwise have a glottal stop; they have a negative interjection of this kind. Does it happen in American Indian languages?

*Lounsbury:* I do not know of any American Indian language that has the glottal stop for the negation.

*Wepman:* On the other hand, if, in talking to an American Indian who spoke no English, one were to shake one's head from side to side, would he accept this as a negation? Or a nod for affirmation?

*Stockwell:* These gestures are not universal.

*Wepman:* Are there universal signs that mean essentially the same thing, without getting involved in the verbal act?

*Hoijer:* As far as the Navaho and Apache groups are concerned, I think the meanings of nodding and shaking are essentially like our own. They do have an interesting variation, however, in indicating direction, which we customarily do by manual gesture. They do this by bunching up their lips and pointing in the particular direction indicated, left and right, up and down.

*Denes:* No need to go outside Europe to find gestures in opposition to "normal": the Bulgarian symbol for "yes" is to shake the head, and for "come here" to move the arm almost threateningly.

*Marschak:* Two Oxford students rowing in the Bosporus were shot at by a sentry—the Turkish sign for "go away" is like our beckoning gesture, palm inwards.

*Wepman:* The non-universality of gestures is quite evident in aphasics; to many aphasics, the word "no" means "yes" and the word "yes" means "no"—that is the way in which the aphasic is schizophrenic.

*Stockwell:* I judge Dr. Ferguson is fairly safe for the moment in making predictions because he has made them to an audience unlikely to be able to test them immediately. It has been observed by historians and philosophers of science that a new idea in a particular science may in fact, almost without its being noticed for a while, change the subject matter, the very universe of discourse, of the science. Something of this sort has happened, I think, in linguistics. For a long time we have claimed to be talking about the way people speak; but a closer look at the structural grammars of this century, particularly after about 1930, makes it hard to avoid the impression that, until recently, the subject matter of linguistics was the distribution of forms in texts, analyzed abstractly as if it were not really necessary to assume that people had distributed them in those texts in accord with abstract rules which exist, somehow, in people's heads. Now, I am quite sure that most linguists will deny the accusation that they have ignored the distributors of forms whose distribution they study. Take nonetheless the notion of the phoneme: for many linguists, it has been simply a distributional notion involving such criteria as complementary distribution and phonetic similarity; only in the last few years have linguists taken seriously the view that it is an essentially psychological entity postulated in a grammar to account for the way speakers divide an auditory continuum. Further, there is the fact that the question of verification of grammatical generalizations has only recently been taken seriously, as in computer parsing and sentence generating programs. I think that the subject matter of linguistics is not so much a description of what people say as the construction of theories about what kinds of abstractions, what kinds of rules, what kinds of capacities, people must have in order to behave linguistically the way they do.

This change in the subject matter of linguistics is a direct outcome of the view that grammar is a set of predictions taking the form of axioms and theorems about the well-formed sentences of a language and their internal structure. In short, a grammar is a set of predictions made by a generative grammar of any of several forms; the axioms are the general schema of linguistic description which specify the form of rules, and the theorems are the implementation of those rules for particular languages. Such a grammar is an extremely powerful account of the quite extraordinary capacities of mature speakers to construct and understand sentences the way they do. It provides not only an account of their ability to discriminate between well-formed sentences and any arbitrary string of words of the language, but also an account of the background against which various kinds of deviant or parasitic construction can be understood.

As I understand his paper, Dr. Ferguson is making a different kind of prediction. Suppose we have a grammar, by which I mean a set of generative rules. In Dr. Ferguson's presentation, I presume it is a set of patterns which can be restated in the form of generative rules. It is a grammar which we consider to be satisfactory with respect to its account of what can be sentences, and of the internal structure of strings that can be sentences. That is, he is assuming the existence of an adequate set of predictions of the fundamental type which, in my view, grammars are obligated to make. Given these, is it the case that more general predictions can be made, for example, about the sequence in which the rules will be mastered by children, about the kinds of errors children will make in the development of their control over the rules, and even about the direction in which linguistic change will occur? Testing such predictions seems to me extremely relevant for the comparison and verification of alternative theories, and I consider the activity of comparison and verification of alternative theories to be at the very core of linguistics as a science.

Recalling Dr. Lenneberg's comments about the extreme difficulty of rating the complexity of language structures, I rather suspect that there is a scale of complexity, even if only grossly describable, in connection with degree of regularity (for example, the number of exceptions like "go/went" to the rules for the formation of past tense) or in connection with extent and type of internal structure (that is, subordinated clauses are structured to a greater depth than are coordinated clauses; certainly, coordinate clauses are learned earlier). There are, I suspect, scales of complexity having to do with functional load, etc. The only way to determine the reality of such a scale of difficulty is by making predictions and testing them. I should very much like to see Dr. Ferguson follow up and test his own predictions. But accurate prediction of the sequence in which the learning of patterns will occur does not, I suggest, depend on the grammatical model used to describe the patterns. While I agree with Dr. Lamb and Chomsky that the simplest grammar must in some sense be suggestive of the nature of the mechanism that handles the rules, it does not follow that the rules will be consistently learned in the sequence of less complex to more complex. I suspect that such factors as frequency and functional load will generally override complexity as parameters for the prediction of learning sequence. Thus it is not clear to me why the hypothesis of order of learning is relevant to the verification of the rules which characterizes the competency which is, in principle, available to the native speaker.

*Marschak:* When off their guard linguists do make predictions, and extremely interesting ones. For instance, I have heard Dr. Lounsbury describe what happens when a conquering nation imposes its language on inhabitants of an isolated mountain valley. We have heard about correlations between kinship vocabulary and property rights or inheritance rights, and between social structure and politeness forms. I suppose some of these hypotheses have already been tested; if not, it would be interesting if they could be.

*Geschwind:* Dr. Ferguson has underlined the importance of testing linguistic predictions in the field, and I agree with him that perhaps linguists have not been as vigorous as they should in doing this. For instance, some years ago Dr. Jakobson made some statements about the loss of phonemes in aphasics in relation to the order of acquisition of phonemes in childhood. I do not think that anyone took up this problem in the right way, i.e., by studying large numbers of children in development and a large number of aphasics to see if the prediction was correct.

*Wepman:* This phenomenon has been studied; actually, Dr. Jakobson and I have discussed it at length. As I understand it, he has more or less dropped the notion that there is a dissolution of the phonemic system in aphasia.

*Geschwind:* The point is that the studies suggested by Dr. Jakobson's predictions were not taken up by the linguists, the very group to whom the statements had been addressed. Nonlinguists might have studied the problem, but the tradition of linguistics has not automatically been oriented to the kind of verification that Dr. Ferguson has advocated. I would like to suggest that it might be interesting to observe how the different forms of negation are affected in fluent and nonfluent Bengali aphasics.

Von Neumann, who dealt with the question of simplicity and complexity in a famous paper (13), pointed out that people have tended to assume that simplicity and complexity were functions of what was observed; he suggested that, on the contrary, simplicity and complexity might be functions of the structure of the observing nervous system rather than of the stimuli themselves. An obvious example is the ease with which most people learn to name colors, in contrast to the difficulty the overwhelming majority have in learning to name specific tones of the scale. This is probably a matter of the structure of the two receptive systems and not of the inherent simplicity or complexity of either task; the auditory system is not built for absolute pitch. We must study the structure of the receiver, not only the external stimulus, in order to decide what is simple or complex.

*Osgood:* That statement should be emphasized. The same problem appears in animal behavior: in testing the effects of lesions, some forms of behavior are observed which would seem to the human to be very simple yet may be extremely complicated and difficult for the animal, whereas other kinds of behavior, such as threading a very complicated maze, may be much easier for it.

*Geschwind:* Another example can be readily observed in the learning behavior of monkeys: a monkey may learn certain complex tasks fairly easily and yet do very badly on a simple non-limbic cross-modal association which looks very easy to a human. It is the structure of the nervous system which determines this.

*Ferguson:* There are one or two points I would like to comment on. The first is Dr. Stockwell's point about the phoneme. The phoneme was first thought of in terms of perception and behavior, and most of the people who have used the concept have been concerned with its usefulness in language teaching or language perception. This has, in some sense, been central to the thinking of almost everyone who has been connected with phoneme  theory.

More important, I suppose, is the question of why linguists write grammars. There are many reasons for writing grammars, and I suggest that we should explore some that are of considerable interest to people outside linguistics. One very good reason for writing a grammar might be to account for the way in which children learn the language. This approach might result in a grammar different from one written for other purposes, but linguists and others can worry about how to reconcile the two grammars, or what it means to have two different grammars. At the present time no one is writing grammars (of adult language) specifically to explain such things as how a child learns his own language, or even how a second language is learned, or how things are perceived.[*]

Dr. Marschak pointed out that linguists are always making predictions, and then he cited a long list of them. I think it would be fair to point out that each one of his examples was not really linguistic; it was somewhere on the borderline, generally "sociolinguistic". The linguist feels almost guilty in making such predictions. He feels he is not in his own home territory, that is, describing the structure of language. The particular examples I

---

[*] *Dr. Carterette's note:* There have been several attempts, however, to induce a child's grammar from a sample corpus of his language. See, for example, Bellugi & Brown (1), Berko (2), Braine (3), Brown & Fraser (4), and Ervin & Miller (6). Berko (2) showed experimentally that a child's grammatical "errors" in extending his grammar often take the form of regularization. Thus, a child deals very simply with the activity of the man who is always *glinging*, who *glings* today, by saying "yesterday he *glinged*". In the context of the child's grammar the adult expression *glang* is not just funny, but wrong.

chose were based on linguistic structure, though I am personally interested in sociolinguistic questions.

Finally, I should apologize for using a prediction which involves simplicity *versus* complexity. There are many other kinds of predictions we can make. In fact, the one I chose from the Jakobson distinctive feature analysis is not in terms of something simpler being learned before something complex. It so happened the particular Bengali example I used was one that involved this question of simplicity, although to a limited extent and in a way in which I think linguists could reach general agreement. There are many other terms in which predictions can be made.

## REFERENCES

1. BELLUGI, U., and BROWN, R. (Eds.), The acquisition of language. *Monog. Soc. Res. Child Dev.*, 1964, **29**(1): 1-191.

2. BERKO, J., The child's learning of English morphology. *Word*, 1958, **14**: 150-157.

3. BRAINE, M. D. S., The ontogeny of English phrase structure: the first phrase. *Language*, 1963, **39**: 1-13.

4. BROWN, R., and FRASER, C., The acquisition of syntax. *Monog. Soc. Res. Child Dev.*, 1964, **29**: 43-79.

5. DE SAUSSURE, F., *Mémoire sur le Système Primitif des Voyelles dans les Langues Indo-Européennes.* Teubner, Leipzig, 1879.

6. ERVIN, S. M., and MILLER, W. R., Language development. *Yearb. Nat. Soc. Study Educ.*, 1963, **62**: 108-143.

7. FERGUSON, C. A., Linguistic theory and language learning. *Monog. Ser. Lang. Ling.*, 1963, **16**: 115-124.

8. ———, Clause negation in Bengali. In: *Proceedings of the XXVI International Congress of Orientalists.* New Delhi (in press).

9. HROZNÝ, F., Die Lösung des hethitischen Problems. *Mit. Deutsch.-Orientges.*, 1915, **56**: 17-50.

10. JAKOBSON, R., FANT, C. G. M., and HALLE, M., *Preliminaries to Speech Analysis; the Distinctive Features and their Correlates*, Technical Report No. 13 (1952), M.I.T. Acoustics Laboratory, M.I.T. Press, Cambridge, 1963.

11 KURYŁOWICZ, J., ə indoeuropéen et *h* hittite. In: *Symbolae in Honorem J. Rozwadowski*, Vol. I. Cracow, 1927: 95-104.

12. SABLESKI, J. A., Equational clauses in Bengali. *Language*, 1965, **41**: 439-446.

13. VON NEUMANN, J., The general and logical theory of automata. In: *Cerebral Mechanisms in Behavior* (L. A. Jeffress, Ed.). Wiley, New York, 1951: 1-41.

# SUMMATION AND REVIEW*

PAUL L. GARVIN
The Bunker-Ramo Corporation
Canoga Park, California

In summing up the results of this conference, I shall speak as a linguist. One of the questions I consider particularly important is, therefore: what is the place of linguistics in this cooperative enterprise and, more specifically, what have linguists contributed so far, what more can they contribute, and how can this contribution best be defined? I should like to present my summary without being parochial. This means that I shall avoid entering into disputes among linguists and refrain from giving my own theory of language.

The first question one can ask about an interdisciplinary gathering is: what disciplines are represented among the people present? Exercising the bias of the linguist I will divide the participants in this conference into linguists and nonlinguists. In order to obtain this simple breakdown, I include among the linguists those of this group who are either psycholinguists or ethnolinguists, as well as those who are acoustic phoneticians. All the others are then considered nonlinguists, and in turn can be divided into two basic categories: the brain researchers and the clinicians, on the assumption that those who are not physiologically or anatomically oriented are interested in some clinical problem such as aphasia.

A dual question arises from this composition of the conference: what does linguistics have to offer the nonlinguists; what do the nonlinguists have to offer the linguists? In my opinion, this dual question can be answered by saying that the major contribution of linguistics to the nonlinguistic disciplines is a frame of reference; the major contributions of these disciplines to linguistics are a link to the physiological substratum of language and a means of validation. In exploring the latter, it is worth noting that one is often dealing not so much with the questions that linguists might actually have put to nonlinguists as with the inferences which the former can draw from the work of the latter. This is because, while nonlinguists seem to be anxious to have linguistic assistance (and often look for it

* Work on this address was done under the sponsorship of the Air Force Office of Scientific Research of the Office of Aerospace Research under Contract No. AF 49(638)-1128.

263

in vain), only a few linguists have so far paid close attention to physiological or clinical studies of the brain.

### A LINGUISTIC FRAME OF REFERENCE

I should first of all like to stress that I am here talking about a frame of reference and not an explanation. While a linguistic frame of reference is of unquestioned usefulness, taking linguistics as an explanatory model will often seem grossly oversimplified, as was shown in some of the discussions at this conference. Two basic considerations are involved in this point of view: what characteristics of language, as studied by linguists, are relevant to its use as a frame of reference; in what way can a linguistic approach to natural language serve as a frame of reference? These two considerations are closely interrelated and will therefore be discussed together. In my discussion, I shall limit myself to aspects of these matters that have actually been brought up at the conference.

Three areas have been of interest to the participants. The first is, what are the general characteristics of language? The second is, what is the significance of particular aspects of language, more specifically of its categories and units, for the understanding of particular problems? The third is the question of linguistic complexity or difficulty.

*General Characteristics of Language.* Linguists and anthropologists often call these universals of language. Two types can be distinguished, namely internal characteristics—those that linguists might want to call structural, and external characteristics—those that linguists might want to call functional.

The internal characteristics of language, its structural properties, cannot be discussed without entering into the linguistic controversies which I promised to avoid. I shall therefore restrict myself to four crucial questions of structure that were suggested by the contributions of the nonlinguistic participants, and not raise any myself. Two of the questions relate to the general problem of the overall characteristics of linguistic structure. The other two relate to more particular problems.

The first general question is that of the phylogeny of language. This question involves the evolutionist notion of primitiveness as a general characteristic of a structure, and hence is directly relevant to the problem of the overall properties of a language. The notion of primitiveness is as yet undefined for language, as was shown in Dr. Hoijer's paper. The traditional interpretations of this notion are based on false assumptions, such as the alleged scarcity of vocabulary in "primitive" languages. This does not mean that a re-evaluation of the notion of primitiveness may not be fruitful. Such a re-evaluation has taken place in anthropology, where the traditional opposition of primitive *versus* civilized has been replaced by the more readily definable opposition of folk *versus* urban. A similar re-evaluation of the notion of primitiveness of a language might be based on some of the subtler structural differences that characterize the distinction between a folk dialect and an urban officially codified standard language.

Another general problem was suggested by the emphasis in the discussion by the clinicians on the difference between what were called the processes of naming and of sentence construction. This difference is illustrated by the traditional distinction made in the field of aphasia between alexia and agrammatism. Comparatively little attention, by contrast, was given by the linguists to the corresponding distinction between the lexical and grammatical dimensions. It was only referred to indirectly when two categories of grammatical rules were posited for a transformational grammar: rewrite rules and dictionary rules. The two questions of detail in the structure of language were raised in the brain research and clinical discussions, respectively. They relate to the aspects of language and to the properties of linguistic units.

The well-known experiments with electrical stimulation of specific areas of the brain have highlighted the question of localization. This problem no longer simply concerns the faculty of language as a global phenomenon. It has to be reformulated in terms of separate localizations for different aspects of language. The question which the linguist is then expected to answer is: what are these different aspects of language that may have separate localizations?

The second question deals with what I consider to be a fundamental property of linguistic units, namely fusion. It was brought up on two occasions during the conference in connection with the phonological aspect of language, once when the question of the "connective tissue" between vowels and consonants was raised, and again when there was some reference to perception experiments which showed that perception does not occur in terms of strings of individual speech sounds, but in terms of integrated wholes such as breath groups. These questions underline the significance of the process of fusion on the phonological level and point to the broader problem of the role of fusion in all levels of language. They further suggest the necessity of taking this important property into account whenever language is used as a frame of reference.

*Functional Properties of Language.* One of the comments made during the conference by Dr. Geschwind, a nonlinguist, was that language functions as a cross-modal sign system. If I interpret it correctly, he meant that language is a sign system which links sensory impressions coming from different sensory modalities. The only aspect of this view in which linguists have been interested, so far, is the problem of synesthesia in relation to speech sounds. It might be worthwhile for linguists to go beyond such limited observations and consider this cross-modal function more systematically. One question that can be asked in this connection is, for instance, to what extent the cross-modal function of language is reflected in either the lexicon or the grammar. An ad-hoc example might be the cross-modal implications of an expression such as "a warm color". This type of question has not been a primary preoccupation of linguists, although it has held the attention of psychologists of language. It is closely related to the problem of the role of language in the cultural conception of reality. Interest in the latter is now on the increase in connection with the linguistic and anthropological study of the cognitive systems of different cultures.

Another universal functional characteristic of language that was brought up in this conference is the well-known property of discreteness. This property means that language functions as a discrete filter for reality by selecting discrete modes of reference irrespective of whether the physical reality is discrete or continuous. It is the prerequisite for the oft-cited function of language to serve as a means for the cultural categorization and segmentation of reality.

*Linguistic Categories and Units.* The most relevant question here is that of the role of linguistic categories and units in the interpretation of clinical processes. The term "linguistic category" is used in its broadest sense to designate any systematic aspect of language, lexical as well as grammatical; the term "linguistic unit" is used to refer to any directly observable or analytically ascertainable discrete entity within the system of a language; the term "process" is used to designate any dynamic aspect of an organism, such as growth or deterioration.

The question of the role of categories and units can be stated more specifically by asking what is the set of categories or units best suited to the purposes of the clinician. An appropriate set of categories may, for instance, help in answering a clinical question such as whether there is a single scale in the deterioration of aphasia, or whether one is dealing with several scales and hence with a multidimensional problem. The related question of the role of linguistic units in assessing the development and deterioration of language was brought up during the conference on several occasions. The types of units of which clinicians seem to be most aware are words and phrases. One might, however, also want to consider whether new insights would not result from viewing some of these problems in terms of the units of transformation theory, such as kernels and transforms, or in terms of the units of some other theory, such as the lexemes or semons of stratificational grammar.

*Complexity.* I should like to stress one basic point in connection with the question of complexity or difficulty as applied to language. This is the importance of differentiating between the complexity of the language phenomena themselves, on the one hand, and the problem of the simplicity or complexity of grammars, on the other. The latter are, after all, constructs of the observer. It is theoretically conceivable to have a complex grammar of a simple language, or a simple grammar of a complex language.

The concept of the complexity or difficulty of a language is often considered related to the notion of primitiveness which I mentioned earlier. It is

**INDEXES**

# NAME INDEX

271

# SUBJECT INDEX

## A

Accent, in aphasia, 88
Acoustic phonetics, *see* Audition
Agnosia, 8
Agrammatism, 70, 73, 121, 165-167, 265
Agraphia, 157
Akinetic mutism, 171
Alexia, 265
Amusia, 82
Anomia, 147, 157, 168
Anosognosia, 26
Aphasia
  adult recovery prognosis in, 41, 45
  afferent, 75-77
  amnestic, 75-78
  Broca's, 9, 69, 79, 83, 157
  central, 79, 157
  child recovery prognosis in, 41, 44, 45
  comprehension intact in, 6
  conduction, 6, 79, 157
    comprehension intact in, 6
    fluent speech in, 6
    paraphasia in, 6
    repetition disturbance in, 6
    writing ability loss in, 5, 6
    written comprehension loss in, 5, 6
  due to hemispherectomy, 47
  dynamic, 73, 77, 83, 87
  efferent, 69-73, 76, 77
    inner speech and, 73
    linguistic defects in, 70
    phonological defects in, 70, 71
  expressive, 130, 131, 157
    in children, 130, 131
  gesture in, 84, 85
  global, 146, 158, 170
  handedness and, 17
  hemiplegia and, 158, 167
  impaired comprehension, 4
  jargon, 143, 144, 146, 162, 170, 171
  kinesthetic, 75
  kinetic, 69
  language acquisition following, 56, 58
  lesion effects, 40, 41, 44, 45, 47
    in children, 118, 137

  in left hemisphere, 45, 47
  in right hemisphere, 45
  permanent residues, 41, 44
  seizures, 45
  speech development, delay in, 44
  speech development, lack of, 44
  linguistic types of, 67-88, 145, 146
  localization of symptoms, 4-6, 9, 77, 82, 83
  mosaicist *versus* phrenological approach
    to, 9-11
  motor, 69, 79, 85, 157
  phoneme loss in, 259
  pragmatic, 145, 146, 154, 156-158, 170
  psycholinguistic approaches to, 141-171
    measurements, 162-167
    parts of speech classification, 149-155,
      167, 168
    testing methods, 142-152
  psychological approach to, 10
  quantitative approach to, 68, 143, 156
  rate of speech in, 162-164, 166, 167
  regression of, in children, 118
  repetition rate in, 164, 165, 167
  schizophrenia and, 67, 68, 257
  semantic, 74, 77, 144-147, 152, 154, 157,
    158, 170
  sensory, 4, 69, 70-72, 74, 76, 77, 79, 82,
    85, 87, 157
    linguistic defects in, 71
    metalingual defects in, 73
    phonemic defects in, 71, 72
    phonological defects in, 71
  speech rate in, 6
  syntactic, 9, 143-147, 152-154, 157
  syntactic pattern in, 74, 75
  verbal, 9, 154
  Wernicke's, 157, 158
  "Wernicke's disease", 7
  word preservation in, 70-74, 82, 88
Aphasic texts, 83
Apraxia, 8, 130
  localization of, lesions in, 8, 9
Asemia, 84
Asymbolia, 85
Audimutitas, in children, *see* Speech, Childhood disorders of

275